Monoclonal Antibodies and Cancer

IMMUNOLOGY SERIES

NOEL R. ROSE

Professor and Chairman
Department of Immunology and
  Infectious Diseases
The Johns Hopkins University
School of Hygiene and Public Health
Baltimore, Maryland

Other Volumes in Preparation

Monoclonal Antibodies and Cancer

edited by

George L. Wright, Jr.

*Department of Microbiology and Immunology
and the Immunology Program
Eastern Virginia Medical School
Norfolk, Virginia*

MARCEL DEKKER, INC.   New York and Basel

Library of Congress Cataloging in Publication Data

Main entry under title:

Monoclonal antibodies and cancer.

(Immunology series ; 23)
Includes indexes.
1. Tumor antigens. 2. Antibodies, Monoclonal.
3. Cancer—Immunological aspects. I. Wright, George L.,
[date] II. Series. [DNLM: 1. Neoplasms—
Immunology. 2. Antibodies, Monoclonal. W1 IM53K v.22 /
QZ 200 M751]
RC268.3.M66   1984   616.99'40792   83-26344
ISBN 0-8247-7073-0

MARCEL DEKKER, INC.
270 Madison Avenue, New York, New York 10016

Current printing (last digit):
10 9 8 7 6 5 4 3 2

PRINTED IN THE UNITED STATES OF AMERICA

FOREWORD

Nothing is more obvious to the biologist than that there is a fundamental difference between a normal cell and a cancer cell. The malignant cell looks different and behaves differently in the test tube or in the animal. Yet nothing has frustrated more distinguished investigators than their inability to identify distinctive antigenic properties of the cancer cell.

On careful reflection, the reasons for this frustration become evident. The cancer cell presents a great variety of antigenic determinants to the immunized host, but only a small number of them are unique for the malignancy. Until now, the investigator had to absorb out a multitude of unwanted antibodies to pick out the few that were fully or largely specific; that is, the ones that reacted predominantly with determinants of the malignant cells.

This bleak picture changed dramatically in 1975 with the introduction of in vitro hybridization as a method of producing monoclonal antibodies. In the few years since the description of this new technique, discovery has followed discovery with breathtaking speed. This book gathers together a cross section of these findings. Antibodies targeting a variety of different solid tumors and leukemias are described. Their immediate application to diagnosis and prognosis is described. The potential of monoclonals as carriers of diagnostic radioisotopes or therapeutic drugs is also considered.

During the first seventy-odd years of tumor immunology, one was inclined to ask: "whether." Now the question has become: "when." An immunological attack on cancer is at last imminent.

Noel R. Rose

PREFACE

The lymphocyte hybridoma technique introduced by Köhler and Milstein, in 1975, for the production of monoclonal antibodies, has already had a tremendous impact in many areas of biology and medicine, including the study of cancer. One of the major questions that has concerned biologists for years has been whether human tumors expressed tumor-specific antigens analogous to the tumor-specific transplantation antigens found associated with virus and chemically induced animal tumors. Although, as this book illustrates, the generation of monoclonal antibodies against human tumors has so far failed to uncover a human tumor-specific antigen, several new specificities have been identified which potentially may have clinical application. Monoclonal antibodies to normal lymphocyte differentiation antigens, for example, have permitted a more specific classification of leukemia and T-cell lymphomas permitting more efficient treatment monitoring and prognosis. The possibility of using these monoclonal antibodies for serodiagnosis and for removing tumor cells from autologous bone marrow appears to be promising as an adjunct in the treatment of leukemia patients. Moreover, many of the antigens identified by monoclonal antibodies on solid human tumors also appear to be differentiation antigens. The effective therapeutic use of monoclonal antibodies to solid tumors may require conjugation of the monoclonal antibodies with plant or bacterial toxins, drugs, or isotopes. Furthermore, the immunoglobulin class or subclass of the monoclonal may be particularly important in obtaining a desired clinical application. For example, the mouse IgG2a subclass appears, at present, to be the major murine immunoglobulin class capable of activating human effector cells (macrophages) to mediated antibody-dependent cytodestruction of human tumor cells. Present studies also suggest that monoclonal antibodies directed against antigens shared by tumor cells and some kinds of normal cells may, under certain situations, be useful for diagnosis, classification, monitoring, and serotherapy of cancer.

The purpose of this volume has been to provide a concise overview of some of the specificities identified on human tumor cells by first-generation monoclonal antibodies. It was not possible in this volume to discuss the studies being done on all human tumors. Whenever possible the authors have compared monoclonal antibodies generated in their laboratory with those produced by other investigators. Detailed descriptions of methods have been purposely omitted, since these can be found in several recent books and monographs. Particular topics covered in this volume relate to the immunohistochemical identification and classification of tumors, problems associated with tumor cell heterogeneity, the need for well-characterized panels of monoclonal antibodies, radioimmunologic imaging of primary and secondary tumors, in vivo and in vitro serotherapy using conjugated and unconjugated monoclonal antibodies, animal models for evaluating the therapeutic application of monoclonal antibodies, and the use of monoclonal antibodies as probes for dissecting tumor-associated antigens. An underlying theme throughout this volume is the problems associated with assessing the specificity of the monoclonal antibodies. Regardless if any of the monoclonal antibodies described in this book will eventually be part of a diagnostic or therapeutic workup, they should prove to be valuable for understanding the dynamics of antigen expression on human tumor cells.

It is hopeful that the reader of this book will find an appreciation for both the problems and rewards in using monoclonal antibodies to study human cancer. Several important contributions have been made and there is every reason to believe that even wider applications will be discovered for this significant advance in biological science. We can look forward with immense enthusiasm and great expectation toward the next phase in the development and application of mouse as well as human monoclonal antibodies for the study, diagnosis, and therapy of human cancer.

A great deal of new data has accumulated since the submission of the original manuscripts for publication of this book. It was decided to include a final "Recent Developments" chapter in order to give the authors an opportunity to update their contributions just prior to publication. I am grateful to those authors who responded to this request to make the book as current as possible at the time of publication. Also I wish to extend my deepest appreciation to Lucy Krauss for her expert secretarial assistance and to Adrienne Cox for help with the index. Without their interest and dedication this project would never have been completed. I am also grateful to the following companies who provided the funds which made it possible to include the color plates of immunoperoxidase and radioimmunologic imaging results: Meloy Laboratories, Revlon Health Care Group; Vector Laboratories, Inc.; DAKO Corporation; Accurate Chemical and Scientific Corporation and Sera-Lab Limited; Hybritech, Inc.; and Ortho Pharmaceutical Corporation.

George L. Wright, Jr.

CONTENTS

CONTRIBUTORS

Paul G. Abrams, M.D. Biological Response Modifiers Program, Division of Cancer Treatment, National Cancer Institute—Frederick Cancer Research Facility, Frederick, Maryland

Robert C. Bast, Jr., M.D. Division of Tumor Immunology, Dana-Farber Cancer Institute; Department of Medicine, Brigham and Women's Hospital; and Department of Medicine, Harvard Medical School, Boston, Massachusetts

Mary Lou Beckett, M.S. Department of Microbiology and Immunology, and Immunology Program, Eastern Virginia Medical School, Norfolk, Virginia

Joseph P. Brown, Ph.D. Program in Tumor Immunology, Fred Hutchinson Cancer Research Center, Seattle, Washington

Franz Buchegger Institute of Biochemistry, University of Lausanne, Epalinges-sur-Lausanne, Switzerland

Desmond N. Carney, M.D., Ph.D., M.R. C.P.F. NCI-Navy Medical Oncology Branch, Division of Cancer Treatment, National Cancer Institute, National Institutes of Health, and the National Naval Medical Center, Bethesda, Maryland

Stefan Carrel, Ph.D. Ludwig Institute for Cancer Research, Lausanne Branch, Epalinges-sur-Lausanne, Switzerland

David Colcher, Ph.D. Laboratory of Tumor Immunology and Biology, National Cancer Institute, National Institutes of Health, Bethesda, Maryland

Frank Cuttitta, Ph.D. NCI-Navy Medical Oncology Branch, the National Naval Medical Center, Bethesda, Maryland

Frank H. DeLand, M.D. Department of Radiation Medicine, Division of Nuclear Medicine, University of Kentucky and Veterans Administration Medical Centers, Lexington, Kentucky

Benoit de Muralt, M.D. Neurosurgical Service, Centre Hospitalier Universitaire Vaudois, Lausanne, Switzerland

Nicolas de Tribolet, M.D. Neurological Service, Centre Hospitalier Universitaire Vaudois, Lausanne, Switzerland

Michael Jim Embleton, Ph.D. Cancer Research Campaign Laboratories, University of Nottingham, Nottingham, England

Silvia Fargion, M.D. NCI-Navy Medical Oncology Branch, Division of Cancer Treatment, National Cancer Institute, National Institutes of Health, and the National Naval Medical Center, Bethesda, Maryland

Joseph Fedorko, M.S. NCI-Navy Medical Oncology Branch, Division of Cancer Treatment, National Cancer Institute, National Institutes of Health, and the National Naval Medical Center, Bethesda, Maryland ·

Adi F. Gazdar, M.D. NCI-Navy Medical Oncology Branch, Division of Cancer Treatment, National Cancer Institute, National Institutes of Health, and the National Naval Medical Center, Bethesda, Maryland

David M. Goldenberg, Sc.D., M.D.* Division of Experimental Pathology, University of Kentucky, and Albert B. Chandler Medical Center, Lexington, Kentucky

Melvyn F. Greaves, Ph.D., M.R.C. Path. Membrane Immunology Laboratory, Imperial Cancer Research Fund, London, England

Teresa Gregorio, M.D. NCI-Navy Medical Oncology Branch, Division of Cancer Treatment, National Cancer Institute, National Institutes of Health, and the National Naval Medical Center, Bethesda, Maryland

Patricia Horan Hand, Ph.D. Laboratory of Tumor Immunology and Biology, National Cancer Institute, National Institutes of Health, Bethesda, Maryland

Ingegerd Hellström, Ph.D., M.D.† Department of Microbiology/Immunology, University of Washington, and Program in Tumor Immunology, Fred Hutchinson Cancer Research Center, Seattle, Washington

Karl Erik Hellström, Ph.D., M.D.† Department of Pathology, University of Washington, and Program in Tumor Immunology, Fred Hutchinson Cancer Research Center, Seattle, Washington

John T. Kemshead, Ph.D. Imperial Cancer Research Fund Oncology Laboratory, Institute of Child Health, London, England

---

Present affiliations:

*Institute for Molecular Immunology, Center for Molecular Medicine and Immunology, University of Medicine and Dentistry of New Jersey, Newark, New Jersey

†Oncogen, Seattle, Washington

Mary E. Kirch, Ph.D. Immunology Unit, Sloan-Kettering Institute, New York, New York

Robert C. Knapp, M.D. Division of Tumor Immunology, Gynecologic Oncology, Dana-Farber Cancer Institute; Department of Obstetrics and Gynecology, Brigham and Women's Hospital; and Department of Obstetrics and Gynecology, Harvard Medical School, Boston, Massachusetts

Donald Kufe, M.D. * Laboratory of Tumor Immunology and Biology, National Cancer Institute, National Institutes of Health, Bethesda, Maryland

Herbert Z. Kupchik, Ph.D. Departments of Microbiology and Pathology, Boston University School of Medicine; The Hubert H. Humphrey Cancer Research Center, Boston University; and the Mallory Institute of Pathology, Boston, Massachusetts

Jean-Pierre Mach, M.D. Ludwig Institute for Cancer Research, Lausanne Branch, Epalinges-sur-Lausanne, Switzerland

John D. Minna, M.D. NCI-Navy Medical Oncology Branch, Division of Cancer Treatment, National Cancer Institute, National Institutes of Health, and the National Naval Medical Center, Bethesda, Maryland

Terry W. Moody, Ph.D.† NCI-Naval Medical Oncology Branch, the National Naval Medical Center, Bethesda, Maryland

James Mulshine, M.D. NCI-Navy Medical Oncology Branch, Division of Cancer Treatment, National Cancer Institute, National Institutes of Health, and the National Naval Medical Center, Bethesda, Maryland

Marianna Nuti, Ph.D. Laboratory of Tumor Immunology and Biology, National Cancer Institute, National Institutes of Health, Bethesda, Maryland

F. James Primus, Ph.D.‡ Department of Pathology, Division of Experimental Pathology, University of Kentucky, Lexington, Kentucky

Steven T. Rosen, M.D.§ NCI-Navy Medical Oncology Branch, the National Naval Medical Center, Bethesda, Maryland

---

*Also affiliated with the Division of Medicine, Dana-Farber Cancer Institute, Boston, Massachusetts

Present affiliations:

†Department of Biochemistry, George Washington University School of Medicine and Health Sciences, Washington, D.C.

‡Institute for Molecular Immunology, Center for Molecular Medicine and Immunology, University of Medicine and Dentistry of New Jersey, Newark, New Jersey

§Section of Medical Oncology, Northwestern University Department of Medicine, Chicago, Illinois

Jeffrey Schlom, Ph.D. Laboratory of Tumor Immunology and Biology, National Cancer Institute, National Institutes of Health, Bethesda, Maryland

Magali Schreyer Ludwig Institute for Cancer Research, Lausanne Branch, Epalinges-sur-Lausanne, Switzerland

James J. Starling, Ph.D. Department of Biochemistry, and Immunology Program, Eastern Virginia Medical School, Norfolk, Virginia

Sylvia Stephenson, M.D. NCI-Navy Medical Oncology Branch, Division of Cancer Treatment, National Cancer Institute, National Institutes of Health, and the National Naval Medical Center, Bethesda, Maryland

Yoshio A. Teramoto, Ph.D. Laboratory of Tumor Immunology and Biology, National Cancer Institute, National Institutes of Health, Bethesda, Maryland

Laida Vodinelich, Ph.D. Membrane Immunology Laboratory, Imperial Cancer Research Fund, London, England

George L. Wright, Jr., Ph.D. Department of Microbiology and Immunology, and Immunology Program, Eastern Virginia Medical School, Norfolk, Virginia

David Wunderlich Laboratory of Tumor Immunology and Biology, National Cancer Institute, National Institutes of Health, Bethesda, Maryland

Monoclonal Antibodies and Cancer

1 APPLICATION OF MONOCLONAL ANTIBODIES TO THE STUDY OF HUMAN CANCER

George L. Wright, Jr. / Eastern Virginia Medical School, Norfolk, Virginia

INTRODUCTION

One of the goals of cancer researchers has been to identify and isolate specific tumor antigens that could be used to improve the diagnosis and therapy of human cancer. The suggestion that human tumor cells might possess specific components capable of distinguishing malignant cells from normal cells and even malignant cells of one tumor type from a histologically different tumor was derived from the discovery of the tumor-specific transplantation antigens found on tumors induced in rodents with chemical carcinogens and oncogenic viruses (1,2). The search for similar transplantation antigens on human tumor cells was stymied from the very beginning. The experimental method so crucial in the discovery of tumor-specific transplantation antigens in animal models, namely, the transplantation of a malignant tumor from a tumor-bearing animal to a normal syngeneic recipient, was not ethically possible. Other approaches and more sensitive methods, for example, radioimmunoassay (RIA) and cell-mediated methodologies, needed to be developed. During this developmental period, doubt began to emerge as to whether tumor-specific antigens did indeed exist on human tumors. The discovery of alpha-fetoprotein (AFP) and carcinoembryonic antigen (CEA) in the mid 1960s (3-5) stimulated renewed interest and hope that human tumors did in fact contain components that were specific to human neoplasms. Although early studies suggested that elevated serum levels of these tumor substances may be diagnostic of hepatocellular cancer (i.e., AFP) and colonic cancer (i.e., CEA), subsequent studies, using more sensitive immunoassays, showed that AFP and CEA may be elevated in other types of cancer and nonmalignant conditions. Because higher concentrations could be demonstrated in the serum from cancer patients, the term *tumor-associated antigen* began to be used to indicate that CEA and AFP were tumor-related but not tumor specific.

The demonstration that sensitive immunoassays could detect small quantities of antigens associated with malignant cells in body fluids was the stimulus for other investigators to attempt to identify tumor antigens associated with other human cancers. Moreover, since it was felt by some cancer immunologists that cell-mediated immunity was the most important immune response directed against cancer, the development of assays to measure this response was thought to be critical not only for understanding the importance and mechanism of cell-mediated immune responses, but to identify the tumor antigens responsible for inciting the specific cell-mediated immune anti-tumor response.

This resulted in a plethora of publications on the study of both cellular and humoral immune responses of cancer patients, with claims and counterclaims for the existence of tumor-specific antigens present on human tumors. However, these studies failed to provide crucial evidence for the existence of specific human cancer antigens. Therefore the general view that tumor-specific antigens have been demonstrated in any human cancer cannot be justified. The long-standing issue continues to be in evaluating the specificity of the putative tumor-antigens (2). Most of the initial claims for specific tumor antigens have subsequently been shown to be based on a quantitative rather than a qualitative difference and therefore these antigens must, at best, be referred to as being tumor associated. It must be understood, however, that most of what is known at present about human cancer cell-surface antigens is derived from testing heterologous antiserum raised in animals against cancer cells or from testing sera and lymphocytes from cancer patients on fresh cancer cells or established cancer cell lines. The candidate tumor antigens so defined have turned out to be (a) differentiation antigens, that is, antigens characteristic of normal cells at some stage of development rather than antigens restricted to cancer cells, such as the surface markers found on both normal lymphocytes and leukemia/lymphoma neoplastic cells; (b) the loss or gain of normal antigens, for example, products of the HLA complex and ABO locus, the latter being found especially but not only with bladder cancer; and (c) antigens shared by fetal tissues and tumors, like CEA and AFP, and now referred to as oncodevelopmental antigens. For a description of many of the better-known cancer markers (antigens) associated with human tumors, the reader is referred to *Human Cancer Markers,* edited by Sell and Wahren (6).

It should be realized that the components on tumor cell surfaces that have been called antigens are so designated because they are capable of eliciting an immune response in an unrelated or nonimmune experimental animal. It still remains to be determined what is the primary biological function of these surface "antigens." The discovery of these cell-surface neoplastic-associated antigens, which can under appropriate conditions distinguish cancer cells from normal cells, has been the starting point of attempts to develop more sensitive and specific tools for the diagnosis and monitoring of human cancer, to control cancer by immunological means, and as probes to explore oncological transformation at the cell membrane level. However, further studies will be required to determine if tumor-specific antigens exist on human tumors and if the host responds to them immunologically before a rational approach for immunodiagnosis and treatment of cancer can be developed. The detection of tumor antigens having the "ideal" characteristics (Table 1) for diagnostic and therapeutic application may be facilitated by a recent major biotechnical advance: the lymphocyte hybridoma technique.

SOMATIC CELL HYBRIDIZATION: BIRTH OF A HYBRIDOMA

Ever since the discovery of naturally occurring human myeloma proteins, immunologists have attempted to find methods of immunization that would produce large amounts of homogeneous and functional antibodies. These homogeneous human myeloma immunoglobulins became instrumental and necessary for elucidating the chemical structure of immunoglobulins. But in spite of the usefulness of these naturally occurring monoclonal antibodies or those from

Table 1 Ideal Properties of Biological Markers of Tumor Activity

Tumor-specific and specific for recurrent tumor

Indicator of tumor burden of host

Prognosticator of outcome

Predictor of recurrence

Lead to more effective treatment

Table 2 Some Important Events Leading to the Development of the Hybridoma Technique

Year	Investigators	Event	Reference
1846	Dalrymple	Discovery of human multiple myeloma	8
1848	Bence Jones	Discovery of unique substance (immunoglobulin) in urine of myeloma patients	9
1906	Ehrlich	Discovery of antibodies	10
1950s	Burnet	Proposed clonal hypothesis to explain monoclonality of antibody formation	11
1951	Rask-Nielson and Gormsen	Discovery of plasma cell tumors in mice	12
1954	Dunn		13
1961	Kritzman et al.	Recognition that myeloma proteins	14
1964	Waldenström et al.	were immunoglobulins and that human myelomas were a source of naturally occurring monoclonal antibodies	15
1962	Potter and Boyce	Induced myelomas in mice that produced large amounts of monoclonal immunoglobulins	16
1964	Littlefield	Showed chemically how to select hybrid cells by poisoning parental lines; developed HAT selective method	17
1966	Fahler et al.	Transformed B lymphocytes with virus to obtain homogeneous antibodies	18
1967	Pettengill and Sorensen	Successful establishment of murine myeloma cell lines	19
1970	Horibata and Harris		20
1970	Laskov and Scharff		21
1970	Laskov and Scharff	Somatic hybridization of myeloma cells to study the genetics of immunoglobulin production	21
1973	Cotton et al.		22
1975	Köhler and Milstein	Development of the lymphocyte hybridoma technique	7

Table 2 (Continued)

1977	Galfré et al.	Used polyethylene glycol to improve fusion efficiency	23
1978	Shulman et al.	Isolated non-immunoglobulin-	24
1979	Kearney et al.	producing murine myeloma cell variants	25
1980	Olsson and Kaplan	Production of human hybridomas by fusing human spleen cells with human myeloma cell line	26

experimentally induced mouse myeloma tumors for facilitating the study of the biochemistry and cell biology of immunoglobulin synthesis, myelomas are not a useful source of monoclonal antibodies to defined antigens. Homogeneous antibodies directed to defined antigens were early recognized as essential to study the genetics of antibody diversity. The solution for obtaining homogeneous (monoclonal) antibodies to specific antigenic determinants came in 1975 with the development of the lymphocyte hybridoma technique by Köhler and Milstein (7).

However, in order to appreciate the full significance of their discovery, it is important to point out that the research aims of these investigators were not the production of monoclonal antibodies, but to use somatic cell myeloma hybrids to study the genetic organization and expression of immunoglobulins. Had the objectives been solely to produce monoclonal antibodies, it is unlikely that these investigators would have been working on both mutant mouse myeloma cell lines and mouse myeloma hybrids in the same laboratory—the combination that led to the first successful experiment to produce monoclonal antibodies to red blood cell antigens (7). The birth of the hybridization technique for generating monoclonal antibodies to defined antigens, as so often happens in biological science, was the result of a series of basic and completely unrelated experiments. Table 2 lists some of these experiments, including the discovery of human plasma cell neoplasms, the discovery of myeloma proteins, the discovery that myeloma proteins were immunoglobulins, and the concept of monoclonality (i.e., each antibody-producing cell produces one antibody type). The methodology that led directly to the hybridoma technology was an extension of the principles of somatic cell hybridization established and used by geneticists for many years to generate somatic cell hybrids in order to study gene expression in animal cells. Crucial to the lymphocyte hybrid experiments was the availability of established mouse myeloma cell lines (19-21) that had been derived from mouse myeloma tumors (12,13,16,27), and the selective medium developed by Littlefield (17) needed for isolation of the lymphocyte hybrids from the nonfused myeloma cells.

THE MOUSE-MOUSE HYBRIDOMA TECHNIQUE FOR PRODUCING
MONOCLONAL ANTIBODIES TO TUMOR ANTIGENS

Although some technical advances have been made, most notably the use of non-immunoglobulin-secreting myeloma fusion partners (24,25) and polyethylene glycol (23) as a fusing agent, the basic lymphocyte hybridoma technique used by Köhler and Milstein is employed for generating monoclonal antibodies to tumor antigens. Below is described a generalized protocol for the preparation of anti-human tumor monoclonal antibodies. The technical details for each step of the protocol can be found in several recent monographs (28-34).

The usual approach is to hyperimmunize mice with tumor cells (either established tumor cell lines or cell suspensions from tumor tissues) or crude cell membrane extracts (either particulate or soluble). The immunization schedule, and choice and preparation of antigenic material are so variable that it is impossible to describe an immunization protocol that always will be successful in generating the desired hybrid. If one approach fails to produce the desired monoclonal antibodies, then alternative strategies, including a different antigen source, modified ways of preparing cell membranes, other animals, or varied immunization routes and schedules are employed for producing specific hybrids. Usually 2-4 days following the last antigen injection, the mice are sacrificed and the spleens removed and teased apart to form a suspension of spleen cells. The spleen cells are mixed with a mouse myeloma cell, usually one of the non-immunoglobulin-secreting variants (Table 3), which is 8-azaguanine resistant—due to loss of the

Table 3 Murine Cell Lines for Hybridoma Procedure

Cell line	Immunoglobulin		Reference
	Origin	Chain secreted	
P3-x63-Ag8	Mouse[a]	IgG_1 (κ)	7
P3-NS1-1-Ag4-1	Mouse	κ[b]	35
MPC11-45·6TG1·7	Mouse	IgG_{2b} (κ)	36
SP/2-Ag14	Mouse	None	24
S194/5°XXO°BU·1	Mouse	None	37
P3-x63-Ag·653	Mouse	None	25
210·TCY3·Ag·1·2·3	Rat[c]	κ	38

[a]Origin of all mouse myeloma lines from strain BALB/c.
[b]κ chains synthesized but not secreted; secreted by hybridomas.
[c]Strain Lou.

enzyme hypoxanthine phosphoribosyl transferase (HPRT)—and has been adapted to grow in continuous culture (i.e., immortalized). Polyethylene glycol is added to the cell mixture to promote fusion of the cell membranes, and the cells are suspended in a tissue culture medium containing hypoxanthine, aminopterin, and thymidine (HAT selective medium). Because only a few cells form viable hybrids, it is necessary to have a method for selecting the hybrids from the unfused cells. The HAT selection method (17) used in the first successful fusion experiments (7) is usually adapted. The unfused myeloma cells die in HAT tissue culture medium because they lack the HPRT enzyme needed to synthesize purines from the salvage pathway, while the aminopterin blocks the de novo synthesis of purines and pyrimidines. The unfused spleen cells do not survive in any culture medium for long periods and eventually die or are overgrown by the hybrids. The hybrid cell resulting from the fusion between the myeloma cell and spleen cell (activated B lymphocyte or immunoblast) survives in HAT medium because the hybrid acquires the HPRT enzyme from the normal spleen cell.

The next step is screening the supernatant (culture media) from growing hybrids for antibody production and specificity. Since the nature of the tumor antigens is unknown, it is necessary to screen many fusion products to find one hybrid producing antibody of the desired specificity. Screening is the most labor intensive and expensive phase of the hybridoma technique, since literally hundreds or thousands of supernatants will most likely have to be screened to find a few hybrids secreting antibodies of the preferred specificity. For initial screening solid-phase radioimmunoassay (RIA) or enzyme-linked immunosorbent assay (ELISA) is usually employed, although indirect immunofluorescence (IF) and immunoperoxidase (IP) assays have also been used. The former assays (RIA and ELISA) are frequently used because they are rapid, sensitive, and provide quantitative data, whereas IF, IP, hemagglutination inhibition (HI), and cytotoxic assays are used to confirm the specificities of the monoclonal antibodies, as are absorption, blocking, and inhibition versions of these assays. Selected hybrids are then cloned by limiting dilution or in semisolid agar, the supernatant of the clones retested, and the active and specific clones recloned and retested. This procedure eliminates contamination from non-antibody-producing clones and cells that have lost their ability to produce antibody as a result of chromosomal loss. Clonality is determined by finding a single immunoglobulin isotype and one heavy and one light chain band in gel electrophoresis. The specificity of antibody is confirmed by more extensive testing using a combination of several of the assays mentioned above. The specific hybrids are frozen and preserved in liquid nitrogen to ensure a continuous supply of monoclonal antibodies.

The screening strategy is most important and key to the successful isolation of a hybrid producing antibody of the desired specificity. Selecting the right strategy can save an insurmountable amount of time and energy by not wasting time and expense on monoclonal antibodies subsequently shown to lack specificity. The selected hybrids will depend largely on the source and form of immunogen used (e.g., cell lines, tumor tissue, membranes, soluble) and the antibody activity wanted (e.g., cytotoxic, high-affinity antibody). Although many different strategies can be developed, two examples are given below.

Strategy When Using Tumor Cell Lines as Immunogen

Mice are immunized with an established prostate tumor cell line. The fusion products are screened using an RIA or ELISA with the prostate tumor cell line (immunogen) and one or more different cell lines of malignant or normal cells as antigen targets. The hybrids that produce antibodies which preferentially bind to the immunogen are doubly cloned and the supernatant subjected to extensive testing on many malignant and normal cell lines by RIA or ELISA and membrane IF (direct binding or following absorption). Important early in this strategy would be to determine if the most specific antiprostate tumor monoclonal antibodies bind to tissue antigens. This can be done on frozen or embedded tissue sections by indirect IF or IP. Another method currently used in our laboratory (39) is a direct binding autoradiographic procedure using crude normal and malignant membrane extracts fixed to wells of microtiter plates as the antigen source. Monoclonal antibodies that are found to have specificity for prostate tumor cell lines but not for prostate tumor tissue would, of course, not be applicable for diagnosis or therapy. This strategy allows the specificity of the monoclonal antibody to be characterized as recognizing a normal or possibly tumor-specific determinant. The argument for not using established tumor cell lines for generating hybrids is that the established cell selected during culture may not be representative of the in vivo tumor, or that antigen modulation has resulted in the loss or gain of membrane antigens. The results from several studies (40-49; see also Chapters 2, 4, and 10 of this volume) using cell lines as immunogens would suggest, however, that at least some tumor cell lines do retain high concentrations of surface tumor-associated antigens, and that monoclonal antibodies directed against these tumor antigens are also found on tumor tissues. An obvious advantage of these cell lines would be to provide a continuous and homogeneous supply of the tumor antigens, which in turn would be a valuable source for purification of the tumor antigens.

Strategy When Using Tumor Tissue as Immunogen

Mice are immunized with cell membranes prepared from surgically removed prostate adenocarcinoma tissue. The fusion products are screened using an autoradiographic or quantitative RIA or IP on several prostate tumor membrane preparations (including the membrane preparation used as the immunogen) from both primary and metastatic tumors, several normal tissue membrane preparations, and membranes prepared from several other types of malignant tissues. The initial screening might be by the qualitative RIA (autoradiographic), and the reactive monoclonal antibodies retested by the quantitative RIA. After the selected hybrids have been cloned, the monoclonal antibodies showing the greatest specificity are retested by RIA or ELISA and IF on cell lines to further assess the specificity of the monoclonal antibodies and to determine if the antibodies bind to any prostate tumor cell lines. The monoclonal antibodies are also tested on frozen or fixed tissue sections of many normal tissues (including tissue of tumor origin) and sections of other types of tumor tissues by IF and/or IP. Important in screening and determining the specificity of the monoclonal antibodies by whichever strategy is selected is to use more than one type of immunoassay. Although simple binding assays, such as RIA and ELISA, are more sensitive than other immunoassays, they may not detect certain specificities. Specificities missed by RIA on cell membranes have been subsequently detected by absorption and IF (48-50). The immunohistochemical techniques, particularly IP, are being recognized as important assays for elucidating the specificity of monoclonal antibodies to tumor antigens (47,51,52; see also Chapters 5,6, and 10). Additional qualitative and semiquantitative information can be gleaned from the histological tissue reactivity. By properly selecting tissue sections displaying both normal and tumor cells, one can easily observe the reactivity of the monoclonal antibodies to either normal or tumor cells or both cell types on the same tissue sections. By comparing tumor samples from different patients with the same histological tumor, one can obtain information relevant to diagnosis or treatment. Based on the IP reaction, it may even be possible to better relate the histological grade of the tumor with the clinical status of the patient. With the present "state of the art," it would appear that the immunoperoxidase technique may provide more pertinent information than can be obtained by assessing monoclonal antibody reactivity with tissue homogenates, membrane preparations (by absorption, binding, or immunoprecipitation methods), or established tumor cell lines. Immunohistochemical techniques may become the best approach for screening monoclonal antibodies for possible usefulness for radioimmunolocalization of tumor metastases and for immunotherapy.

An additional desirable control in assessing the specificity of monoclonal antibodies to human tumor cells is to test their reactivity to erythrocytes and peripheral blood lymphocytes to rule out cross-reactivity to HLA and ABO antigens.

Early reports suggested that tumor-specific monoclonal antibodies had been produced; but after more extensive testing such antibodies have been found to react with different histological tumors and certain fetal or adult normal cells (53,54). It is becoming clear that specificity testing is extremely difficult, but immensely important (2). To test exclusively on cell lines is not sufficient, because, as mentioned before, they may not represent the tumor cell present in vivo and usually are derived from a limited spectrum of tissue. Furthermore, the absence of reaction with a particular cell type may in reality be a measurement of the sensitivity of the technique used, again emphasizing the need to confirm the specific reactivity of the monoclonal antibodies by several different immunoassays.

PRODUCTION OF HUMAN MONOCLONAL ANTIBODIES

A potential problem with the immunization of rodents with human tumor cells is that most of the hybridomas produce monoclonal antibodies against species-specific antigens. Another is the potential risk of developing serum sickness (i.e., immune complex disease) using rodent monoclonal antibodies for passive immunotherapy in humans. Anticipation of these and other potential problems with mouse monoclonal antibodies has led to efforts to develop human monoclonal antibodies. Human myeloma cells or immortalized B lymphocytes capable of fusing with human lymphocytes would be useful for (a) producing human monoclonal antibodies to human allogeneic antigens present on human tumor cells (as recognized by the human immune system), (b) detecting preexisting immune responses to the tumor antigens or autoantigens that are produced in the tumor patient's draining lymph nodes, and (c) producing human antibody for possible therapeutic application.

An alternative for producing human monoclonal antibodies has been attempts to transform B lymphocytes with viruses (18, 55-58). Recently Steinitz and associates (56) succeeded in the transformation of antigen-specific lymphocytes with Epstein-Barr (EB) virus. This procedure requires transformation of presensitized peripheral blood lymphocytes from donors with high natural antibody titer to a particular antigen and enrichment of the specific antigen-binding lymphocytes prior to viral transformation. This approach has led to the production of potentially clinically useful human monoclonal antibodies (57,58). However, most of the EB-transformed lymphoblastoid lines secrete relatively low amounts of antibody. Another problem with this technique is that it will be limited to only a few antigens, since it is not ethical to immunize humans with antigen mixtures specifically for this purpose. Another ethical consideration is the possible transfer of a potential cancer-producing virus with the human antibodies used for therapy. These problems could perhaps be overcome by EB transformation of peripheral blood or tonsillar lymphocytes following in vitro immunization to a particular antigen. The potential usefulness of this method for producing monoclonal antibodies to human tumor antigens must await further developments.

The production of human monoclonal antibodies by the hybridoma technique has not been very productive to date. One of the first attempts to produce human anti-tumor monoclonal antibodies employed the fusion of human lymphocytes obtained from the tumor patient's draining lymph nodes with mouse myeloma cells (51). Although successful, the labor involved in obtaining a few stable hybrids secreting desirable human monoclonal antibodies is far greater than that in fusing with mouse lymphocytes because of the preferential loss of human chromosomes. This leads to frequent loss of human immunoglobulin production, although the hybrid may continue to grow. The human-mouse approach is essentially a "fishing" expedition. One has to assume that at least one clone of lymphocytes in the draining lymph node has been sensitized to the patient's tumor antigen. The search for a hybrid secreting monoclonal antibody to the tumor antigen is intensified, requiring the possible need to sort out monoclonal antibodies to a variety of nontumor antigen specificities, for example, autoantigens, infectious disease antigens, and private antigens.

The most likely reason for the limited progress made to date in the production of human-human hybridomas has been the lack of a suitable human myeloma fusion partner. Recently Olsson and Kaplan (26) described the first successful human-human hybrid producing a human monoclonal antibody. They obtained an 8-azaguanine-resistant variant, designated SKO-007 (which secretes IgE), that was derived from the human myeloma cell line U266, and fused it with cells from a spleen removed from a Hodgkin's disease patient to generate an IgM-secreting hybrid with specificity to dinitrochlorobenzene. Although this monoclonal antibody is probably of no clinical value, their results indicate the feasibility of this technical approach. They also were subsequently successful in generating IgM monoclonal antibodies to sheep red blood cells and endotoxin after in vitro immunization of Hodgkin's spleen cells and normal peripheral blood lymphocytes, respectively, followed by fusion with the SKO-007 line. This indicated that the human-human hybridoma technique could also be performed in vitro. Unfortunately, the SKO-007 line became contaminated with mycoplasma shortly after these successful reports and only recently has been cured of this bacterial contaminant. A stable variant of the SKO-007 line with high fusibility has once again been obtained and only recently sent to other laboratories. Therefore whether the SKO-007 myeloma cell line will result in clinically useful human anti-cancer monoclonal antibodies is unknown.

Extensive research efforts by other investigators has resulted in recent reports of at least five other human-human hybridoma systems. In at least two of these reports (59,60) successful fusions were performed with human lymphocytes immunized in vitro and fused with human lymphoblastoid lines. A list of these human-human hybridoma systems is presented in Table 4. Some or all of the following problems, however, exist with all of these systems, including the

Table 4 Possible Human Lymphocyte Lines for Hybridoma Procedure

| Cell line | Immunoglobulin | | Reference |
	Origin	Chain secreted	
SKO-007	Myeloma	IgE (λ)	26
GM 1500 6TG·A1·2	Myeloma	IgG$_2$ (κ)	62
RPMI 8226	Myeloma	λ	63
WI·2·729HF$_2$	Lymphoblastoid	None	59,60
LICR-LON-HMy$_2$	Lymphoblastoid[a]	IgG$_1$ (κ)	64
LSM 2·7	Myeloma	None	65
HFB-1	Myeloma	None	66

[a]May not be true myeloma cell line, as line expresses EB virus nuclear antigens (64,67).

SKO-007 human-human hybridoma system: (a) the need to conduct experiments in vitro rather than in vivo because of ethical considerations, (b) the toxicity of the fusion step, (c) presence of EB virus-positive lymphoblastoid lines, (d) human myeloma or lymphoblastoid lines secreting immunoglobulin, (e) most of the human monoclonal antibodies being low-affinity IgM antibodies, and (f) most of the human-human hybrids secreting low levels of monoclonal antibodies. Like the SKO-007 hybridoma system, it has yet to be determined if any of these human-human hybridoma systems will have any utility for producing human monoclonal antibodies to human tumor antigens. None of the human myeloma or lymphoblastoid lines described thus far would appear to have the necessary requirements, for example, stable variant, non-immunoglobulin-secreting, and high fusion frequency, to be good fusion partners when compared with some of the murine myeloma lines (e.g., P3-x-68-Ag8·653, NS-1). Although there still remain a number of technical difficulties with the in vitro immunization procedure, the key to successful application of this approach for generating human monoclonal antibodies to tumor antigens will be (a) to derive a suitable non-immunoglobulin-secreting human myeloma or B-lymphocyte cell line, (b) determine the appropriate lymphocyte source (i.e., lymph nodes, peripheral blood lymphocytes, tonsils) for in vitro sensitization; and (c) determine the optimal in vitro conditions for immunization (namely, the need for growth factors, prestimulation with mitogens, antigen preparation and concentration, length of immunization period, and influence of genetic restriction). The reader is referred to an excellent review by Reading (61) concerning the methods and mechanisms for in vitro immunization and monoclonal antibody formation. Extensive and rigorous efforts are being undertaken with this objective in mind.

Table 5 Potential Uses of Monoclonal Antibodies for the Diagnosis and Therapy of Cancer

Diagnosis

    Early detection of localized disease

    Differential diagnosis, i.e., benign or malignant tumor

    Correlate clinical status of malignancy with biological status, i.e., stage and grade of tumor

        Increase or deletion of normal antigens

        Gain, loss, or quantitative increase of tumor antigens

    Radiolocalization of micrometastatic lesions

Screening high-risk populations

Monitoring prognosis

    Correlate tumor antigen patterns with stage and grade of tumor

Monitoring therapy

Therapy

    Passive immunization with cytotoxic monoclonal antibodies

    With monoclonal antibodies coupled with drugs, toxins, or isotopes

Monitoring the cancer patient's immune system before and after surgery

    Determine the number and ratio of different types of immune and hematopoietic stem cells

POTENTIAL APPLICATION OF MONOCLONAL ANTIBODIES TO HUMAN CANCER

The hope of the cancer immunologist and oncologist is that monoclonal antibodies directed to human tumors will revolutionize the approaches for the diagnosis and therapy of cancer (Table 5). In evaluating the potential clinical applications of murine or human monoclonal antibodies, three questions must be asked: (a) Do tumor-specific antigens exist on human tumors? (b) How specific do anti-tumor monoclonal antibodies have to be? (c) And what are the real advantages of monoclonal antibodies over conventional anti-tumor antibodies? The advantages and disadvantages of monoclonal versus conventional antibodies have been discussed in detail in recent reviews and monographs (28,31,68-70) and are listed in Table 6. The preparation of large quantities of homogeneous monospecific antibodies that bind to individual cell types is perhaps the most important benefit of the hybridoma technology. So in this sense monoclonal

Table 6   Advantages and Disadvantages of Hybridoma Methodology for
Producing Monoclonal Antibodies

Advantages

    Impure antigens can be used to generate pure antibodies

    Production of homogeneous antibodies: monoclonal and monospecific

    Provide a continuous and unlimited supply of highly specific, chemically pure
    antibodies

    Extensive and tedious absorption to remove unwanted antibodies not required

Disadvantages or problems

    Almost impossible to obtain an antibody-producing hybridoma to weak im-
    munogens

    Low frequency of fusion—usually only one hybrid developing per 2×10^5
    spleen cells

    Labor intensive—usually taking 4-6 months to generate a stable hybridoma

    Monoclonal antibodies may be very sensitive to physical conditions such as
    pH and temperature that may change the reactivity and functional activity

    Some monoclonal antibodies unable to induce large amounts of ascitic fluid

    Since monoclonal antibodies recognize only single antigenic determinants,
    they cannot form the complex lattice necessary for precipitation

    Some classes or subclasses of antibodies do not fix complement

    Some antibodies are of low affinity (especially IgM antibodies)

    Undesirable cross-reactivity not eliminated by absorption

---

antibodies offer a definition of new specificities, standardization, and unlimited
supply, but they do not work in all assay systems, and in other respects they
may actually be inferior to heterogeneous antibodies. The detection and measurement of the level of expression of an antigenic determinant on cell surfaces
by monoclonal antibodies reflects a number of complex variables, including the
affinity of the antibody, the nature and accessibility of the determinant, the
density (number) of determinant sites, and the type of immunoassay used. The
assays used to measure binding of monoclonal antibodies to cell surfaces, such
as radioimmunoassays, immunofluorescent assays, immunoperoxidase assays,
cytotoxic assays, and immunoprecipitation assays, which vary markedly in levels
of sensitivity and within-assay test variability, can result in strikingly different results. For example, they may have too low an affinity for use in RIA. Because
they bind only to one antigenic site, monoclonal antibodies cannot form the

complex lattice network necessary to form precipitates with the antigen, and some classes or subclasses of antibodies do not fix complement. Therefore the possibility exists that a negative reaction will become positive if a different assay is used. Again this stresses the importance of determining the specificity of monoclonal antibodies by more than one assay. However, these problems are not insurmountable. For example, if cytotoxic or high-affinity monoclonals are desired and are not found on the initial fusion experiment, additional fusion experiments can be performed until a hybridoma is found producing the desired antibody. Because of the expense and labor intensiveness of the hybridoma technique, it is advisable to include early in the screening strategy assays that will measure the desired antibody function. If situations would benefit by a heterogeneous mixture of antibodies, a mixture of monoclonal antibodies may produce the desired reaction. For example, Brown and associates (53,71) found that two monoclonal antibodies directed against different determinants on the same melanoma p97 antigen acted synergistically and enhanced the sensitivity of their assay for measuring the antigen in malignant and normal tissue. They also showed that two monoclonals directed to the p97 antigen also were synergistic to give strong complement-dependent cytotoxicity, when either antibody alone was ineffective (72). Similarly, Goodfliech and associates (73) found that the binding of one monoclonal antibody could be enhanced approximately 100-fold by the addition of a second monoclonal antibody of a different specificity. Technical advances such as these and a better understanding of how to best use monoclonal antibodies will shrink the list of proposed disadvantages.

The question as to whether neoantigens are present on human tumors still remains unanswered despite the large number of monoclonals that have already been produced against several human tumors. The initial claims for human tumor-specific antigens detected by monoclonal antibodies are completely unfounded. The evidence available at the time of this writing indicated that no anti-human tumor monoclonal antibody had been generated that uncovered a tumor-specific antigen after extensive testing of both normal and malignant tissues. The closest example of a human tumor-specific antigen may be the class I or "private" tumor antigens reported by Old (2) that are found only on autologous tumors. However, a tumor-specific antigen, by definition, in my opinion, would be an antigen found on all tumors of the same histological type, but not expressed on normal adult cells or different types of neoplasms. Initial reports describing monoclonal antibodies specific to one or several types of tumors were subsequently found, after extensive testing, to react to normal tissues, but at a much lower concentration. Some of these cross-reactivities with normal tissues, fetal and/or adult, have turned out to be possible differentiation antigens. Others have been identified as reacting to glycolipid antigens, including rare types found on erythrocytes (48,54). The cross-reactivity to antigens expressed on normal tissues may still have clinical utility if they are present in substantially higher (i.e., 10-100 times) quantities in tumor cells than in normal cells. A good example of the usefulness of such monoclonal antibodies is those directed against the differentiation antigens expressed on normal T cells and malignant lymphoid cells (74-76, also see Chapter 8). These monoclonal antibodies are already commercially available and are being used to classify lymphoid malignancies in order to determine which subtypes have uniform prognosis and respond to therapy. Based on this type of information, patients with less severe forms of cancer may be spared unnecessarily harsh treatment. Detection of antigen-bearing leukemia cells in the bone marrow of patients with acute myeloblastic leukemia has provided early signs of relapse (76). Early detection of relapse may allow effective therapy before the disease progresses beyond control. Monoclonal antibodies to lymphocyte differentiation antigens have also recently been used to treat certain types of leukemia (77-81). The potential certainly exists then to generate a panel of monoclonal antibodies with which to serologically characterize the normal cell lineage of solid tumors, and then to use these antibodies to develop diagnostic, prognostic, and therapeutic approaches in a manner similar to the promising use of the monoclonal anti-lymphocyte markers.

The foregoing discussion would suggest that not all clinical applications may require highly specific monoclonal antibodies, that is, directed to tumor-specific antigens. The diagnosis of cancer via the detection of tumor antigens shed in serum or urine might require only that the monoclonal antibody react with the antigen, even if it reacts with other substances not found in these body fluids. The monoclonal antibody DU-PAN-2, recently described by Metzgar et al. (47) and produced against human pancreatic adenocarcinoma cells, may be an example that monoclonal antibodies do not have to be entirely specific for cancer cells to have clinical application. This antibody is present on pancreatic adenocarcinoma and gastric carcinomas as well as on some carcinomas from ovary, breast, colon, and lung. It is also present on normal pancreatic ductal cells. A competition radioimmune assay has been developed and is being used to detect the DU-PAN-2 antigen in pleural and ascitic fluids and sera from patients with adenocarcinomas originating from a variety of organ and tissue sites. Preliminary results on the detection and serial monitoring of serum levels of DU-PAN-2 antigen indicate that this test may be valuable as a diagnostic and/or clinical management aid (82). On the other hand, specificity is critical for radiolocalization of tumor cells in normal tissue and for cytotoxic therapy. So the clinical circumstances or application would appear to dictate how specific the monoclonal antibody needs to be. It would appear from the results obtained thus far that it is unlikely that a universal cancer monoclonal reagent or a "pan-tumor cell" reagent, even for a histological class of tumors, will be developed. For example, the monoclonal antibody 19-9, produced at the Wistar Institute

(44,83,84), defines a monosialoganglioside glycolipid antigen that is found only in meconium and on tumor cells, suggesting that the antigen may be an oncofetal antigen. The 19-9 monoclonal antibody was raised against colorectal carcinoma cells but does not recognize an antigen specific for colorectal carcinomas, as it is also found on other gastrointestinal tumors (namely, pancreatic and gastric tumors). A serodiagnostic assay has been developed and currently is being evaluated as an immunodiagnostic aid for gastrointestinal cancers (85-87).

The lack of binding of a monoclonal antibody to a tissue or serum specimen within a histological class of tumors may not reflect that the immunodiagnostic assay was insensitive and failed to detect the antigen but, rather, that the tumor did not express the antigen. Heterogeneity within and among tumors has been observed in human and animal systems with respect to hormone receptors, response to drugs, growth rates, metastatic potential, and antigenic properties (88, 90). The definition of phenotypic variation and antigenic modulation of antigen expression among and within breast adenocarcinomas using monoclonal antibodies has been elegantly demonstrated by Horan Hand et al. (89, see also Chapter 5). Such widespread variation of antigen expression has important implications toward the design of immunodiagnostic and therapeutic approaches for cancer and would support the contention that a panel of monoclonals will be required to identify all antigens expressed by each histological class of tumors. What is the meaning of the heterogeneity of tumor antigen expression as revealed by these monoclonal antibodies at the cellular level? There is evidence that considerable disturbance occurs in the carbohydrate structure of tumor cell membranes resulting from cell transformation. Abnormalities of carbohydrate composition, lectin agglutinability, and in the size of the glycopeptides isolated from malignant cell membranes have been observed (91). Monoclonal antibodies produced to antigens on the murine blastocyst-teratocarcinoma systems have revealed the existence of stage-specific antigens, suggesting that the carbohydrate structure of membrane glycoproteins undergo a series of programmed changes in the differentiation of normal cells as well as neoplastic cells (92). This is strikingly evident for lymphoreticular neoplasms. The importance of monoclonal antibodies directed against stage-specific antigens may be to dissect the several populations of cells in a tumor. If cell populations at different stages of differentiation exist in some tumors, then this may be one of the easier explanations for heterogeneity. If a monoclonal reacts to one tumor but not to another of the same histological type (including stage and grade), this may be due not only to different malignant cell populations (i.e., subtypes), but to cell cycle dependence of antigen expression, antigen modulation, or alterations of the structural genes resulting in a loss or shift in antigen expression. Furthermore, point mutation may alter one amino acid in the antigenic determinant, distorting the binding site, and as a result the monoclonal antibody can no longer bind to the antigen. A polyclonal antiserum, on the other hand, most likely would have specificity for a variant of the antigenic determinant and bind to the altered antigenic determinant. A case in point is a study recently conducted to compare the reactivity of monoclonal antibodies to prostatic acid phosphatase (93) with the reactivity of conventional xenogeneic anti-prostatic acid phosphatase antibodies. The xenogeneic antibodies reacted with 40 of 40 prostate tissues, using an IP assay, whereas the highest number of positives with seven different monoclonal antibodies was 24 of 40 (94). However, by the pooling of several monoclonal antibodies, the sensitivity of the reaction could be enhanced (i.e., 34 positive of 40 tested). One conclusion for the lack of reactivity of a monoclonal antibody to tumor cells of a patient with the same histological type of tumor that the monoclonal antibody was generated against is that the tumor cell population represents a different subclass of the tumor which fails to express the specific antigen (44,47,95,96). But in order to rule out that the lack of binding is the result of tumor cell heterogeneity or one of the other reasons mentioned above, a panel of monoclonal antibodies with various specificities will be required to fully address these biological questions. Such a panel of monoclonal reagents would most likely enhance their specificity for diagnosis and perhaps even for therapy. Depending on the desired result, the panel of monoclonal antibodies could be used independently or as a mixture. The double determinant assay described by Brown and associates (71), in which two monoclonals bind different determinants on the same antigen, markedly increased the sensitivity for detecting the antigen on tissue cells. Another study (73) showed that one determinant recognized by a monoclonal antibody became much more prominent after another monoclonal antibody had reacted with the target cells. This finding suggests the possibility that some antigenic determinants are generated by changes in conformation that are secondary to antigen-antibody interactions, a phenomenon which could be useful for developing highly sensitive diagnostic tests.

It seems likely that panels of monoclonal anti-human tumor antibodies will be useful for diagnosing the presence of the tumor cell or antigen shed in body fluids and in frozen or fixed histological tissue sections, as well as for radioimmunologic localization of tumors in vivo. A panel of monoclonal reagents with a range of specificities might possibly not only detect the malignant cell, but also classify the subtypes of tumor cells within the histological class of tumors (97). The availability of reagents against a battery of tumor markers that define a particular tumor cell lineage, coupled with a sensitive immunoassay, might permit the detection of tumors while still small (i.e., less than 10^7 tumor cells) and localized and in which the cure rate is highest. A library of monoclonals used with an immunohistochemical assay, namely, the immunoperoxidase test, should become an invaluable tool to the pathologist for detecting microfoci, identifying occult tumors, and developing a more specific scheme for the classification and grading of human tumors. The latter may make it possible to more effectively correlate tissue biological status with the clinical status, specifically in terms related to patient prognosis. The immunohistochemical pattern of monoclonal reactivity (no change or loss of tumor markers) of biopsy sections, taken before and after therapy, might reflect the effectiveness or ineffectiveness of therapy. Radiodiagnosis of tumors in situ, particularly micrometastases, via scintigraphic methods should also be facilitated by using a mixture of labeled monoclonal antibodies with defined antigenic specificities. Radiolabeled conventional antibodies have been used to localize tumors in vivo with various rates of success (98-102). Monoclonal antibodies should facilitate this approach because they can be obtained with appropriate specificities. Regardless of whether this approach becomes clinically applicable for detecting tumors in situ, it may become a prerequisite in evaluating the targeting potential of a monoclonal being evaluated for serotherapy.

Despite glowing expectations, the reality of cancer immunotherapy, even in experimental animal models, has not resulted in the type of dramatic tumor rejection that had been envisioned by immunologists at the inception of immunotherapy. The introduction of the hybridoma technology has spurred renewed interest in serotherapy of human tumors.

Several factors that can influence the use of antibodies for serotherapy and which must be considered before a rational approach for immunotherapy with monoclonal antibodies can be designed are listed in Table 7. The question of how specific the monoclonal will have to be will depend on those issues already discussed and perhaps on the type and location of the tumor. It most assuredly will depend on the immunotherapeutic situation. For example, the in vitro "cleansing" of autologous bone marrow for transplantation need not require specific monoclonal antibodies as would most likely be required for in vivo administration. Since the exact effector cell systems reactive with monoclonal antibodies are unknown, it will be important to identify and understand the function of these systems in order to monitor the in vivo fate of the administered monoclonal antibody. It may be necessary to potentiate the effector system to maximize the effect of the anti-tumor monoclonal antibodies. In selected situations, greater effect of the antibody might be obtained with Fab or $F(ab')_2$ fragments of the antibody to prevent binding to Fc-like receptors on normal cells and tissues. If effector systems are not activated by monoclonal antibodies, then it may be necessary to couple drugs or toxins to the antibody for effective delivery of a cytotoxic kill. (The use of conjugated antibodies is discussed below.) The class or subclass of murine monoclonal antibodies may be key to obtaining the desired therapeutic effect. For example, mouse IgG_{2a} monoclonal antibodies are effective in killing human tumors growing in nude mice, whereas IgG_1, IgG_{2b}, IgG_3, and IgM are not tumoricidal (103-107). The in vivo killing of tumor

Table 7 Factors That Can Influence the Effective Use of Monoclonal Antibodies for the Immunotherapy of Human Cancer

Specificity of the antibody

Fate of the antibody in vivo

Presence of antigenic modulation

Presence of antigenic negative cells

Presence of circulating free tumor antigen

Production of an immune response against the foreign mouse monoclonal antibodies by the patient

cells by IgG_{2a} but not by IgG_{2b} has also been demonstrated in a murine tumor model (109). By excluding complement-mediated lysis and killer or natural killer cell lysis, macrophages appeared to be the most likely effector cell. However, monoclonal antibodies to cell surface substances have been shown to reversibly inhibit cell division in in vitro models (110-112), suggesting that the monoclonal antibody binds to a regulating molecule responsible for stimulation and cessation of DNA synthesis. Most likely in vivo the macrophages are activated by the IgG_{2a} monoclonal antibodies and kill those tumor cells that bind specifically to the antibody. It would appear that a subclass of macrophages with Fc receptors, having a high affinity for IgG_{2a}, are involved in this type of antibody-mediated cytodestruction of tumor cells (106-108). A subclass of human macrophages with affinity for mouse IgG_{2a} monoclonals has been identified that also mediates cytotoxicity against human tumors (106,107). Clinical trials have begun using IgG_{2a} anti-colorectal tumor antibodies to treat patients with colorectal cancer (102; Z. Steplewski, personal communication). Similarly, Reisfeld and colleagues have shown that mouse effector cells conjugated with mouse antimelanoma monoclonal antibodies could inhibit the growth of established human melanoma tumors in nude mice (113). Clinical trials have started to evaluate the utility of antimelanoma monoclonal antibody-effector cell conjugates for immunoprophylaxis following surgical resection of tumors (113; R. A. Reisfeld, personal communication). It would appear likely that effective therapy with cytotoxic monoclonal antibodies administered by themselves will require assistance from natural humoral (complement) and cell-mediated (killer cell, natural killer cell, macrophage) effector mechanisms. Binding of the antibody to the tumor membrane antigen might activate the complement system via the classic pathway resulting in cell lysis. This would require monoclonal antibodies capable of binding complement via the Fc region of the antibody. Monoclonal antibodies could also mediate antibody-dependent cell lysis by the classic pathway by first binding to the tumor membrane antigen (via the Fab site), with subsequent binding to killer cells or macrophages via their Fc membrane receptors. Serotherapy with monoclonals will undoubtedly be most effective for *dispersed* tumor cells such as found for leukemias and lymphomas, because the antibody can more effectively home in on individual tumor cells. Preliminary trials in treating leukemia patients with monoclonal antibodies to T-lymphocyte differentiation antigens have met with partial success (77-79). It would seem that immunotherapy might possibly be effective against some solid tumors, provided that they have an adequate blood supply to allow the monoclonal antibody to penetrate and be dispersed throughout the tumor. Another factor that must be considered when employing monoclonal antibodies for serotherapy of cancer is the problem of antigenic modulation. Monoclonal antibodies will be most effective if given when the tumor cells have maximal expression of antigen. Since antigenic modulation is reversible, proper timing of doses will be important. One must appropriately monitor not only the level of antigen expression, but also the tumor (antigen) phenotype to assure that antigen negative variants do not escape therapy. The administration of a panel of monoclonal antibodies of different specificities could overcome this potential problem. It will also be more desirable for immunotherapeutic purposes if the tumor antigen is shed minimally or not at all into the circulation, otherwise the administered monoclonal will be bound by the free antigen to form soluble immune complexes. When this occurs, the monoclonal will not reach its target (i.e., tumor), but, more important, there is the risk of inducing immune complex disease. Passive immunotherapy with foreign antibodies has generally given disappointing results that were attributed to the low antibody specificity and risk of developing serum sickness. Although it has not been adequately determined if pure mouse monoclonal antibodies will have associated toxicities, it is quite conceivable that repeated administration of murine monoclonals could result in severe hypersensitivity reactions, whereas one or two injections might be tolerated. Since the mouse antibodies are foreign proteins, the patient could potentially make antibodies against the monoclonals. Further administration of murine monoclonal antibodies would not be effective because the host antibodies would bind to them, preventing the monoclonal from binding to the tumor cells. This problem has been observed with repeated administrations of mouse monoclonal antibodies for serotherapy of lymphoma (R. Miller, personal communication) and colorectal cancer (112). However, the administration of large doses (300-1000 mg) of monoclonal antibody per single injection may overcome the problem by the induction and maintenance of a state of high dose tolerance to the foreign antibody (112; H. Koprowski, meeting communication). Human monoclonal antibodies in this regard would appear to take precedence over mouse monoclonals for therapeutic situations. Human antibody preparations have been used repeatedly without incident, which supports the notion that human monoclonals would also be safe for clinical use. However, their therapeutic use could present a new problem. Since each monoclonal antibody consists of a unique idiotype determinant, the patient's immune response might produce an anti-idiotype antibody that could bind to the idiotype, blocking binding of the monoclonal to the tumor cell. It is still too early to determine if this will be a problem in human subjects; it has as yet not been a problem in experimental animal immunotherapy.

It seems likely that effective tumor cell killing by monoclonal antibodies via direct cytolysis or by activating the natural effector immune mechanisms may be inefficient and require augmentation by cytotoxic agents. One type of assistance that can potentially be provided is to attach cytotoxic agents such as chemotherapeutic drugs (114–117), radioisotopes (118), or bacterial or plant toxins (114,119–122) to monoclonal antibodies. The monoclonal antibody provides the carrier for the cytotoxic "warhead" and delivers the "warhead" to the tumor. Preliminary studies, mostly using conventional antibodies, suggest that this may be a feasible approach. However, selective in vivo cytotoxic activity against malignant cells has not been reliably demonstrated, perhaps because of the use of heterologous antibodies that lack high-affinity tumor-associated specificity. Disassociation of the toxic "warhead" before reaching the tumor, tissue distribution, and accessibility of antigenic sites within the tumor are some major problems that will have to be thoroughly evaluated before routine use of targeted cytotoxic monoclonal reagents will be possible. Furthermore, delivery of the conjugated antibodies to tumors located in privileged sites such as the central nervous system may be dependent on the class of monoclonal antibody or the size of the antibody-toxin complex. When and if the technical difficulties can be worked out, this form of immunotherapy has considerable potential.

It can be envisioned that monoclonal antibodies will play an important role in other aspects of oncology such as affinity purification of the tumor antigens (123), development of new immunoassays (124,125), helping to delineate the cell function of the substances detected by the monoclonals, monitoring more precisely the cancer patient's anti-tumor immune responses, and the possibility of manipulating the patient's immune response, especially anti-suppressor activity. More basic will be the use of the monoclonals as probes to understand the difference between normal and malignant cells in hopes of elucidating the oncological process at the cell membrane level.

CONCLUSIONS

The introduction of the lymphocyte hybridoma technology in 1975 by Köhler and Milstein (7) not only offers to improve the quality and discriminating power of diagnostic and investigative serology, but also promises to provide new reagents that will be useful in the diagnosis and treatment of many diseases, including cancer. The application of monoclonal antibodies to the study of cancer, however, is only in the beginning stages. It is too early to determine if any new information will be gleaned using monoclonal reagents that will have direct bearing on improving the diagnosis and treatment of cancer. A number of potential technical problems and ethical considerations still must be resolved, but these appear to be solvable. The hope that the hybridoma technique would finally reveal the presence of human tumor-specific antigens has not been substantiated by the data reported thus far. The technique is labor intensive, requiring months to obtain a stable clone, which is then followed by extensive testing of the culture supernatant for antibody specificity. Thus the obvious question must be asked: Is it worth the effort? The answer must be a resounding yes! It is clear that new specificities have been identified on cancer cells by monoclonal antibodies. Although most have not been specific for tumor cells, they do appear to be directed to unique antigens present in higher concentration on cancer cells than found on normal cells. Having a panel of monoclonal antibodies that define the various specificities which might be associated within a specific histological tumor cell lineage, such as for the T-cell differentiation antigens used for defining leukemia cell populations, should enhance the specificity in detecting cancer markers in body fluids and immunopathological diagnosis of human malignancies. Such a panel of monoclonal reagents should help define more clearly the subtypes of cancer than is possible by present methods. Now that we have learned a lesson on developing a specificity testing strategy, the focus should be on extensive and detailed analysis of the specificity of the monoclonals before jumping into biochemical characterization of the antigens and diagnostic immunoassay development. In this way, one can take the best advantage of the monoclonals for constructing diagnostic and therapeutic tools. The role that monoclonal antibodies can play in the classification and diagnosis of tumors is already becoming apparent and promises to be immense and applicable within the next few years. On the other hand, the ultimate role monoclonal antibodies will play in serotherapy of cancer remains both unknown and questionable. Because monoclonal antibodies can be made that react with antigens not previously identified, they represent important new probes for elucidating complex biological processes of tumor cells, perhaps even to help understand the oncogenic process at the membrane level. The discussion in this chapter has focused on monoclonal antibodies to tumor antigens for potential therapeutic and diagnostic use. This is not the only envisioned use for monoclonal antibodies in cancer. Monoclonal antibodies directed against cells and regulatory molecules of the immune system are being developed and will have tremendous application for the monitoring and modulation of the cancer patient's immunocompetence and anti-tumor responses. The combination of recombinant DNA technology with the lymphocyte hybridoma technology should also bring forth new reagents for cancer diagnosis and therapy. Already monoclonal antibodies have been successfully used to purify interferon and other medically important substances produced by the recombinant technology. Thus it is with great expectation that we view the next phase of the application of monoclonal reagents to the diagnosis and therapy of cancer.

REFERENCES

1. G. Klein, *Cancer Res. 28*:625 (1968).
2. L. J. Old, *Cancer Res. 41*:361 (1981).
3. G. I. Abelev, S. D. Perova, N. I. Khramkova, Z. A. Postnikova, and I. S. Irlin, *Transplantation 1*:174 (1963).
4. Y. Tatarinov, *Vopr, Med. Khim 10*:90 (1964).
5. P. Gold and S. O. Freedman, *J. Exp. Med. 121*:467 (1965).
6. S. Sell and B. Wahren (eds.), *Human Cancer Markers,* Humana Press, Clifton, N. J., 1982.
7. G. Köhler and C. Milstein, *Nature 256*:495 (1975).
8. J. Dalrymple, *Dublin J. Med. Sci. 2*:85 (1846).
9. H. Bence Jones, *Phil. Trans. Soc. 1*:55 (1848).
10. P. Ehrlich, *Proc. R. Soc. London (B.) 66*:242 (1906).
11. F. M. Burnet, *The Clonal Selection Theory of Acquired Immunity,* Vanderbilt Univ. Press, Nashville, 1959.
12. R. Rask-Neilsen and H. Gormsen, *Cancer 4*:387 (1951).
13. T. B. Dunn, *J. Nat. Cancer Inst. 14*:1281 (1954).
14. J. Kritzman, H. G. Kunkel, J. McCarthy, and R. C. Mellors, *J. Lab. Clin. Med. 57*:905 (1961).
15. J. Waldenström, S. Winblad, J. Hällen, and S. Llüngman, *Acta Med. Scand. 176*:619 (1964).
16. M. Potter and Boyce, *Nature 193*:1086 (1962).
17. J. W. Littlefield, *Science 145*:709 (1964).
18. J. L. Fahler, I. Fingold, A. S. Rabson, and R. A. Manaker, *Science 152*:1259 (1966).
19. G. S. Pettengill and G. D. Sorensen, *Exp. Cell Res. 47*:608 (1967).
20. K. Horibata and A. S. Harris, *Exp. Cell Res. 60*:61 (1970).
21. R. Laskov and M. D. Scharff, *J. Exp. Med. 131*:515 (1970).
22. R. G. H. Cotton, D. S. Secher, and C. Milstein, *Eur. J. Immunol. 3*:135 (1973).
23. G. Galfré, S. C. Howe, C. Milstein, G. W. Butcher, and J. C. Howard, *Nature 266*:500 (1977).
24. M. Shulman, C. D. Wilde, and G. Köhler, *Nature 276*:269 (1978).
25. J. F. Kearney, A. Radbruch, B. Liesegang, and K. Rajewsky, *J. Immunol. 123*:1548 (1979).

26. L. Olsson and H. S. Kaplan, *Proc. Nat. Acad. Sci. U.S.A.* 77:5429 (1980).
27. M. Potter, in *Multiple Myeloma and Related Disorders,* Vol. 1 (H. A. Azar and M. Potter, eds.), Harper and Row, New York, 1973, p. 195.
28. R. H. Kennett, T. J. McKern, and K. B. Bechtol (eds.), *Monoclonal Antibodies,* Plenum, New York, 1980.
29. F. Melchers, M. Potter, and N. L. Warner, *Curr. Top. Microbiol. Immunol.* 81:1 (1978).
30. G. J. Hämmerling, U. Hämmerling, and J. F. Kearney (eds.), in *Research Monographs in Immunology,* Vol. 3, Elsevier/North-Holland, Amsterdam, 1981, pp. 1-587.
31. J. G. R. Hurell (ed.), *Monoclonal Hybridoma Antibodies: Techniques and Applications,* CRC Press, Boca Raton, Fla., 1982, pp. 1-231.
32. W. C. Raschke, in *Human Cancer Markers* (S. Sell and B. Wahren, eds.), Humana Press, Clifton, N. J., 1982, p. 1.
33. G. Köhler, *Hybridoma Techniques,* Cold Spring Harbor Laboratory, New York, 1980.
34. G. Galfré and M. R. Clark, in *Monoclonal Antibodies and Developments in Immunoassay* (A. Alberlini and R. Ekins, eds.), Elsevier/North-Holland, Amsterdam, 1981, p. 23.
35. G. Köhler and C. Milstein, *Eur. J. Immunol.* 6:511 (1976).
36. D. H. Margulies, W. M. Kuehl, and M. D. Scharff, *Cell* 8:405 (1976).
37. I. S. Trowbridge, *J. Exp. Med.* 148:313 (1978).
38. G. Galfré, C. Milstein, and B. Wright, *Nature* 277:131 (1979).
39. J. J. Starling, G. L. Wright, Jr., P. F. Schellhammer, L. Ladaga, M. Beckett, and S. Sieg, manuscript in preparation.
40. H. Koprowski, Z. Steplewski, D. Herlyn, and M. Herlyn, *Proc. Nat. Acad. Sci. U.S.A.* 75:3405 (1978).
41. R. G. Woodbury, J. P. Brown, M. Y. Yeh, I. Hellström, and K. E. Hellström, *Proc. Nat. Acad. Sci. U.S.A.* 77:2183 (1980).
42. S. Carrel, R. S. Accolla, A. L. Carmagnola, and J. -P. Mach, *Cancer Res. 40:* 2523 (1980).
43. K. Imai, A. -K. Ng, and J. Ferrone, *J. Nat. Cancer Inst. 66:*489 (1981).
44. M. Herlyn, Z. Steplewski, D. Herlyn, and H. Koprowski, *Proc. Nat. Acad. Sci. U.S.A.* 76:1438 (1979).
45. R. H. Kennett and F. Gilbert, *Science 203:*1120 (1979).
46. J. F. Schnegg, A. C. Diserens, S. Carrel, R. S. Accolla, and N. Tribolet, *Cancer Res. 41:*1209 (1981).
47. R. S. Metzgar, M. T. Gaillard, S. J. Levine, F. L. Tuck, E. H. Bossen, and M. J. Borowitz, *Cancer Res. 42:*601 (1982).
48. R. Veda, S. Ogata, D. M. Morrissey, C. L. Finstad, J. Szkudlarek, W. R. Whitmore, H. F. Oettgen, K. O. Lloyd, and L. J. Old, *Proc. Nat. Acad. Sci. U.S.A.* 78:5122 (1981).
49. J. J. Starling, S. M. Sieg, M. L. Beckett, P. F. Schellhammer, L. E. Ladaga, and G. L. Wright, Jr., *Cancer Res. 42:*3084 (1982).

50. M. J. Embleton, B. Gunn, V. S. Byers, and R.W. Baldwin, *Br. J. Cancer 43*: 582 (1981).
51. J. Schlom, D. Wunderlich, and Y. A. Teramoto, *Proc. Nat. Acad. Sci. U.S.A.* 77:6841 (1980).
52. J. O. -D. McGee, J. C. Woods, F. Ashall, M. E. Bramwell, and H. Harris, *Lancet 2*:7 (1982).
53. J. P. Brown, R. G. Woodbury, C. E. Hart, I. Hellström, and K. E. Hellström, *Proc. Nat. Acad. Sci. U.S.A.* 78:539 (1981).
54. Z. Steplewski and H. Koprowski, *Fed. Proc. 41*:2660 (1982).
55. J. T. Abelson and L. S. Rabstein, *Cancer Res. 30*:2213 (1970).
56. M. Steinitz, in *Research Monographs in Immunology*, Vol 3, *Monoclonal Antibodies and T-Cell Hybridomas* (U. Hämmerling, G. J. Hämmerling, and J. F. Kearney, eds.), Elsevier/North-Holland, Amsterdam, 1981, p. 447.
57. S. Tsuchiya, S. Yokoyama, O. Yoshie, and Y. Ono, *J. Immunol. 124*:1970 (1980).
58. V. R. Zurawski, Jr., E. Haber, and P. H. Black, *Science 199*:1439 (1978).
59. R. L. Lundak and R. M. Malachowski, *Abst. Ann. Meet. Am. Soc. Microbiol. Abstr.* E-42 (1981).
60. L. E. Strike, S. A. Murray, W. H. Fletcher, and R. L. Lundak, *Fed. Proc. 41*: 1900 (1982).
61. C. L. Reading, *J. Immunol. Methods 53*:261 (1982).
62. C. M. Croce, A. Linnenbach, W. Hall, Z. Steplewski, and H. Koprowski, *Nature 288*:488 (1980).
63. S. A. Clark, W. H. Stimon, A. R. Williamson, and H. M. Dick, *J. Supramol. Struct. Cell. Biochem. Suppl. 5*:40 (1981).
64. P. A. W. Edwards, C. M. Smith, A. M. Neville, and M. J. O'Hare, *Eur. J. Immunol. 12*:641, 1982.
65. H. Lazarus, M. Posner, S. Schlossman, and J. Schwaber, *Fed. Proc. 41*:1911 (1982).
66. R. J. Hartzman, K. W. Hunter, and J. N. Woody, *Fed. Proc. 41*:1917 (1982).
67. T. Yokochi, R. D. Holly, and E. A. Clark, *J. Immunol. 128*:823 (1982).
68. D. E. Yelton and M. D. Scharff, *Annu. Rev. Biochem. 50*:657 (1981).
69. B. A. Diamond, D. L. Yelton, and M. D. Scharff, *N. Engl. J. Med. 304*:1344 (1981).
70. C. Milstein, *Sci. Am. 243*:66 (1980).
71. J. P. Brown, K. E. Hellström, and I. Hellström, *Clin. Chem. 27*:1592 (1981).
72. I. Hellström, K. E. Hellström, and M. -Y. Yeh, *Int. J. Cancer 27*:281 (1981).
73. R. Goodfliesh, S. V. Hunter, Z. Maciorowski, and M. D. Poulik, *Fed. Proc. 39*:919 (1980).
74. M. F. Greaves, *Cancer Res. 41*:4752 (1981).
75. J. Ritz, J. M. Pesando, J. Notis-McConarty, L. A. Clavell, S. E. Sallan, and S. F. Schlossman, *Cancer Res. 41*:4771 (1981).
76. T. F. Zipf, R. I. Fox, J. Dilley, and R. Levy, *Cancer Res. 41*:4786 (1981).
77. R. A. Miller, D. G. Maloney, R. Warnke, and R. Levy, *N. Engl. J. Med. 306*: 517 (1982).

78. R. A. Miller, D. G. Maloney, J. McKillup, and R. Levy, *Blood 58*:78 (1981).
79. J. Ritz, J. M. Pesando, S. E. Sallen, L. A. Clavell, J. Notis-McConarty, P. Rosenthal, and S. F. Schlossman, *Blood 58*:141 (1981).
80. R. A. Miller, D. Maloney, R. Warnke, R. McDougall, G. Wood, T. Kawakami, J. Dilley, M. L. Goris, and R. Levy, in *Progress in Cancer Research and Therapy*, Vol. 21, *Hybridomas in Cancer Diagnosis and Treatment* (M. S. Mitchell and H. F. Oettgen, eds.), Raven Press, New York, 1981, p. 133.
81. R. G. Andrews, I. D. Bernstein, and B. Torok-Storb, in *Progress in Cancer Research and Therapy*, Vol. 21, *Hybridomas in Cancer Diagnosis and Treatment* (M. S. Mitchell and H. F. Oettgen, eds.), Raven Press, New York, 1982, p. 147.
82. R. S. Metzgar, M. T. Gilland, M. Borowitz, V. N. Daasch, F. L. Tuck, N. W. Rodriquez, and P. D. Fernsten, *Hybridoma 2*:110 (1983).
83. J. Magnani, J. M. Brockhaus, D. F. Smith, V. Ginsberg, M. Blaszczyk, K. Mitchell, Z. Steplewski, and H. Koprowski, *Science 212*:55 (1981).
84. H. Koprowski and Z. Steplewski, in *Research Monographs in Immunology*, Vol. 3, *Monoclonal Antibodies and T-Cell Hybridomas* (G. J. Hämmerling, U. Hämmerling, and J. F. Kearney, eds.), Elsevier/North Holland, Amsterdam, 1981, p. 161.
85. M. Herlyn, H. F. Sears, Z. Steplewski, and H. Koprowski, *J. Clin. Immunol. 2*:135 (1982)
86. H. F. Sears, M. Herlyn, B. Del Villano, Z. Steplewski, and H. Koprowski, *J. Clin. Immunol. 2*:141 (1982).
87. J. R. Hart and J. J. Fidler, *Biochim. Biophys. Acta 651*:37 (1981).
88. R. J. Kerbel, *Nature 280*:358 (1979).
89. P. Horan Hand, M. Nuti, D. Colcher, and J. Schlom, *Cancer Res. 43*:728 (1983).
90. L. Warren, A. B. Clayton, and G. R. Tuszywski, *Biochim. Biophys. Acta 516*: 97 (1978).
91. D. Sotter and B. Knowles, *Proc. Nat. Acad. Sci. U.S.A. 77*:457 (1980).
92. C. -I. Lee, C. -Y. Li, Y. -H. Jou, G. P. Murphy, and T. M. Chu, *Ann. N.Y. Acad. Sci. 390*:52 (1982).
93. M. Nadji and A. R. Morales, *Ann. N.Y. Acad. Sci. 390*:133 (1982).
94. H. Koprowski, H. Sears, M. Herlyn, and Z. Steplewski, *Science 212*:53 (1981).
95. F. Cuttitta, S. Rosen, A. F. Gazdar, and J. D. Minna, *Proc. Nat. Acad. Sci. U.S.A. 78*:4591 (1981).
96. D. Colcher, P. Hand, M. Nuti, and J. Schlom, *Proc. Nat. Acad. Sci. U.S.A. 78*:3199 (1981).
97. D. Y. Mason, N. Naiem, Z. Abdulaziz, J. R. G. Nash, K. C. Gatter, and H. Stein, in *Monoclonal Antibodies in Clinical Medicine* (A. J. McMichael and J. W. Fabre, eds.), Academic, London, 1982, p. 585.
98. B. Ballou, G. Levine, T. R. Hakala, and D. Solter, *Science 206*:844 (1979).
99. V. Moshakis, R. A. J. McIlhinney, D. Raghavan, and A. M. Neville, *Br. J. Cancer 44*:91 (1981).

100. J. -P. Mach, F. Buchegger, M. Forni, J. Ritschardi, C. Berche, J. D Lumbroso, M. Schreyer, C. Giradet, R. S. Accola, and S. Carrel, *Immunol. Today 2*:239 (1981).
101. D. M. Goldenberg (ed.), Radioimmunodetection of Cancer Workshop, *Cancer Res. 40*: 2953–3087 (1980).
102. D. M. Goldenberg, F. DeLand, E. E. Kim, S. Bennett, F. J. Primus, J. R. vanNagel, Jr., N. Estes, P. DeSimone, and P. Rayburn, *N. Engl. J. Med. 298*: 1384 (1978).
103. D. Herlyn, Z. Steplewski, M. Herlyn, and H. Koprowski, *Cancer Res. 40*: 717 (1980).
104. D. Herlyn, M. Herlyn, Z. Steplewski, and H. Koprowski, *Eur. J. Immunol. 9*:657 (1979).
105. H. Koprowski, Z. Steplewski, D. Herlyn, and M. Herlyn, *Proc. Nat. Acad. Sci. U.S.A. 75*:3405 (1978).
106. D. Herlyn and H. Koprowski, *Proc. Nat. Acad. Sci. U.S.A. 79*:4761 (1982).
107. Z. Steplewski, D. Herlyn, G. Maul, and H. Koprowski, *Hybridoma 2*:1 (1983).
108. A. J. Langlois, T. Matthews, G. J. Rolson, H. -J. Thiel, J. J. Collins, and D. P. Bolognesi, *J. Immunol. 126*:2337 (1981).
109. R. L. Byrd, Z. L. Jonak, and R. H. Kennett, in *Progress in Cancer Research and Therapy*, Vol. 21, *Hybridomas in Cancer Diagnosis and Treatment* (M. S. Mitchell and H. F. Oettegen, eds.), Raven Press, New York, 1982, p. 219.
110. M. McGrath, E. Pillemer, and J. L. Weissman, *Nature 285*:259 (1980).
111. J. R. Harper, T. F. Bumol, and R. A. Reisfeld, *Fed. Proc. 41*:2669 (1982).
112. H. Koprowski, D. Herlyn, and Z. Steplewski, *Hybridoma 2*:114 (1983).
113. R. A. Reisfeld, J. R. Harper, G. Schulz, and T. F. Bumol, *Hybridoma 2*:115 (1983).
114. G. Möller (ed.), *Immunol. Rev. 62*:5-216 (1982).
115. M. V. Pimm, J. A. Jones, M. R. Price, J. G. Middle, M. J. Embleton, and Robert W. Baldwin, *Cancer Immunol. Immunother. 12*:125 (1982).
116. M. T. B. Davis and J. F. Preston, *Science 213*:1385 (1981).
117. T. Ghose and A. H. Blair, *J. Nat. Cancer Inst. 61*:657 (1978).
118. H. S. Kaplan, in *Progress in Cancer Research and Therapy*, Vol. 21, *Hybridomas in Cancer Diagnosis and Treatment* (M. S. Mitchell and H. F. Oettegen, eds.), Raven Press, New York, 1982, p. 255.
119. D. G. Gilliland, Z. Steplewski, R. J. Collier, K. F. Mitchell, T. H. Chang, and H. Koprowski, *Proc. Nat. Acad. Sci. U.S.A. 77*:4539 (1980).
120. H. E. Blythman, P. Casellas, O. Gros, P. Gros, F. K. Jansen, F. Paolucci, B. Pau, and H. Vidal, *Nature 290*:145 (1981).
121. V. Raso, J. Ritz, M. Basala, and S. F. Schlossman, *Cancer Res. 42*:457 (1980).
122. F. K. Jansen, H. E. Blythman, D. Carriere, P. Casellas, O. Gros, P. Gros, F. Paolucci, B. Pau, P. Poncelet, G. Richer, H. Vidal, and G. A. Voisin, in *Research Monographs in Immunology*, Vol. 3, *Monoclonal Antibodies and T-Cell Hybridomas* (U. Hämmerling, G. J. Hämmerling, and J. F. Kearney, eds.), Elsevier/North-Holland, Amsterdam, 1981, p. 229.

123. D. S. Secher and D. C. Burke, *Nature* 285:446 (1981).
124. R. Ekins, in *Monoclonal Antibodies and Developments in Immunoassay* (A. Albertini and R. Ekins, eds.), Elsevier/North-Holland, Amsterdam, 1981, p. 3.
125. E. D. Sevier, G. S. David, J. Martinis, W. J. Desmond, R. M. Bartholomew, and R. Wang, *Clin. Chem.* 27:1797 (1981).

2 MONOCLONAL ANTIBODIES TO MELANOMA-ASSOCIATED ANTIGENS

Karl Erik Hellström, Ingegerd Hellström, and Joseph P. Brown / University of Washington and Fred Hutchinson Cancer Research Center, Seattle, Washington

INTRODUCTION

Melanomas are among the human neoplasms that have been investigated most intensively from the immunological point of view. Initially they were chosen for immunological studies because of the occurrence of spontaneous remissions, which suggested a host immune response (1)*, and also because melanoma cells grow well in culture and can be readily distinguished from other cell types (2). Lymphocytes from many melanoma patients were found to be cytotoxic to melanoma cells in vitro (3,4), indicating that melanomas express cell-surface antigens that can be recognized by melanoma patients. Further evidence of immunity to melanomas came from work performed with leukocyte migration inhibition (5,6) and leukocyte adherence inhibition assays (7). The reactivity pattern observed suggested that more than one shared, melanoma-associated antigen was involved (8). However, the target antigens were not identified biochemically, and various amounts of natural killer cell activity in different lymphocyte suspensions complicated the interpretation of studies on lymphocyte-mediated anti-tumor cytotoxicity (9-11).

---

*The literature survey was completed on July 1, 1982.

Serological studies have several advantages over studies of cell-mediated immunity when one is attempting to define tumor-associated antigens. The two most important advantages are that highly sensitive techniques can be used to determine antigen specificity and that antibodies can be used to purify the antigens for structural characterization. Sera from melanoma patients have been studied extensively, and they have been reported to contain antibodies both to antigens that are unique for each melanoma (12) and to antigens that are shared by many different melanomas but absent from other tumors (13,14). The strongest serological evidence for the unique and shared antigens has come from work of Shiku et al. (15), in which antibodies were tested for binding to the patients' own, cultured melanoma cells, and specificity of antibody binding established by absorption with autochthonous and allogeneic melanoma cells, as well as with various other cells. However, specific antibodies were detected in only a few patients and the antibody titers were generally too low for further characterization of the target antigens.

The hybridoma technique (16) made it possible to obtain mouse monoclonal antibodies specific for melanoma-associated antigens, and thus to gain new insight into the nature of such antigens and to develop novel approaches to the diagnosis and therapy of melanoma. In this chapter we shall review the major findings obtained.

MELANOMA-ASSOCIATED ANTIGENS IDENTIFIED BY MONOCLONAL ANTIBODIES

Hybridomas defining melanoma-associated antigens have been obtained by immunizing mice with human melanoma cells; no human monoclonal antibodies (17,18) specific for melanoma-associated antigens have been reported. In most cases, cultured melanoma cells were used as immunogens, although supernatants from melanoma cultures and melanoma biopsy material have also been employed. Antigens defined by xenogeneic immunization, it is important to note, are not necessarily the same as those recognized by the human immune system in patients with melanoma.

Spleen cells from mice immunized with melanoma cells have been fused with azaguanine-resistant mouse myeloma cells, such as P3-NS1-1Ag3-1 (NS-1) and SP2/0-Ag14 (SP2/0), using polyethylene glycol, hybrids being selected in a medium containing hypoxanthine, aminopterin, and thymidine (16). In most cases, the hybridomas were screened for production of antibodies to melanoma-associated antigens by using binding assays, in which spent culture medium from closed hybridomas was tested for reactivity to cultured tumor cell lines (19). The melanoma line SK-MEL 28 (15) has been included in many of these studies and expresses most of the antigens to which monoclonal antibodies have been obtained. Hybridomas have also been screened by immunoprecipitation of target antigens from lysates of radiolabeled cells followed by sodium dodecyl sulfate-polyacrylamide gel electrophoresis (SDS-PAGE) and autoradiography (20). The latter method is most useful when one wishes to obtain an antibody to an antigen of known molecular weight (mol wt), for example, to additional epitopes of a previously defined antigen. A third screening procedure is immunoperoxidase staining of frozen or formalin-fixed, paraffin-embedded tissue sections (21-24). Its major advantages are that the antigens detected must be expressed in vivo and that antibody binding to both neoplastic and normal cells can be evaluated at the same time.

Many hybridomas have been described that make monoclonal antibodies to antigens expressed in larger amounts at the surface of melanoma cells than of other cells. The following 15 antigens are those, in our view, that are the most melanoma-specific of those defined by monoclonal antibodies. We first list protein antigens followed by glycolipid antigens. As is apparent from this listing, some antigens, like p97 (25) have been studied extensively, while for others little information is available.

28,000 mol wt protein: This antigen, defined by antibody WM56-1 (IgG_1) has been detected on cultured melanoma cells, but not on various control cells (23).

69,000 mol wt protein: This antigen, defined by antibody I182-11 (Z. Steplewski, personal communication), is expressed on most melanomas, on teratocarcinomas, and on nevi. Antibody-dependent cellular cytotoxicity to the antigen has been detected.

70,000 mol wt glycoprotein: This antigen, defined by IgG_1 antibody ME3-TB7 (26,27), is present on most melanoma, neuroblastoma, and astrocytoma cell lines. Much weaker antibody binding has been seen to normal cells.

74,000 mol wt glycoprotein: This antigen, defined by IgG_{2a} antibody 15-75, is present on most cultured melanoma and carcinoma cells (28). Its expression in vivo is unknown.

94,000 mol wt glycoprotein: A glycoprotein with a molecular weight of approximately 94,000 has been described by Saxton's group (29,30). This protein, defined by antibodies 376-92 (IgG_{2a}) and 705-56 (IgG_{2b}), is present on cultured melanomas, on melanoma biopsies, on carcinoma cells, and, more weakly, on epithelial cells and fibroblasts. It has not been detected on normal melanocytes. Both complement-dependent cytotoxicity and antibody-dependent cellular cytotoxicity have been detected. A similar antigen defined by antibody 376.96S has been described by Ruberto et al. (31) and Imai et al. (32).

p97 (gp95): The best-characterized melanoma antigen is p97, a 97,000 mol wt cell-surface sialoglycoprotein (20,25,33-36). Thirteen antibodies to five different epitopes of p97 and representing three different classes (IgG_1, IgG_{2a}, IgG_{2b}) have been obtained (33; J. P. Brown, unpublished findings). Three of these epitopes are present on a 40,000 mol wt proteolytic fragment of p97 (33). Sequential immunoprecipitation and competition experiments with different monoclonal antibodies have shown that gp 95, an antigen described subsequently by Dippold et al. (37), is identical to p97 (33). The antigen is synthesized by melanoma cells and appears to form an integral part of the cell membrane (33; J. P. Brown, K. Nishiyama, I. Hellström, and K. E. Hellström, unpublished findings).

Binding assays of cultured cells have revealed that melanoma cells express up to 400,000 molecules of p97, while carcinoma cells, fibroblasts, and lymphoid cells express fewer than 10,000 molecules of p97 (33; J. P. Brown, K. Nishiyama, I. Hellström, and K. E. Hellström, unpublished findings). By using monoclonal antibodies to two epitopes to p97 in a two-site immunoradiometric assay (34,38), p97 has been quantitated in biopsy samples from tumors and normal tissues. The antigen was detected in very small amounts in virtually all adult tissues, but in substantial amounts in fetal colon (34). However, melanomas contain much more p97 than any normal, adult tissues, with about 50% of melanomas expressing 50 times more p97 than lung, liver, and intestine. Immunofluorescence studies have failed to detect p97 in cells from bone marrow (39). Its expression on resting and on phytohemagglutinin-activated lymphocytes is very weak (38). Antibodies to p97, tested in the presence of complement, are not detectably inhibitory to hematopoietic stem cells (B. Torok-Storb, personal communication).

Antigen p97 can be detected by the peroxidase anti-peroxidase technique in frozen sections of most primary and metastatic melanomas and compound nevi, but not in normal adult tissues, including normal adult melanocytes, except for myoepithelial cells lining sweat glands (24; H. J. Garrigues, W. Tilgen, I. Hellström, W. Franke, and K. E. Hellström, unpublished findings). The antigen does not undergo antigenic modulation (I. Hellström, unpublished findings). It has not been possible to isolate p97-negative clones from tumors expressing large amounts of p97; however, variation in the expression of p97 (gp95) among different cell cultures established from the same metastatic melanoma has been described (40). The antigen can serve as a target for both complement-dependent cytotoxicity (41) and antibody-dependent cellular cytotoxicity (I. Hellström, unpublished findings). As shown by sequential immunoprecipitation assays (35), it is not the same as the transferrin receptor (42,43).

The N-terminal amino acid sequence of p97 is homologous to the N-terminal sequences of transferrin and lactoferrin (35). Antiserum to denatured p97 binds to transferrin and lactoferrin, while monoclonal antibodies to native p97 do not. Antigen p97 thus appears to be a member of the transferrin family, but it is membrane-associated instead of soluble. Like other transferrins p97 binds iron (35).

Nu-4b: Antibody 69I15 Nu-4B identifies an antigen expressed in cells from most melanomas and astrocytomas (23,44), in nevi, and in smaller amounts in some cultured fibroblasts. The antigen is a protein with polypeptide chains of molecular weights 116,000, 95,000, 29,000, and 26,000. It is present in vivo (45) and has been demonstrated in histological sections (23). An IgG_{2a} antibody to the antigen gives antibody-dependent cellular cytotoxicity. It does not suppress the growth of human melanoma in athymic mice. It does not appear to be present on any normal skin cells, including melanocytes. Since the amount of the antigen in tissues has not been determined quantitatively, it is possible that some normal adult cells and some carcinoma cells express small amounts of the antigen. Nevertheless, it appears to be sufficiently specific for melanoma to be of great interest.

gp150: This is a glycoprotein defined by an IgG_1 antibody, R_{23} (37), and expressed by most melanomas and astrocytomas and on some carcinomas. It is also expressed on endothelial cells, smooth muscle cells, and cultivated kidney epithelium (37). The same antigen has been identified by a monoclonal antibody obtained by Saxton et al. (30).

p155: This is a protein antigen, identified by hybridoma 6.1 (IgM) and present on about 50% of melanomas (46). It is also expressed by kidney carcinomas, but only weakly on cells from other tissues. It is present in vivo.

184,000 mol wt glycoprotein: This antigen, defined by antibody 51-52 (IgG_{2a}), is present on most melanomas and some carcinomas (23). It is absent from lymphocytes and erythrocytes but can be detected on lymphoblastoid cell lines. Both antibody-dependent cellular cytotoxicity and complement-dependent cytotoxicity have been observed.

p210: This is a protein antigen, identified by hybridoma 5.1 (IgG_1) and present on about 50% of melanomas and carcinomas as well as on normal adult and fetal brain (46). It is expressed in vivo.

High molecular weight antigen(s): Both Reisfeld's (47,48) and Ferrone's (31,49) groups have described high molecular weight antigens. Most work has been done using Reisfeld's antibody 9.2.27 (IgG_{2a}) and Ferrone's antibodies 225.28S (IgG_{2a}), 653.40s (IgG_1), and 763.24 (IgG_1). The antigen described by Reisfeld's group is a glycoprotein with a molecular weight of ~250,000 that is sialylated and either associates with a chondroitin-sulfate-like proteoglycan in melanoma cells or provides the core glycoprotein for the synthesis of such a proteoglycan in melanoma cells (48). Ferrone's group has described two antigen components, one greater than 500,000 daltons and the other around 280,000 daltons (31,49). The antigens are present in most melanomas and some astrocytomas, as well as in nevi and occasionally in carcinomas. They are absent from other neoplastic and normal cells, including B- and T-cell lines and peripheral blood leukocytes. Since they are expressed in vivo (48, 49), they may be useful diagnostic markers and, perhaps, therapeutic targets. IgG_{2a} antibodies to the antigens can suppress tumor growth in athymic mice and give both complement-dependent cytotoxicity and antibody-dependent cellular cytotoxicity (R. A. Reisfeld, personal communication). It remains unclear whether or not the two very similar antigens studied by Reisfeld's and Ferrone's groups are identical.

A similar or identical antigen is defined by antibody 48.7 (IgG_1). This anti-body binds strongly to cells from approximately 75% of melanomas, more weakly to cells from some carcinomas and to cultured fibroblasts, and not detectably to B- and T-cell lines (50). It binds to melanoma sections, using peroxidase-anti-peroxidase techniques, but not to sections of other tumors or to a larger variety of normal human tissues, except that there is some antigen expression in endo-thelial cells (50).

GD_3: Antibodies R_{24} (37), which is an IgG_3, and 4.2 (51), which is an IgM, define glycolipid antigen(s) expressed in about 90% of cultivated human mela-nomas, in astrocytomas, and in biopsy samples of most melanomas. Very small amounts of antigen(s) have been detected in other tumors (37), and weak cross-reactive binding to some other carcinomas has been noted (51). Normal tissues are also negative, except that R_{24} binds to cultured melanocytes. The antigen(s) defined by the two antibodies are sensitive to neuraminidase and are heat resistant, and both are present in the ganglioside fraction of cells (37,51). Recent studies (52,53) show that the antigen(s) defined by both R_{24} amd 4.2 are GD_3 sialoganglio-sides. This, together with their distribution, indicates that the antigens recognized by the two antibodies are probably the same; at least they seem to be closely re-lated. According to a recent study by Nudelman et al. (53), the ceramide portion of antigen 4.2 is larger than that found in GD_3 from normal brain. This may ex-plain why the antigen is not immunologically detected at the surface of brain cells, in spite of the fact that brain contains much GD_3. Complement-dependent cyto-toxicity against the antigen defined by antibody 4.2 has been demonstrated (I. Hellström et al., unpublished findings).

WM9-19: Hybridoma WM9-19 forms an IgM antibody that defines a glycolipid antigen expressed primarily on melanoma cells (23).

3.1: Antigen 3.1 (54) is identified by three monoclonal antibodies: 3.1 (IgG_1), 3.2 (IgG_{2a}), and 3.3 (IgG_{2b}). It has not been detected by immunoprecipitation/ SDS-PAGE, and it is resistant to heating. When cultured cells were studied, antigen 3.1 was detected only on a small subgroup of melanomas, the strongest expression being on cells from the metastatic melanoma, M1804, which was used for the im-munization. IgG_2 antibodies to the antigen are cytotoxic in the presence of com-plement (55) and give antibody-dependent cellular cytotoxicity in the presence of human leukocytes (56). Antigen 3.1 undergoes genetic variation so that antigen-negative cells can be selected from antigen-positive clones (51). Since it could be detected in biopsy samples from many normal tissues (38), in spite of the fact that it is highly melanoma-specific as long as cultured cells are studied, antigen 3.1 does not qualify as a truly melanoma-associated antigen and is included in this section for historic reasons.

Based on the data summarized for these 15 antigens, three conclusions can be made about melanoma-associated antigens defined by monoclonal mouse anti-bodies. First, most of them are differentiation antigens that are expressed more strongly on melanoma cells than on the majority of normal adult cells. Second, the same melanoma can express several of the antigens, which implies that a combination of monoclonal antibodies to different antigens should identify most (essentially all?) melanomas. A combination of antibodies may, indeed, be needed for diagnostic and therapeutic procedures, also in view of the finding that the antigens can undergo clonal variation within the same tumor. Third, the number of antigens detected by monoclonal mouse antibodies is likely to be limited, with several laboratories having already identified some of the same antigens in their attempts to develop new monoclonal antibodies to human melanoma. This is true for the GD_3 antigen, when the same cell line, SK-MEL 28, was used for immunization, and for p97 (gp95), where either the same (SK-MEL 28) or a different (KZ2) cell line was used. It is also true for the high molecular weight antigen(s), where the group discovering the antigen immunized with material released into the culture medium from explanted melanoma cells while subsequent work used a short-term melanoma explant for immunization. It remains to be seen to what extent additional melanoma antigens will be defined by immunization of mice or of other species or by making human hybridomas.

SPECIFICITY OF MELANOMA-ASSOCIATED ANTIGENS

When monoclonal antibodies to human melanomas were first described, some of the antigens detected were believed to be present on all melanoma cells and completely absent from all normal and other neoplastic cells. However, more extensive and more sensitive tests of cultured cells and tissue samples have shown, as illustrated above, that many of the original claims for tumor specificity were overly optimistic. Thus the antigens that have been most thoroughly studied, for example, p97 (34,36), have been found to be differentiation (oncofetal) antigens shared by melanoma cells and certain fetal cells and present in trace amounts on normal adult cells. Although other antigens, according to published data, appear to be entirely melanoma-specific (see, e.g., Refs. 23 and 27), these antigens have not been subjected to specificity tests as rigorous as those used for p97, the high molecular weight antigen, Nu-4B, or GD_3. The possibility is great, therefore, that they are no more melanoma-specific than the others.

Even if no monoclonal antibodies have been convincingly demonstrated to react with antigens that are unique for melanomas, this does not mean that the antibodies that are available are of little interest; rather, one should consider the degree of specificity that is required for an antibody to be useful clinically (57,58). In many cases, absolute specificity is not required, and other factors, such as antigen density, may be more important.

Thus we believe the degree of specificity for antigens such as p97, the high molecular weight proteoglycan antigen(s), the Nu-4B antigen, and GD_3, to take some examples, is sufficient for many diagnostic and therapeutic purposes, since these antigens are present in melanoma cells at much higher concentration than in other tumor cells or adult normal cells. For example, many melanomas express an amount of p97 more than 50 times greater than that for normal adult tissues (33). The difference in sensitivity between normal and neoplastic cells to killing by natural killer cells (59) or to the cytotoxic effect of anti-cancer drugs is rarely this great. Even if any antigens would be found that are present in equal amounts on melanoma cells and normal skin melanocytes, they might still be useful markers for diagnosis and they might also be used for targeting therapeutic agents into tumors, since cytotoxicity to normal melanocytes may constitute an acceptable risk. It is interesting in this context that Bernstein's group (60) was able to successfully treat mouse T-cell leukemias by an anti-Thy-1 antibody, even when the antibody could react also with normal T cells.

Of all tumor-associated antigens that have so far been defined by monoclonal antibodies, the antigens that operationally are most tumor-specific are the idio-typic determinants of B-cell leukemias. These are shared by a patient's leukemic cells and the clone of normal B cells from which the leukemia originated (61). Since the only normal cells recognized by the antibody represent that clone, idiotype-specific antigens may be ideal as therapeutic targets (62,63), and two recent therapeutic studies bear this out (64,65). There is, however, a drawback in that a different idiotype-specific antibody must be raised against each patient's tumor. Whether any idiotype- (clone-) specific antigens occur among solid tu-mors, such as melanomas, is not known; however, no evidence for this has been observed to date in numerous experiments to generate monoclonal antibodies.

One still hopes, of course, that it might be possible, in the future, to obtain monoclonal antibodies that are more specific for melanoma than the antibodies available today and which still define antigens of sufficient concentration at the cell surface to be of clinical use. If, indeed, some patients recognize antigens that are entirely confined to their melanomas(15), monoclonal antibodies to these anti-gens might, for example, be obtained by hybridizing the patient's lymphocytes (17,18,66,67) or transforming them with Epstein-Barr virus (68). There is also the possibility that melanoma cells express cell-surface antigens that are directly associated with their neoplastic state, for example, as a result of the activation of an oncogene (69). Since monoclonal antibodies to such antigens would be of great interest, particular efforts should be made to obtain them.

CLINICAL APPLICATIONS

Monoclonal antibodies to melanoma-associated antigens will, it is hoped, be of both diagnostic and therapeutic value. Clinical application of antibodies to mela-noma antigens should, in addition to providing information pertinent to melanoma, provide models for future studies of other neoplasms, such as carcinoma of the lung or breast. We shall first discuss diagnosis, where several possibilities may be considered.

First, one might use anti-melanoma antibodies to correlate the presence of certain cell-surface antigens with clinical prognosis, an approach that has been useful in leukemia (43,70,71). To facilitate this, one should look for antibodies to antigens that can distinguish melanomas with different prognoses, for example, nodular from superficially spreading melanoma or melanomas from compound nevi, as well as for antibodies to antigens distinguishing metastatic from primary tumors (if any such antigens exist).

Second, antibodies may be used for the detection of melanoma in histological sections, which may be helpful, for example, when diagnosing a metastasis from an unknown primary tumor. Antigens strongly expressed by most melanomas and either absent from or expressed very weakly in other neoplasms, would be the ones most useful for this. There is already evidence that the Nu-4B antibodies can be used in that respect (72). Combinations of monoclonal antibodies to several different melanoma-associated antigens may be useful for this, since virtually all melanomas may then be recognized.

Third, antibodies might be used to assay serum for melanoma-associated antigens, in a way analogous to the measurement of alpha-fetoprotein or carcinoembryonic antigens, but with the advantage of increased specificity. This could be helpful both in monitoring tumor destruction in response to therapy and in detecting imminent relapses. The extent to which an antigen is released from neoplastic as compared to normal cells will obviously influence its usefulness for this. For colon carcinoma, a tumor-type specific monosialoganglioside antigen has been described (23,73,74), which is diagnostically promising in that patients with advanced colon carcinoma have elevated serum antigen levels (23). However, no antigen so far identified has been detected in sera from melanoma patients in amounts sufficient to be clinically useful.

A fourth potential diagnostic use of antibodies is for the localization of tumor metastases by injecting antibodies labeled with radioisotopes such as ^{131}I, ^{123}I, ^{125}I and, [111]In (75-78). Since antibodies may localize in tumor tissues also for nonimmunological reasons, the experiments will be most meaningful if both specific and control antibodies are used; when feasible, these may be labeled with two different radioisotopes and injected simultaneously. Recently Larson and collaborators (79) have performed a study in which ^{131}I-labeled monoclonal anti-p97 antibody or Fab fragments were given to patients with advanced melanoma. About 80% of known metastases were detected by imaging, and studies on tumor biopsy samples showed three- to fivefold greater uptake in tumors of specific antibody (or Fab) than of control antibody (or Fab). Since this degree of antibody uptake in tumors was lower than expected from in vitro studies (where melanomas often express a 50-fold greater amount of p97 than normal adult tissues), a number of practical problems need to be solved, for example, problems concerning the pharmacology of injected radiolabeled antibodies (or Fab). Nevertheless, the fact that a several-fold concentration of antibodies in tumor can be obtained is promising in two ways: It points toward ways of developing new diagnostic techniques that may become routinely applicable for tumor detection, and it indicates that a sufficient amount of antibodies can localize in tumors for therapeutic trials to be considered.

Therapeutic applications of monoclonal antibodies to tumor antigens have also attracted much attention. There are several possibilities.

One should first consider giving antibody alone. Most of the evidence suggesting this approach comes from in vitro studies, where the antibody effects include complement-dependent cytotoxicity (23,55,56), antibody-dependent cellular cytotoxicity (56,80), and directly inhibitory effects of antibody on neoplastic cells (81). It is interesting that a combination of antibodies to two epitopes of p97 gives efficient complement-dependent cytotoxicity of melanoma cells in vitro, under conditions where neither of the two antibodies alone is significantly cytotoxic. When the antibodies are combined, strong cytotoxicity can be seen even at concentrations as low as 2 ng/ml, a serum level that can easily be obtained in vivo (41). However, in all the in vitro studies performed with mouse antibodies, rabbit or guinea pig complement had to be used, with human complement generally being ineffective. In vivo, some effective anti-tumor responses of antibody have been reported with lymphoid tumors (60,82).

Antibody can also be employed as a carrier of anti-tumor agents. At least four types of such agents can be conjugated with the antibody, namely, radioisotopes, toxins, chemotherapeutic agents, and molecules modifying the immune response.

First, antibody (or Fab fragments) might be labeled with a sufficient dose of radioisotope to deliver a therapeutic level of radiation to the tumor (83). This could be with a gamma-emitter such as ^{131}I, or possibly with an alpha-emitter. Although highly radiosensitive tumors are more suitable candidates for this approach than melanomas, it should be possible also to treat melanomas.

Second, conjugates ("immunotoxins") can be prepared between antibody and a toxin such as ricin (84-87) or diphtheria toxin (84,88,89). This is best done by conjugating relatively nontoxic A chains with antibody (90); the antibody carries the A chain to the cell, whose protein synthesis is inhibited. A melanoma-specific immunotoxin has been made in the form of a conjugate between ricin A chain and anti-p97 antibody (91). This conjugate was found to kill melanoma cells in vitro expressing medium to high levels of p97, but to spare cells expressing small amounts of p97 (less than 5000 molecules per cell). It was much more effective in the presence of ammonium chloride, an observation now being explored in order to develop agents that, like ammonium chloride, are lysosomotropic and which can be given in concentrations that are effective in vivo (92).

Immunotoxins can kill both dividing and nondividing cells, a clear advantage. Whether they will be effective in vivo is unclear, a major problem being the degree of stability of the conjugates. Therefore it is important to develop practically feasible procedures by which immunotoxins can destroy tumor cells more rapidly. It is encouraging that Vitetta's group (93), even without using such procedures, has been able to cure transplanted mouse lymphomas by combining the injection of immunotoxin with other therapeutic modalities that were ineffective by themselves. Even if efficient tumor cell destruction could be regularly achieved in vivo, some therapeutic difficulties may still result from the fact that immunotoxins are effective only against those neoplastic cells that express the respective target antigen. This is in view of the fact that both temporary (94) and permanent losses (see, e.g., Refs. 40, 55, and 95) of tumor-associated antigens have been documented, so that treatment with an immunotoxin might lead to the enrichment of cells lacking the antigen to which the antibody is directed. However, we do not, at this point in time, consider this problem to be one of the most worrisome, and it can probably be overcome by using a combination of immunotoxins specific for different melanoma-associated antigens on the same cells. Another possible complication might arise from the fact that the uptake by a cell of as little as one immunotoxin molecule can kill it, leading to toxic side effects, even when normal cells express only trace amounts of the target antigens. By adjusting the concentrations of injected immunotoxins, however, it should be possible to prevent damage to the major proportion of the normal cells.

A third approach is to use conjugates between antibodies and chemotherapeutic agents, which either may be taken up by the cells to which the conjugates are bound or dissociate in the tumor area so as to release free drug. Several different conjugates have been prepared, most of which have used xenoantibodies (96-98). Recently conjugates have been made between monoclonal antibodies and Vindesine, including such with anti-p97 antibody. The latter conjugate has been found to be selectively cytotoxic for melanoma cells expressing high levels of p97 (98).

A fourth approach is to use anti-tumor antibodies for transporting agents to the tumor site that can induce tumor-destroying immunological mechanisms. For example, one may use antibodies to locally induce hypersensitivity reactions or to increase the ability of natural killer cells to destroy tumor. In the former case, the antibodies would play a role analogous to that achieved when one locally applies a sensitizing agent such as bacille Calmette-Guerin (99,100), or dinitrochlorobenzene (101). Such application often induces local tumor destruction. The problem of it rarely having a systemic effect on foci of disseminated tumor cells may be rectified by using conjugates with antibodies. With respect to tumor destruction by natural killer cells, Baldwin (102) recently prepared conjugates between monoclonal antibodies and interferon and showed that such conjugates can induce tumor killing by natural killer cells in vitro. Whether or not they are effective in vivo needs to be tested.

In most cases in which monoclonal mouse antibodies are repeatedly injected into patients, a complication is the development of antibodies to mouse immunoglobulins. Although these problems are less severe when Fab fragments rather than whole antibodies are used, antibodies to mouse immunoglobulin are generally observed after several injections have been given (79). Procedures should be considered for overcoming this. For example, one should consider trying to induce specific immunological unresponsiveness to mouse immunoglobulin. When tumor antigen-specific human monoclonal antibodies become available, antibody formation to xenogeneic immunoglobulin would be avoided. However, even the human antibodies are likely to be immunogenic to patients by inducing the formation of antibodies to allotypic and idiotypic determinants.

Another therapeutic approach is to immunize patients with one or several of the melanoma-associated antigens so as to induce an active immune response. Although it may not be practical to purify sufficient amounts of antigen from tumor cells, one may be able to use synthetic peptides based on the amino acid sequence of the proteins. The rationale for using them is the finding that immunization with synthetic oligopeptides can induce antibodies recognizing the native proteins (103).

Finally, one may attempt to induce immunity in tumor patients by giving anti-idiotypic antibodies obtained by using monoclonal anti-melanoma antibodies as immunogens. This approach is based on the demonstration, in animal systems, that both cell-mediated and humoral responses can be induced by injecting anti-idiotypic antibodies (82,104). It has the advantage of being able to mimic conformational rather than only sequential determinants in the antigen molecule.

The extent to which synthetic peptides and anti-idiotypic antibodies will be useful by inducing active anti-tumor immunity depends upon whether a host response can be induced to antigens present in trace amounts in normal tissues. Since immunological tolerance to many normally occurring cellular antigens can be broken, with autoimmunity as the result, the greatest problem may be whether or not an immune response to melanoma-associated differentiation antigens would cause unacceptable damage to normal cells expressing trace amounts of the given antigens. The degree of complication due to such damage is likely to vary for different antigens.

CONCLUSIONS

Monoclonal antibodies have been obtained that are specific for a number of cell-surface antigens associated with human melanomas. Most antigens identified by these antibodies are differentiation antigens that are expressed more strongly on melanoma cells than on normal adult cells. Some of the antibodies may be suitable for diagnosis and therapy.

ACKNOWLEDGMENTS

This work was supported by grants CA 14135, 19148, 19149, CA 25558, and CA 27841 from the National Institutes of Health and grant IM 241A from the American Cancer Society. The authors wish to acknowledge collaboration with M. -Y. Yeh, S. M. Larson, R. G. Woodbury, H. J. Garrigues, P. Casellas, K. Nishiyama, and S. M. Loop.

REFERENCES

1. T. C. Everson and W. H. Cole, in *Spontaneous Regression of Cancer,* Saunders, Philadelphia, 1966, p. 560.
2. K. E. Hellström and I. Hellström, *Ann. Rev. Med. 23*:19 (1972).
3. I. Hellström, K. E. Hellström, G. E. Pierce, and J. P. S. Yang, *Nature 220*: 1352 (1968).
4. I. Hellström, K. E. Hellström, H. O. Sjögren, and G. A. Warner, *Int. J. Cancer 8*:185 (1971).
5. A. J. Cochran, R. M. Mackie, C. E. Ross, L. J. Ogg, and A. M. Jackson, *Int. J. Cancer 18*:274 (1976).
6. J. L. McCoy, L. F. Jerome, J. H. Dean, E. Perlin, R. K. Oldham, D. H. Char, M. H. Cohen, E. L. Felix, and R. B. Herberman, *J. Nat. Cancer Inst. 55*: 19 1975.
7. W. J. Halliday, A. E. Maluish, J. H. Little, and N. C. Davis, *Int. J. Cancer 16*: 645 (1975).
8. I. Hellström and K. E. Hellström, *Fed. Proc. 32*:156 (1973).
9. R. W. Baldwin, *Adv. Cancer Res. 18*:1 (1973).
10. R. B. Herberman and R. K. Oldham, *J. Nat. Cancer Inst. 55*:749 (1975).
11. K. E. Hellström and J. P. Brown, in *The Antigens* (M. Sela, ed.), Academic, New York, 1979, p. 1.
12. M. G. Lewis, R. L. Ikonopisov, R. C. Nairn, T. M. Phillips, G. Hamilton-Fairly, D. C. Bodenham, and P. Alexander, *Br. Med. J. 3*:547 (1969).
13. D. L. Morton, R. A. Malmgren, E. C. Holmes, and A. S. Ketcham, *Surgery 64*:233 (1968).
14. S. Cornain, J. E. de Vries, J. Collard, J. C. Vennegoor, I. V. Wingerden, and P. Rumke, *Int. J. Cancer 19*:981 (1975).
15. H. Shiku, T. Takahashi, H. F. Oettgen, and L. J. Old, *J. Exp. Med. 144*:873 (1976).
16. G. Köhler and C. Milstein, *Nature 256*:495 (1975).
17. L. Olsson and H. S. Kaplan, *Proc. Nat. Acad. Sci. U.S.A. 77*:5429 (1980).
18. C. Croce, A. Linnenbach, W. Wall, Z. Steplewski, and H. Koprowski, *Nature 288*:488 (1980).
19. J. P. Brown, K. E. Hellström, and I. Hellström, *Methods Enzymol. 92*:160 (1980).
20. J. P. Brown, P. W. Wright, C. E. Hart, R. G. Woodbury, K. E. Hellström, and I. Hellström, *J. Biol. Chem. 255*:4980 (1980).

21. L. A. Sternberger, in *Immunocytochemistry*, Wiley, New York, 1979, p. 104.
22. D. Colcher, P. Horan Hand, M. Nuti, and J. Schlom, *Proc. Nat. Acad. Sci. U.S.A. 78*:3199 (1981).
23. H. Koprowski and Z. Steplewski, in *Research Monographs in Immunology*, Vol. 3, *Monoclonal Antibodies and T-Cell Hybridomas* (U. Hämmerling, G. J. Hämmerling, and J. F. Kearney, eds.) Elsevier/North-Holland, Amsterdam, 1981, p. 161.
24. H. J. Garrigues, W. Tilgen, I. Hellström, W. Franke, and K. E. Hellström, *Int. J. Cancer 29*:511 (1982).
25. R. G. Woodbury, J. P. Brown, M. -Y. Yeh, I. Hellström, and K. E. Hellström, *Proc. Nat. Acad. Sci. U.S.A. 77*:2183 (1980).
26. S. Carrel, R. S. Accolla, A. L. Carmagnola, and J. -P. Mach, *Cancer Res. 40*: 2523 (1980).
27. S. Carrel, R. S. Accolla, N. Gross, and J. -P. Mach, in *Research Monographs in Immunology*, Vol. 3, *Monoclonal Antibodies and T-Cell Hybridomas* (U. Hämmerling, G. J. Hammerling, and J. F. Kearney, eds.), Elsevier/North-Holland, Amsterdam, 1981, p. 174.
28. J. P. Johnson, M. Demmer-Dieckmann, T. Meo, M. R. Hadam, and G. Riethmuller, *Eur. J. Immunol. 11*:825 (1981).
29. R. E. Saxton, B. D. Mann, D. L. Morton, and M. W. Burk, *J. Biol. Response Modifiers* (in press).
30. R. E. Saxton, B. D. Mann, D. L. Morton, and M. W. Burk, *Hybridoma* (in press).
31. G. Ruberto, K. Imai, P. G. Natali, B. S. Wilson, S. Ferrone, in *Progress in Cancer Research and Therapy*, Vol. 21, *Hybridomas in Cancer Diagnosis and Treatment* (M. S. Mitchell and H. F. Oettgen, eds.), Raven Press, New York, 1982, p. 191.
32. K. Imai, B. S. Wilson, A. Bigotti, P. G. Natali, and S. Ferrone, *J. Nat. Cancer Inst. 68*:761 (1982).
33. J. P. Brown, K. Nishiyama, I. Hellström, and K. E. Hellström, *J. Immunol. 127*:539 (1981).
34. J. P. Brown, R. G. Woodbury, C. E. Hart, I. Hellström, and K. E. Hellström, *Proc. Nat. Acad. Sci. U.S.A. 78*:539 (1981).
35. J. P. Brown, R. M. Hewick, I. Hellström, K. E. Hellström, R. F. Doolittle, and W. J. Dreyer, *Nature 296*:171 (1982).
36. R. G. Woodbury, J. P. Brown, S. M. Loop, K. E. Hellström, and I. Hellström, *Int. J. Cancer 27*:145 (1981).
37. W. G. Dippold, K. O. Lloyd, L. T. C. Li, H. Ikeda, H. F. Oettgen, and L. J. Old, *Proc. Nat. Acad. Sci. U.S.A. 77*:6114 (1980).
38. J. P. Brown, K. E. Hellström, and I. Hellström, *Clin. Chem. 27*:1592 (1981).
39. M. E. Dantas, J. P. Brown, M. R. Thomas, W. A. Robinson, and L. M. Glode, *Cancer* (in press).
40. A. P. Albino, K. O. Lloyd, A. N. Houghton, H. F. Oettgen, and L. J. Old, *J. Exp. Med. 154*:1764 (1981).

41. I. Hellström, J. P. Brown, and K. E. Hellström, *J. Immunol.* *127*:157 (1981).
42. I. S. Trowbridge and F. Lopez, *Proc. Nat. Acad. Sci. U.S.A.* *79*:1175 (1982).
43. M. F. Greaves, *Cancer Res.* *41*:4752 (1981).
44. K. F. Mitchell, J. P. Fuhrer, Z. Steplewski, and H. Koprowski, *Proc. Nat. Acad. Sci. U.S.A.* *77*:7267 (1980).
45. Z. Steplewski, M. Herlyn, D. Herlyn, W. H. Clark, and Z. Koprowski, *Eur. J. Immunol.* *9*:94 (1979).
46. S. M. Loop, K. Nishiyama, I. Hellström, R. G. Woodbury, J. P. Brown, and K. E. Hellström, *Int. J. Cancer* *27*:775 (1981).
47. A. C. Morgan, D. R. Galloway, and R. A. Reisfeld, *Hybridoma* *1*:27 (1981).
48. T. F. Bumol and R. A. Reisfeld, *Proc. Nat. Acad. Sci. U.S.A.* *79*:1245 (1982).
49. P. G. Natali, K. Imai, B. S. Wilson, A. Bigotti, R. Cavallere, M. A. Pellegrino, and S. Ferrone, *J. Nat. Cancer Inst.* *67*:591 (1982).
50. I. Hellström, H. J. Garrigues, L. Cabasco, G. H. Mosley, J. P. Brown, and K. E. Hellström, *J. Immunol.* *130*:1467 (1983).
51. M. -Y. Yeh, I. Hellström, K. Abe, S. Hakomori, and K. E. Hellström, *Int. J. Cancer* *29*:269 (1982).
52. C. S. Pukel, K. O. Lloyd, L. R. Trabassos, W. G. Dippold, H. F. Oettgen, and L. J. Old, *J. Exp. Med.* *155*:1133 (1982).
53. E. Nudelman, S. Hakomori, R. Kannagi, S. Levery, M. -Y. Yeh, K. E. Hellström, and I. Hellström, *J. Biol. Chem.* *257*:12752 (1982).
54. M. -Y. Yeh, I. Hellström, J. P. Brown, G. A. Warner, J. A. Hansen, and K. E. Hellström, *Proc. Nat. Acad. Sci. U.S.A.* *76*:2927 (1979).
55. M. -Y. Yeh, I. Hellström, and K. E. Hellström, *J. Immunol.* *126*:1319 (1981).
56. I. Hellström, K. E. Hellström, and M. -Y. Yeh, *Int. J. Cancer* *27*:281 (1981).
57. K. E. Hellström, J. P. Brown, and I. Hellström, in *Contemporary Topics in Immunology* (N. L. Warner, ed.), Plenum, New York, 1980, p. 117.
58. E. S. Lennox, in *Progress in Cancer Research and Therapy,* Vol. 21, *Hybridomas in Cancer Diagnosis and Treatment* (M. S. Mitchell and H. F. Oettgen, eds.), Raven Press, New York, 1982, p. 5.
59. R. B. Herberman, in *Natural Cell-Mediated Immunity Against Tumors* (R. B. Herberman, ed.), Academic, New York, 1982.
60. I. D. Bernstein, M. R. Tam, and R. C. Nowinski, *Science* *207*:68 (1980).
61. A. Hatzubai, D. G. Maloney, and R. Levy, *J. Immunol.* *126*:2397 (1981).
62. H. N. Eisen, N. Sakato, and S. J. Hall, in *Cancer and Transplantation* (G. P. Murphy, ed.), Grune and Stratton, New York, 1975, p. 71.
63. G. T. Stevenson, E. V. Elliott, and F. K. Stevenson, *Fed. Proc.* *36*:2268 (1977).
64. T. J. Hamblin, A. K. Abdul-Ahad, J. Gordon, F. K. Stevenson, and G. T. Stevenson, *Br. J. Cancer* *42*:495 (1980).
65. G. G. Miller, P. I. Nadler, Y. Asano, R. J. Hodes, and D. H. Sachs, *J. Exp. Med.* *154*:23 (1981).

66. R. C. Nowinski, C. Berglund, J. Lane, M. Lostrom, I. Bernstein, W. Young, S. Hakomori, L. Hill, and M. Cooney, *Science 210*:537 (1980).
67. J. Schlom, D. Wunderlich, and Y. Teramoto, *Proc. Nat. Acad. Sci. U.S.A. 77*:6841 (1980).
68. M. Steinitz, in *Research Monographs in Immunology,* Vol. 3, *Monoclonal Antibodies and T-Cell Hybridomas* (U. Hämmerling, G. J. Hämmerling, and J. F. Kearney, eds.), Elsevier/North-Holland, Amsterdam, 1981, p. 447.
69. J. M. Bishop, *Sci. Am. 246*:80 (1982).
70. J. Ritz, J. M. Pesando, J. Notis-McConarty, L. A. Clavell, S. E. Sallan, and S. F. Schlossman, *Cancer Res. 41*:4771 (1981).
71. T. F. Zipf, R. I. Fox, J. Dilley, and R. Levy, *Cancer Res. 41*:4786 (1981).
72. M. Herlyn, W. H. Clark, Jr., M. J. Mastrangelo, D. Guerry IV, D. E. Elder, D. LaRosse, R. Hamilton, E. Bondi, R. Tuthill, and Z. Steplewski, *Cancer Res. 40*:3602 (1980).
73. M. Herlyn, Z. Steplewski, D. Herlyn, and Z. Koprowski, *Proc. Nat. Acad. Sci. U.S.A. 76*:1438 (1979).
74. J. L. Magnani, M. Brockhaus, D. F. Smith, V. Ginsburg, M. Blaszczyk, K. F. Mitchell, Z. Steplewski, and H. Koprowski, *Science 212*:55 (1981).
75. R. S. Accola, F. Buchegger, S. Carrel, and J. -P. Mach, in *Research Monographs in Immunology,* Vol. 3, *Monoclonal Antibodies and T-Cell Hybridomas* (U. Hämmerling, G. J. Hämmerling, and J. F. Kearney, eds.), Elsevier/North-Holland, Amsterdam, 1981, p. 209.
76. B. Ballou, G. Levine, T. R. Hakala, and D. Solter, *Science 206*:844 (1979).
77. D. M. Goldenberg, F. DeLand, E. Kim, S. Bennett, F. J. Primus, J. R. Van Nagell, N. Estes, P. DeSimone, and P. Rayburn, *N. Engl. J. Med. 298*:1384 (1978).
78. J. -P. Mach, F. Buchegger, M. Forni, J. Ritschard, C. Berche, J. -D. Lumbroso, M. Schreyer, C. Girardet, R. S. Accolla, and S. Carrel, *Immunol. Today 2*:239 (1981).
79. S. M. Larson, J. P. Brown, P. W. Wright, J. A. Carrasquillo, I. Hellström, and K. E. Hellström, *J. Nuclear Med. 24*:123 (1983).
80. D. Herlyn, M. Herlyn, Z. Steplewski, and H. Koprowski, *Eur. J. Immunol. 9*:657 (1979).
81. I. S. Trowbridge and M. B. Omary, *Proc. Nat. Acad. Sci. U.S.A. 78*:3039 (1980).
82. R. A. Miller, D. G. Maloney, R. Warnke, and R. Levy, *N. Engl. J. Med. 306*:517 (1982).
83. H. S. Kaplan, in *Progress in Cancer Research and Therapy,* Vol. 21, *Hybridomas in Cancer Diagnosis and Treatment* (M. S. Mitchell and H. F. Oettgen, eds.), Raven Press, New York, 1982, p. 255.
84. H. E. Blythman, P. Casellas, O. Gros, P. Gros, F. K. Jansen, F. Paolucci, B. Pau, and H. Vidal, *Nature 290*:145 (1981).
85. F. K. Jansen, H. E. Blythman, D. Carriere, P. Casellas, O. Gros, P. Gros, F. Paolucci, B. Pau, P. Poncelet, G. Richer, H. Vidal, and G. A. Voisin, in *Research Monographs in Immunology,* Vol. 3, *Monoclonal Antibodies and*

T-Cell Hybridomas (U. Hämmerling, G. J. Hämmerling, and J. F. Kearney, eds.), Elsevier/North-Holland, Amsterdam, 1981, p. 229.

86. H. Miyazaki, M. Beppu, T. Terao, and T. Osawa, *Gann 71*:766 (1980).
87. V. Raso, J. Ritz, M. Basala, and S. F. Schlossman, *Cancer Res. 42*:457 (1982).
88. D. G. Gilliland, Z. Steplewski, R. J. Collier, K. F. Mitchell, T. H. Chang, and H. Koprowski, *Proc. Nat. Acad. Sci. U.S.A. 77*:4539 (1980).
89. Y. Masuho, T. Hara, and T. Noguchi, *Biochem. Biophys. Res. Commun. 90*: 320 (1981).
90. K. Sandvig, S. Olsnes, and A. Pihl, *Eur. J. Biochem. 84*:323 (1978).
91. P. Cassellas, J. P. Brown, O. Gros, P. Gros, I. Hellström, F. K. Jansen, P. Poncelet, R. Roncucci, H. Vidal, and K. E. Hellström, *Int. J. Cancer 30*: 437 (1982).
92. P. Casellas, H. Blythman, P. Gros, G. Richer, and F. K. Jansen, in *Protides of the Biological Fluids, Colloquium 30* (H. Peeters, ed.), Pergamon, Oxford, 1983, p. 359.
93. E. S. Vitetta, K. A. Krolick, M. Miyama-Inaba, W. Cushley, and J. W. Uhr, *Science 11*:219 (1983).
94. L. J. Old, E. Stockert, E. A. Boyse, and J. H. Kim, *J. Exp. Med. 127*:523 (1968).
95. E. M. Fenyo, E. Klein, G. Klein, and K. Swiech, *J. Nat. Cancer Res. 40*:69 (1968).
96. T. Ghose and A. H. Blair, *J. Nat. Cancer Inst. 61*:657 (1978).
97. E. Hurwitz, R. Levy, R. Maron, M. Wilchek, R. Arnon, and M. Sela, *Cancer Res. 34*:1175 (1975).
98. G. F. Rowland, R. G. Simmonds, J. R. F. Corvalan, R. W. Baldwin, J. P. Brown, M. J., Embleton, C. H. J. Ford, K. E. Hellström, I. Hellström, J. T. Kemshead, C. E. Newman, and C. S. Woodhouse, in *Protides of the Biological Fluids, Colloquium 30* (H. Peeters, ed.), Pergamon, Oxford, 1983, p. 375.
99. R. C. Bast, Jr., B. Zbar, T. Borsos, and H. J. Rapp, *N. Engl. J. Med. 290*: 1413 (1974).
100. D. L. Morton, F. R. Eilber, E. C. Holmes, J. S. Hunt, A. S. Ketcham, M. J. Silverstein, and F. C. Sparks, *Ann. Surg. 180*:635 (1974).
101. E. Klein, O. A. Holterman, B. Papermaster, H. Milgrom, D. Rosner, L. Klein, M. J. Walker and B. Zbar, *Nat. Cancer Inst. Monogr. 39*:229 (1973).
102. R. W. Baldwin, M. J. Embleton, G. R. Flannery, J. M. Pelham, M. V. Pimm, M. R. Price, and R. A. Robbins, in *Protides of the Biological Fluids* (H. Peeters, ed.), Pergamon, Oxford, 1983, p. 381.
103. M. Z. Atassi, *Immunochemistry 15*:909 (1978).
104. J. A. Bluestone, S. O. Sharrow, S. L. Epstein, K. Ozato, and D. H. Sachs, *Nature 291*:233 (1981).

3 MONOCLONAL ANTIBODIES TO NEUROBLASTOMA ANTIGENS

John T. Kemshead / Imperial Cancer Research Fund Oncology Laboratory, Institute of Child Health, London, England

INTRODUCTION

Neuroblastoma is a malignancy of cells forming the adrenergic component of the sympathetic nervous system, first described by Virchow in 1865 (1). The most common sites of tumor origin are extracranial, being the adrenal gland and sympathetic ganglia running along the spinal cord from the neck to the abdomen (2,3). However, tumors arising in other areas such as the lip, bladder, cerebrum, and sciatic nerve have also been reported (4,5).

Neuroblastoma is almost exclusively restricted to children and is the most common extracranial solid tumor in childhood (6,7). Early diagnosis is often difficult, and where metastatic spread of the tumor occurs, treatment involves a combination of surgery, radiotherapy, and chemotherapy (8,9). However, despite increasing cure rates for other forms of pediatric malignant disease, the prognosis for children with metastatic neuroblastoma has not improved over recent years (10). Using conventional doses of chemotherapeutic reagents, patients can often obtain a partial or complete remission (11), but the response is nearly always transient. To attempt to obtain longer remission periods (and hopefully cures), current treatment protocols have increased both the doses and combinations of chemotherapeutic agents used for the malignancy (12). This approach has culminated in the use of high-dose chemotherapy, for example L-phenylalanine mustard (melphalan) in amounts where the drug is also toxic to hemopoietic cells in bone marrow. To avoid ablation of hemopoietic cell progenitors, bone marrow is aspirated from patients just prior to chemotherapy (13). The use of melphalan, with a short plasma half-life of approximately 20 min, allows marrow to be safely reinfused back into patients some 8-12 hr after infusion of the drug (14,15). To prevent reseeding of tumor not exposed to high-dose chemotherapy, the marrow used in the autologous transplantation technique has to be free of malignant cells (16).

Identification of small numbers of neuroblasts in either marrow aspirates or trephine marrow biopsies is extremely difficult by conventional histological techniques, as the tumor cells individually resemble some mononuclear components of normal bone marrow (17). The desire to easily identify metastatic spread of neuroblastoma has lead to a search for markers specific to these malignant cells. This review will briefly discuss the range of markers that have been associated with neuroblastoma, followed by a detailed description of monoclonal antibodies selected for binding to these malignant cells. Finally, current work using monoclonal antibodies to remove neuroblastoma cells from bone marrow will be discussed.

MARKERS ASSOCIATED WITH NEUROBLASTOMA

Histological Characteristics

In 1910 Wright (18) suggested that neuroblastoma cells could be characterized by their tendency to clump together to give the impression of rosettes or fibril bundles. Although this characteristic is still used in diagnosis today, it is not consistently associated with the malignancy and is less useful where cells have been taken from sites such as bone marrow and are thus disturbed by aspiration. As previously stated, identification of metastatic spread of neuroblastoma to sites such as bone marrow is often difficult, as the tumor cells can appear identical to normal hemopoietic blast cells (17). Furthermore, by conventional histological criteria it is often difficult to distinguish neuroblastoma cells from other small, round cell tumors, and where other diagnostic parameters prove inadequate, misdiagnosis of malignancy can occur.

Intracellular Markers

Catecholamines: Neuroblastoma tumor cells frequently express properties of normal cells developing to form elements of the sympathetic nervous system (16), for example, often synthesizing and secreting catecholamines (19). The presence of either elevated catecholamine or catecholamine breakdown products in the urine of patients with neuroblastoma is used as a major diagnostic marker for the malignancy (20). 3-Methoxy-4-hydroxymandelic acid (VMA), HMA, and 3-methoxy-4-hydroxyphenylalanine glycol (HMPG) are examples of catecholamine catabolites routinely screened for in the urine of patients with neuroblastoma (21,22). Estimates of these major degradative products are relatively simple as colorimetric assays are employed, although more complex techniques are required for the detection of minor breakdown products (23,24). Many of these assays are prone to interference from breakdown products of normal dietary components, for example, vanilla (25). Furthermore, to account for diurnal variations in catecholamine excretion, assays are usually undertaken on 24-hr urine samples (26). Even with these precautions, measurement of catecholamine catabolites can vary from one day to another, adding to the problem of using such indicators for diagnosis. To attempt to overcome at least some of these problems, a radioimmune assay to detect catecholamines and or their breakdown products may be appropriate. Certainly heteroantisera capable of distinguishing epinephrine from norepinephrine have been produced (27). We have attempted to produce monoclonal antibodies to catecholamines using synthetic, stable analogs to epinephrine and norepinephrine. Mice were immunized with these haptens coupled to either sheep red blood cells or bovine serum albumin. Assay of the products of several fusions only resulted in antibodies that cross-reacted with the amino acid tyrosine. Although the immunization schedules used in these studies closely followed those used to produce heteroantisera to catecholamines, no monoclonal antibodies specifically recognizing these antigens were obtained.

Even if successful, measurement of elevated catecholamine breakdown products in urine is not an ideal marker for neuroblastoma, as this physiological change does not occur in all patients with the malignancy (20,28). However, it has been suggested that as assays become more sensitive, the number of patients presenting with this abnormality will increase (29). More sensitive assays will also allow serum samples to be screened for abnormal catecholamine levels (30, 31).

Epinephrine and norepinephrine can be identified in some neuroblastoma cells by the technique of formalin-induced fluorescence (32). This technique, although very sensitive, is quite complex; thereby antibodies against catecholamines could also prove an alternative for detecting catecholamines within neuroblastoma cells (27). However, in parallel with the observation that not all neuroblastoma patients excrete catecholamine catabolites, not all neuroblastoma cells synthesize epinephrine and/or norepinephrine (11,16). Therefore these substances cannot be used as definitive markers for neuroblastoma.

Enzymes: Enzymes involved in the synthesis and degradation of epinephrine and norepinephrine can also be used as neuroblastoma cell markers (33). Hetero-antisera to tyrosine hydroxylase, the rate-limiting enzyme in catecholamine bio-synthesis, has been used to distinguish neuroblastoma from other malignant cells (34). This enzyme is not unique to neuroblastoma cells, however, as it is also found in other neuroectodermally derived tissue such as melanocytes and mela-noma cells (35). Monoclonal antibodies to tyrosine hydroxylase have been pro-duced following immunization of BALB/c mice with highly purified enzyme pre-parations (36), but these reagents have not yet been used in the diagnosis of ma-lignancy. The intracellular levels of tyrosine hydroxylase in the human neuro-blastoma cell line TR14 have been shown to change when 3',5'-dibutryl cyclic AMP is added to the culture medium (37). In addition, in the presence of the nucleo-tide, TR14 cells take on the appearance of mature neurons, suggesting that the reagent induces differentiation to a more mature state (38) (Fig. 1).

A marker originally thought to be specific for neurons is the 14-3-2 protein or alpha-antigen described by Moore and Perez (39). This antigen has been iden-tified as an enolase (2-phospho-D-glycerate hydroxylase, EC.4.2.1.11), with dif-ferent isoenzyme forms existing in neurons and glial cells (40). Although mono-clonal antibodies to this enzyme have not yet been described, heteroantisera to rat neuron-specific enolase have shown the enzyme to be present in human amine precursor uptake and decarboxylation cells, that is, neurons of the diffuse neuro-endocrine system and tumors related to these cells (41,42). While neuroblastoma was not specifically mentioned in this study, three out of three ganglioneuro-blastomas were found to contain neuron-specific enolase (a less malignant tumor than neuroblastoma involving a more mature cell type).

A colorimetric assay has been used to determine levels of neuron-specific eno-lase in homogenates of neuroblastoma tissue and human cell lines (43). These studies showed that neuroblastoma biopsies contained less neuron-specific eno-lase than more differentiated tumors, such as ganglioneuroma (43). Several neuro-blastoma cell lines (SH-SY5Y, SK-N-MC, SK-N-SH, and IMR32) were found to contain considerably lower amounts of the enzyme than equivalent volumes of fresh biopsy material (43). As with the cell line TR14, where morphological differentiation of human neuroblastoma cell lines can be brought about by using 3',5'-dibutyryl cyclic AMP, a small increase in neuron-specific enolase was detected (44). As with many markers associated with neuroblastoma, there is heterogeneity in the expression of antigen within the malignancy. This could be related to the relative differentiation state of the tumor cells (45).

Chromosomal Abnormalities: Any consistent karyotypic change found uniquely associated with a particular tumor can be used as a marker for malignancy. The best example of such a marker is the shortening of the long arm of chromosome $22=22q^-$ (Philadelphia chromosome), which occurs in chronic myeloid leukemia (46). Several abnormalities have, at one time or another, been thought to be associated with human neuroblastoma (47). The first of these described was the elongation of the long arm of one or several chromosomes that were characterized by amorphous staining, and therefore termed homogeneous staining regions (48). Another abnormality is the appearance of small extra pieces of chromosomal material not linked by a centromere, termed double minutes (49). These can number up to more than 100 per cell and may result from the breakdown of homogenous staining regions (46). These abnormalities do not always occur in all cases of neuroblastoma and recently have been found associated with other malignancies (50). No chromosomal marker has yet been described for neuroblastoma, although recent studies reveal a greater incidence in abnormalities in chromosome 1 as compared with other malignancies (51).

Toxin and Heteroantisera Binding to Neuroblastoma Cells

Toxins: Toxins, like monoclonal antibodies, can show exquisite specificity in their binding to cell receptors. In addition, toxins usually have very high affinities for their receptors, making them, conceptually, useful reagents for the identification of different neural cell types. Tetanus toxin has been described as a nerve-specific marker (binding to both central and peripheral nerves) in the rat (52). Little is known about the mechanism of toxicity of tetanus, but it has been shown to bind to the gangliosides GD_{1b} and GT_1 found in the cell membrane (53,54). Recently it has been suggested that tetanus may also bind to identical receptors in the membranes of some fibrous astrocytes (55). Despite its theoretical usefulness as a marker for human neuroblastoma cells, no definitive studies have been reported on the binding of tetanus toxin to these tumor cells. Botulinin toxin is another candidate as a marker for neuroblastoma cells, as this is thought to bind to peripheral nerves but not to those present in the central nervous system (56). However, the extreme toxicity of this reagent makes it unsuitable as a general laboratory reagent.

Using [3H] bungarotoxin, Kemshead has found the receptor for acetylcholine to be present on two out of five human neuroblastoma cell lines investigated (57). Whether this result is indicative of the acetylcholine receptor being present on fresh tumor cells is not yet established. Should fresh tumor cells show greater and more uniform expression of this receptor, it could be an excellent marker for the detection of metastatic spread of neuroblastoma to bone marrow, as [3H] bungarotoxin has not been found to bind to a variety of hemopoietic cells or cell lines. In contradiction to this latter observation, studies on mice suggest that thymic lymphocytes bear a surface antigen that is recognized by antibodies to the nicotinic acetylcholine receptor (58).

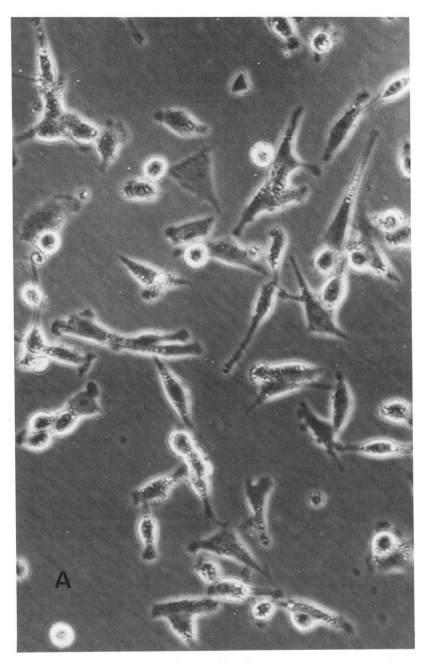

Figure 1 Human neuroblastoma cell line TR14 cultured in the presence and absence of 3′,5′-dibutyryl cyclic AMP. TR14 human neuroblastoma cells were grown in RPMI 1640 medium supplemented with 10% fetal calf serum, penicillin, streptomycin, and glutamine. (A) Cells grown without cyclic nucleotides.

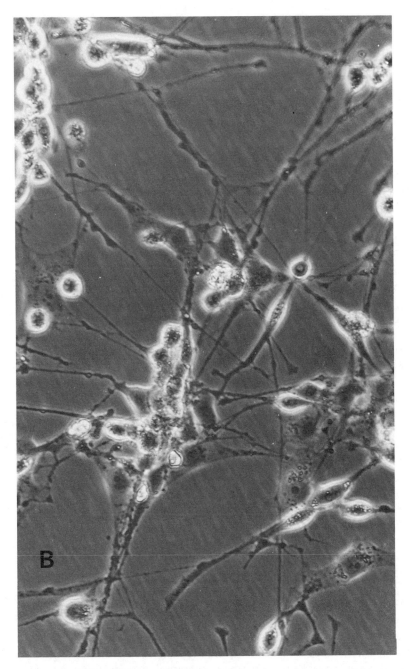

(B) Cells incubated with 10mM $3',5'$-dibutyryl cyclic AMP for 48 hr. In these cultures, processes analogous to neurites were identified, suggesting a morphological differentiation to a more mature cell type.

Like [^{3}H] bungarotoxin, cholera toxin has also been shown to bind differentially to several human neuroblastoma cell lines, although no line examined has failed to interact with the toxin (57). This toxin has been shown to specifically recognize the ganglioside GM_1 in cell membranes (59). Furthermore, this ganglioside has been found in the cell membranes of neural tissue as well as a variety of other normal and malignant cell types (60).

Heteroantisera: A variety of human neuroectodermally derived tissues and/or cell lines have been used in an attempt to raise antisera specific to human neuroblastoma cells (45,61,62). However, to date no one has successfully and reproducibly raised an antiserum detecting a tumor-specific antigen associated with this malignancy (16,47). Probably the expression of a viral gene product is the simplest reason to explain how tumor-specific antigens arise within malignant cells (63). In neuroblastoma there is no direct evidence to suggest a viral etiology of the tumor, and thus no reason to expect viral antigens to be consistently expressed in these cells. Recent work, using DNA hybridization techniques has suggested that some fresh neuroblastoma samples and cell lines express genes encoded for by cytomegalovirus (63). However, as some fresh biopsies do not contain cytomegalovirus genes, it is difficult to suggest that this finding is necessarily linked with the malignancy.

Using normal neural tissue to immunize rabbits (human fetal brain), Casper et al. (61) have raised an antiserum that detects antigens shared between neuroblastoma and normal neural tissue. Following extensive absorption, indirect immunofluorescence, and radiobinding, assays indicated that the reagent reacted with fetal brain, adult brain, neuroblastoma, and embryonal rhabdomyosarcoma (61). No reactivity to either glial cells or hemopoietic cells was detected, and no evidence was presented to biochemically identify the antigen recognized by this reagent.

Seeger et al. (62) have immunized rabbits against the human neuroblastoma cell line LAN 1. Following absorption, the antiserum raised was found to bind to a differentiation antigen, common to neuroblastoma, oat cell carcinoma, Wilms' tumor, and sarcoma cells (62). In addition, the antiserum bound to cells in normal fetal and adult brain as well as the adrenal gland (62). The antigens detected by this antiserum were again not defined biochemically, but in normal tissue appeared restricted to neural cells, since no binding to glia was detected (62). These two reagents illustrate a finding common to heteroantisera raised against either fresh neural material or human cell lines, that is, they detect antigens shared between several different neuroectodermally derived cell types. This conclusion, however, has always been open to criticism, because insufficient absorption of reagents could always explain the observed cross-reactivity of these heteroantisera.

Some of the best high-titer and well-characterized heteroantisera to neural tissue are those reacting with the Thy-1 molecule in rodents (64-66). These have been made using highly purified Thy-1 as antigen and require little or no absorption to confirm their specificity (67). Using one of these reagents, Kemshead et al. (68) have demonstrated the human equivalent of the Thy-1 antigen on several human neuroblastoma cell lines and fresh tumor tissue. Along with many antigens associated with neuroblastoma, there appears heterogeneity (possibly quantitative or qualitative) in the expression of human Thy-1 on the cell lines examined (68). The neuroblastoma cell line TR14 has been estimated to have an average of 2×10^6-2.25×10^6 molecules of Thy-1 per cell (68). The specificity of rabbit anti-rat Thy-1 antisera to the human homolog of this molecule was demonstrated by blocking all reactivity of the reagent by prior incubation with an excess of highly purified human Thy-1 (69). It has been estimated that approximately 25% of the total anti-rat Thy-1 antibodies in the heteroantiserum bind to the human homolog of Thy-1 (68). These serological data suggest that the primary sequence of the Thy-1 antigen is at least partially conserved between rat and man (68). Primary amino acid sequence data on rat and human Thy-1 confirm structural similarity between certain areas of the two molecules, although each also has regions that are unique (69).

Human and mouse neuroblastoma cell lines differ in their expression of Thy-1. The murine C1300 neural line lacks detectable levels of Thy-1, unless the cells are incubated with agents that induce differentiation (70,71). Even with highly specific heteroantisera, it remains unclear as to whether Thy-1 is restricted in its expression to rodent neurons (66,67). This was suggested by Barclay and Hyden (66) following immunohistological studies on adult rat brain, and confirmed by studies on short-term primary cultures of central nervous system tissue. However, by keeping cells in culture for longer periods of time, Raff et al. (72) have demonstrated Thy-1 on some glial cells (30-60%) of astrocytes, but not microglia or oligodendrocytes. Also, analyses of rodent glial cell lines (stabilized from chemically induced carcinogenesis) indicate that some express Thy-1, while others lack the antigen. Therefore, in the rodent, Thy-1 is present on neurons and at least some glial cells.

Analysis of the expression of Thy-1 on human neural cell lines showed that the antigen is present on the astrocytoma line UCH 203, the medulloblastoma line H314/123, and the retinoblastoma line GM 1142/13 (68). Thy-1 antigen was not detected on the human melanoma cell line M5 (68). The pattern of Thy-1 expression on these cell types has been confirmed using a series of fresh human tumors and by the use of several monoclonal antibodies (73,74); J. T. Kemshead and J. Garson, unpublished observations).

The anatomical localization of Thy-1 in human neural tissue has been studied using monoclonal antibodies. McKenzie and Fabre (75) have shown the antigen to be present in large amounts throughout human brain, but their data do not reveal which cell type is specifically binding the monoclonal antibody. Outside the central nervous system, Thy-1 has not been detected on cells of the adrenal medulla (75; J. Garson and J. T. Kemshead, unpublished observations). As neuroblastoma cells possess the antigen, and since both the adrenal medulla and the tumor represent elements of the adrenergic component of the sympathetic nervous system, this observation is difficult to interpret.

Although Thy-1 is present on the neural tissue of most species examined, its precise association with different neural cell types seems variable (66,76). This is also true outside the nervous system; for example, in rodents Thy-1 is expressed on thymocytes, but this is not the case in the human (77). Studies on anti-Thy-1 antibody binding to fresh leukemia cells suggests the antigen may be found on an early pre-B or pre-T leukemic cell (Ritter, Sauvage, and Pegram, unpublished observations). Analysis of normal bone marrow showed that less than 0.1% of the cells reacted with a monoclonal antibody to Thy-1, an important observation if one wishes to use this reagent for diagnosis of metastatic spread of neuroblastoma to bone marrow (68).

Monoclonal Antibodies to Neuroblastoma Cells

As stated previously, the interest in producing monoclonal antibodies to human neuroblastoma cells has been primarily to aid in the detection of metastatic spread of the tumor to sites such as bone marrow. Many protocols for the detection of monoclonal antibodies to neuroblastoma cells have used hemopoietic cells and cell lines in the initial screening protocol (78-80). The antibodies resulting from this approach have a high degree of specificity for neuroblastoma cells, but often show cross-reactivity with other cell types, particularly neuroectodermally derived cells. Some of these monoclonal antibodies will be described in detail.

Monoclonal Antibodies Detecting Antigens Shared by Neuroblasts and Hemopoietic Cell Subsets: The first monoclonal antibodies to human neuroblastoma cells were described by Kennett and Gilbert (78) in 1979. These were made following fusion of spleen cells from BALB/c mice immunized with IMR6 cells preincubated with hyperimmune mouse serum directed against the human lymphoblastoid cell line 8866 (78). Two antibodies were described, and the most specific was designated PI 153/3. Using a radiobinding assay, this monoclonal antibody was shown to react with human neuroblastoma, retinoblastoma, and glioblastoma tumors, as well as fetal brain cells (78). After absorption experiments, little binding of the monoclonal antibody was found to human adult brain or bone marrow (78). However, extensive analysis of the reactivity of this antibody to a panel of fresh leukemic cells showed that PI 153/3 also binds to pre-B common acute lymphoblastic leukemic cells (81). Subsequent studies in our laboratory have also demonstrated that this monoclonal antibody reacts with a population of cells in normal bone marrow, these being of pre-B- and B-cell origin.

Kennett et al. (82) have suggested that to obtain a differential diagnosis of metastatic spread of neuroblastoma to bone marrow with PI 153/3, it is necessary to use a second monoclonal antibody, one that binds specifically to B-lineage cells and not to neuroblastoma.

Using the human neuroblastoma cell lines CHP 134 and IMR5, radiolabeled with either [^{3}H] L-fucose or [^{3}H] D-glucosamine, Momoi et al. (83) have shown that the antigen recognized by PI 153/3 is a membrane glycoprotein with a molecular weight of 20,000. Similar studies on the common acute lymphoblastic leukemic cell line Reh have demonstrated that this monoclonal antibody detects an identical molecular weight antigen on hemopoietic cells (83). Using absorption experiments combined with indirect immunofluorescence assays on frozen sections of neural tissue, we have shown that the PI 153/3 antigen appears uniformly distributed throughout major areas of fetal brain (J. Garson, S. Brown, and J. T. Kemshead, manuscript in preparation). In agreement with Kennett, we found less antigen recognized by the monoclonal antibody in adult brain, although it is unquestionably still present (78). PI 153/3 antigen would therefore appear to be a differentiation antigen present on some neuroectodermally and mesodermally derived cell types that is gradually lost during development to a more mature cell type.

Our first attempts to make a monoclonal antibody specific to neuroblastoma cells also involved immunizing mice with a human neuroblastoma cell line, CHP 100 (84). Table 1 illustrates the monoclonal antibodies, reactive to neural cell antigens, made in our laboratory between 1979 and 1981. The only useful monoclonal antibody produced by these immunization protocols was the MIN1 antibody, and like Kennett's reagent, the antibody was found to cross-react with a subset of hemopoietic cells, promyelocytes and more mature cells of the myeloid lineage (79). Extensive absorption experiments and analysis of antibody binding using frozen sections of tissues revealed that the antigen reacting with MIN1 is restricted in its distribution to these two cell types (J. Garson and J. T. Kemshead, unpublished observations). The MIN1 antigen is a membrane glycoprotein with a molecular weight of 120,000-150,000 (obtained under reducing conditions) (P. Teteroo, unpublished observations). Furthermore, monoclonal antibody UJ 308 made by immunizing mice with human fetal brain (Table 1) and monoclonal antibodies made against hemopoietic cells by Knapp (TIMD5) and van der Reijden (B4) appear to recognize an antigen of a similar molecular weight. If this proves to be true, then the antigen recognized by these reagents must be highly immunodominant, since it has been detected following immunization of mice with four different cell types.

In our laboratory, using cell lysates from the promyelocytic cell line HL60, we have preliminary data suggesting that the antigen recognized by UJ 308 binds to a cell membrane protein of 30,000 daltons (obtained under reducing conditions).

Table 1 Monoclonal Antibodies Binding to Human Neuroblastoma Cells Made at the Imperial Cancer Research Fund Oncology Laboratory, 1978–1981

Antibody designation	Immunogen	Reference
MIN1	Human neuroblastoma cell line CHP 100	79
UA1	Human fetal brain	127
UJ 13A		126
UJ 308		85
UJ 127:11		86
UJ 181.4		127
UJ 223.8		127
UJ 167.11		127
α-Thy-1	Purified antigen	87

Incomplete reduction results in a series of bands on acrylamide gels of 60, 90, 120, 150, 180, 210 kilodaltons, suggesting that under nonreducing conditions the UJ 308 antigen is a polymer of 30,000 dalton subunits (J. Fritschy and J. T. Kemshead, unpublished observations). These data are therefore not incompatible with those of P. Teteroo, P. M. Lansdorp, Geurts van Kessel, A. Hagemijer, and A. E. G. Borne. Further biochemical characterization is necessary to confirm these initial findings. Hopefully these biochemical studies will help to explain why neuroblasts, neuroectodermal in origin, and cells of the granulocytic lineage (mesodermal) share common antigenic determinants.

Expression of MIN1 antigen has been found to vary as promyelocytes mature to granulocytes (79). Bone marrow cells incubated with MIN1 and fluorescein-conjugated goat anti-mouse Ig were analyzed in a fluorescence-activated cell sorter (88). Cells in the brightest fraction (i.e., those binding the most MIN1 monoclonal antibody) were always found to be the most mature cells, whereas histological staining revealed promyelocytes to be in the fraction giving very weak fluorescence (79).

A similar result was obtained using the human cell line HL 60, established from a patient with acute promyelocytic leukemia (89). Cells of this line can be induced to differentiate in the presence of agents such as dimethylsulfoxide (DMSO) and phorbol esters (90). Dimethylsulfoxide-induced HL 60 cells have been shown to bind more MIN1 antibody than undifferentiated control populations, many of which resemble promyelocytes (J. T. Kemshead, unpublished observations).

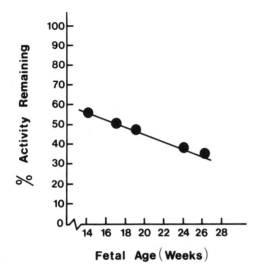

Figure 2 Absorption of monoclonal antibody MIN1 with human fetal brain obtained at different gestation periods. Antibody MIN1 was absorbed with equivalent volumes of human fetal brain taken from fetuses aborted at different ages (14-26 weeks). Following absorption, the residual antibody was tested in a modified radioimmunoassay using CHP 100 human neuroblastoma cells as targets. The percentage of MIN1 remaining in solution after absorption was plotted against fetal age for each dilution of antibody assayed. An example of the curves obtained is given for MIN1 diluted at 1:1200.

Absorption studies also suggest that the MIN1 antigen is differentially expressed during development of the human nervous system. Using equivalent amounts of neural tissue from fetuses of different ages, we have shown that as the age of the fetal tissue increases, more antibody is absorbed from solution. Fetal brain at 26 weeks gestation absorbs approximately 1½ times the amount of MIN1 antigen as an equivalently packed volume of material taken from a fetus aborted at 13 weeks. While complete absorption curves were analyzed to obtain this conclusion, the data can be simply assimilated by presenting the residual binding of MIN1 antibody to human neuroblastoma, following absorption of one dilution of the reagent with brain taken from aborted fetuses of five different ages (Fig. 2). This result can be explained in two ways: (a) a quantitative change in the amount of antigen expressed per neural cell occurs during development (analogous to myeloid cells) or (b) the composition of the cell types making up the absorbing material changes with respect to fetal age. At present, no evidence is available to determine which of these possibilities is correct.

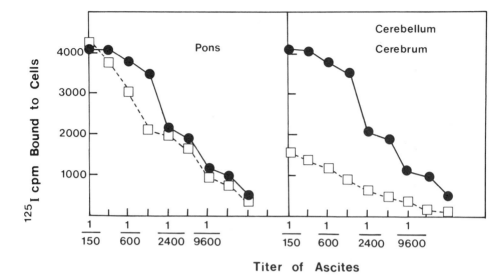

Figure 3 Absorption of MIN1 with different areas of adult brain. Dilutions of MIN1 were absorbed for 30 min at 4°C with equivalently packed volumes of different areas of human adult brain. Following absorption, antibody remaining in solution was tested in a modified radioimmunoassay using CHP 100 human neuroblastoma cells as targets. (●———●, MIN1 antibody not absorbed with brain; □———□, antibody remaining in solution following absorption with different areas of adult brain.)

Since the MIN1 antigen is clearly present in adult neural tissue, we have attempted to determine if it is uniformly distributed throughout the brain. The MIN1 antibody was absorbed with equivalently packed volumes of tissue dissected from different areas of a single brain. Both the adult cerebellum and cerebrum, but not the pons, could absorb the MIN1 monoclonal antibody (Fig. 3). This pattern of reactivity differed markedly from similar absorption studies with other antibodies, for example, 127.11 (86), where almost all the monoclonal antibody was selectively absorbed by adult pons. Analysis of the binding of MIN1 to sections of human neural tissue should ultimately reveal more information as to the specific cell types reacting with the monoclonal (J. Garson, manuscript in preparation). Unfortunately, fixation of tissue in all but the mildest of reagents destroys the antigen recognized by MIN1, making the histological characterization of the cells binding the monoclonal antibody extremely difficult.

As yet, very little work has been done on the distribution of the MIN1 antigen on tissues from different species. The antibody cannot be absorbed from solution using either mouse or rat brain, and indirect immunofluorescence studies indicate that the antigen is not expressed on mouse neuroblastoma cells (a subline of C1300). This result is not surprising, considering mice were used for the initial immunization of tissue prior to cell fusion, and molecules foreign to murine tissue will probably be recognized as the most immunodominant.

Two other antibodies binding to both hemopoietic and neuroblastoma cells have been described by Wikstrand and Bigner (91). Although bone marrow was not listed as one of the tissues tested for reactivity to 4D2c16 and 7H10c14, both fetal and adult spleens were found to absorb out these antibodies (91). Wikstrand and Bigner suggest that these monoclonal antibodies, generated by immunizing mice with human fetal brain, are different from the PI 153/3 antibody (78), since the former antibodies do not bind to the C-ALL cell line SB (91). However, like Kennett's antibody, 4D2c16 and 7H10c14 do not bind to adult brain (91). The antigens recognized by 4D2c16 and 7H10c14 have not been identified; therefore it is not possible to rule out that one of the reagents may recognize an antigenic determinant similar or identical to that recognized by PI 153/3.

Radiobinding and absorption studies have shown that both 4D2c16 and 7H10c14 bind to fetal liver, gliomas and melanomas (91). In addition, 4D2c16 binds to fetal skin fibroblasts, and 7H10c14 to tumor cells from a patient with non-Hodgkin's lymphoma (91).

All the above antibodies are examples of reagents that can show cross-reactivity with hemopoietic cell subsets. They are less than ideal for detecting metastatic spread of tumor to bone marrow; however, it is possible to use reagents such as MIN1 and UJ 308, because granulocytes can be morphologically distinguished from neuroblasts (80). Several reagents have recently become available that do not show cross-reactivity with hemopoietic cells. These will be discussed in the following section.

Monoclonal Antibodies Binding to Neuroblastoma and Not to Hemopoietic Cells: Of the panel of monoclonal antibodies made in our laboratory that have specificity of binding to neuroblastoma cells, but not hemopoietic progenitors in bone marrow, three monoclonal antibodies have been studied in detail (Table 1). The first of these is the monoclonal antibody to the human homolog of Thy-1. With this reagent, previous findings have been confirmed using a heteroantiserum that binds to this antigenic determinant (68). The other two reagents, UJ 127:11 and UJ 13A, can be used to illustrate several conclusions reached when using the whole panel of antibodies listed in Table 1:

1. The reagents are useful in the diagnosis of metastatic spread of neuroblastoma to bone marrow.
2. The reagents show different patterns of reactivity to different neuroectodermally derived tissue.

3. Because of the previous conclusion, the reagents recognize different antigenic determinants, although this has not always been demonstrated biochemically.
4. Many of the antigens recognized by the monoclonal antibodies are species restricted.
5. The antigens are usually destroyed by all but the mildest of fixation procedures.
6. The reagents may be useful in unraveling the complex differentiation pathways involved in the maturation of neurons and glial cells.
7. Along with other monoclonal antibodies made to glial tumors, the reagents are extremely useful in aiding in the differential diagnosis of tumors arising in the central nervous system.

Antibody UJ 127:11 has been shown to differentiate between human neurons and glial cells. The antibody reacts with three of three human neuroblastoma cell lines assayed (CHP 100, CHP 212, and TR14), but does not bind to the astrocytoma cell line, UCH 203 (86,92). A similar pattern of reactivity has been found using frozen sections of fresh tumor tissue: UJ 127:11 binds to fresh neuroblastoma, but not to glioblastoma tumors (10 biopsies) or to normal activated glia found at the margin of a secondary deposit of adenocarcinoma in brain (J. Garson, J. T. Kemshead, and H. Coakham, manuscript in preparation).

Absorption studies on fetal and adult brain, in addition to the analysis of the reactivity of UJ 127:11 to frozen sections of neural material taken at autopsy, indicate that this monoclonal antibody binds to normal nervous tissue. Since current embryological studies indicate that neural and some glial cells arise from a common precursor cell present in the neural crest (93), the antibody UJ 127:11 would appear to recognize a differentiation antigen of the nervous system, present on early nerve cells (neuroblasts) but not on glial or glioblast cells. UJ 127:11 antigen, however, is present on other neuroectodermally derived tissue. For example, the melanoma cell line M5 binds approximately three times more monoclonal antibody than the neuroblastoma cell line CHP 100, while the retinoblastoma line GM 1142/13 does not react with UJ 127:11.

Absorption studies using equivalent volumes of fetal spleen, kidney, liver, muscle, and intestine showed that UJ 127:11 did not bind to these tissues, suggesting that this antigen is restricted in its distribution to neuroectodermally derived tissue (J. T. Kemshead, J. Fritschy, and S. Brown, manuscript in preparation). The expression of the UJ 127:11 antigen within both the fetal and adult nervous system is being investigated. Absorption studies using fetal brain indicate the presence of UJ 127:11 antigen in the pons. This monoclonal antibody was absorbed by fetal adrenal, cerebellum, cerebrum, or hypothalamus (J. T. Kemshead, J. Fritschy, and S. Brown, manuscript in preparation). However, studies on frozen sections of adult brain (taken at autopsy) suggest a more uniform spread of the antigen (J. Garson and J. T. Kemshead, unpublished observations). These results may suggest that the expression of UJ 127:11 antigen changes during neural development; however, considerably more work is necessary to confirm this possibility.

The antigen bound by UJ 127:11 has been identified following surface labeling of either human neuroblastoma or melanoma cells with ^{125}I (using the lactoperoxidase technique) (94). Following sodium dodecyl sulfate-polyacrylamide gel electrophoresis (SDS-PAGE), the antigen has been shown to be a protein of 220-240 kilodaltons (under both reducing and nonreducing conditions), indicating that the antigen consists of a single polypeptide chain (86). The UJ 127:11 antigen is a glycoprotein. With two-dimensional electrophoresis (nonequilibrated isoelectric focusing in the first dimension and SDS-PAGE in the second), the isoelectric point of the protein has been determined to be approximately 4.2.

Because human fibronectin is also a glycoprotein of approximately 220,000 daltons (95), we have attempted to exclude the possibility that UJ 127:11 binds to either human plasma or cell-surface fibronectin. Purified plasma fibronectin, at concentrations of up to 1.0 mg/ml, proved ineffective at blocking the binding of the ^{125}I-labeled monoclonal antibody to melanoma cells, whereas unlabeled UJ 127:11 blocked the binding of the radiolabeled antibody (Fig. 4). Also, UJ 127:11 does not precipitate any protein (determined by SDS-PAGE) when ^{125}I-radiolabeled purified fibronectin is used as the antigen. These studies show that monoclonal antibody UJ 127:11 does not react with human plasma fibronectin. Furthermore, serological studies comparing the binding of a monoclonal antibody made against muscle cell-surface fibronectin and UJ 127:11 suggest that these two reagents are recognizing different antigens. These experiments, however, cannot rule out the possibility that monoclonal antibody UJ 127:11 is recognizing a determinant on a form of fibronectin unique to melanoma and neuroblastoma cells. This is probably unlikely, since the staining patterns of UJ 127:11 and several heteroantisera to fibronectin on frozen sections of fresh neural tissue appeared dissimilar (J. Garson and J. T. Kemshead, unpublished observations).

Despite biochemical characterization of the UJ 127:11 antigen, the function of the molecule remains obscure. Currently we are investigating whether the addition of the monoclonal antibody to cultures of neuroblastoma cells perturbates biological functions of the cells, such as growth rate.

Monoclonal antibody UJ 13A binds to a much broader spectrum of neuroectodermally derived tissues than UJ 127:11. Neuroblastoma (six of six), glioblastoma (one of one), and retinoblastoma (two of two) cell lines were found to bind UJ 13A, but no reactivity was found to either medulloblastoma (one of one) or melanoma lines (three of three) (J. T. Kemshead, unpublished observations). This antibody binds to cells in all areas of fresh fetal and adult brain

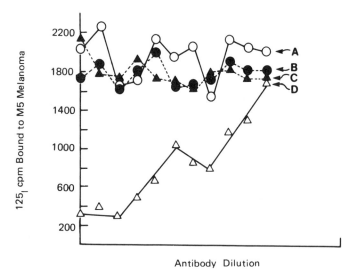

Figure 4 Binding of [^{125}I] 127:11 to human melanoma cells in the presence of either fibronectin or rabbit antifibronectin. A total of 2 × 10^5 M5 cells (human melanoma) were incubated with doubling dilutions of (A) fibronectin, (B) rabbit anti-fibronectin, (C) W6/32 monomorphic anti-HLA monoclonal, (D) non-labeled 127:11 antibody and a constant amount of [^{125}I] UJ 127:11 (150,000 cpm/per well). After 30 min at 4°C, unbound antibodies were washed from the cells and ^{125}I binding determined in a LKB ultragamma counter. The initial concentration of fibronectin and antibodies was 100 μg/ml.

tissues. Quantitative expression of the UJ 13A does not significantly change during fetal development (126). In accordance with the wide expression of the UJ 13A antigen on neuroectodermally derived cell lines, frozen sections showed the antigen to be present on cells in the adrenal medulla and fetal retina. Using transverse frozen sections of autonomic nerves (e.g., vagus) taken from children at autopsy, we have demonstrated that UJ 13A binds to all nerve fibers in these preparations. Similar studies on transverse sections of several peripheral motor nerves shows only 40–60% of nerve fibers stained within each nerve bundle. This result suggests that the UJ 13A antibody may detect an antigen on all autonomic nerve fibers, but absent from some motor nerves. However, the possibility that the monoclonal antibody is detecting an antigen very susceptible to autolysis, and thus lost from some peripheral nerve fibers at autopsy, still has to be excluded (126).

Apart from tissues arising from the neuroectoderm, both UJ 13A and UJ 127:11 antigens have a very restricted tissue distribution. Analysis of several fetal and adult tissues (by absorption and frozen section) indicates that the only nonneural tissue possibly reactive with UJ 13A is fetal kidney. To date, only absorption studies have been undertaken and we are not certain if the absorbing material was contaminated with fetal adrenal. Analysis of fetal and adult tissue by frozen section should resolve this point, although it is our experience that many antibodies bind nonspecifically to kidney. Analysis of bone marrow (fetal, pediatric, or adult) shows that less than 0.1% of cells (background levels) bind to either UJ 127:11 or UJ 13A, making them very useful for the detection of metastatic spread of neuroblastoma to bone marrow (74). Since UJ 13A binds to neurons and glia but not to colon epithelial cells, this reagent has also been useful in distinguishing primary neural tumors from metastases of brain adenocarcinomas (J. Garson, unpublished observations).

UJ 13A is an immunoglobulin of the IgG_{1a} class, and ascites taken from BALB/c mice have a titer of approximately 1:500,000 (126). Attempts to biochemically characterize the UJ 13A antigen using neuroblastoma cell lines radiolabeled with either [^{35}S] methionine or ^{125}I have not proved successful. The molecule is restricted in its species distribution. It has not been found in brains from fish or birds, but has been detected in neural tissue from horse, monkey, dog, cow, and guinea pig (B. Lacey and J. T. Kemshead, unpublished observations).

Two other monoclonal antibodies have been described with similar reactivities to UJ 13A. The first of these (UA1) can only be differentiated from UJ 13A in that it binds strongly to the human melanoma cell line M5 (Table 1). The other antibody has been described by Reynolds and Smith (97) and was produced from a fusion of BALB/c spleen cells with mice immunized with the human neuroblastoma cell line HSAN 1.2.

Eisenbarth et al. (98) have also described a monoclonal antibody (A2B5) that binds to several human neuroblastoma cell lines and fresh tumor biopsies. This antibody reacts across all species examined and was made following immunization of mice with chick retinal cells (98). Biochemical characterization of the A2B5 antigen has shown it to be a ganglioside (designated Gq). A2B5 has also proved useful in the diagnosis of metastatic spread of neuroblastoma to bone marrow, since it reacts with less than 0.1% of hemopoietic cells in normal pediatric marrow (99). While the binding of A2B5 to neurons of all species is unquestioned, the reactivity of this monoclonal antibody to glial cells remains controversial. In our laboratory we have not detected the binding of the antibody to the human glial cell line UCH 203 (J. T. Kemshead, unpublished observations). In addition, in primary cultures of human fetal brain, those cells that are glial fibrillary acidic protein positive (astrocytes) do not react with A2B5 (F. Walsh, personal communication). However, analysis of frozen sections of both glial tumors and biopsies of normal adult brain suggest that A2B5 does bind to glial cells (J. Garson, personal communication). Because the A2B5 antigen has a wide species distribution, analysis of neural material from a variety of animals should resolve whether A2B5 reacts with neural and/or glial cells.

Finally Seeger et al. (100) immunized mice with a human melanoma cell line to produce a monoclonal antibody (AB376) that binds to human melanoma, glioma, neuroblastoma, and sarcoma cell lines. Lymphocytes, erythrocytes, and fibroblasts were shown not to express the antigen (101). The AB376 antigen was found, by absorption studies, to be present on a variety of fetal tissue, but was more restricted in its distribution upon adult cells. Within the neuroectoderm, expression of AB376 antigen is rather unusual. Both fetal and adult brain do not possess detectable levels of the molecule. To explain this finding, Seeger et al. have suggested that either absorption studies may not be sensitive enough to reveal the presence of a subpopulation of neural cells binding the antibody in brain, or the antigen is only expressed on central nervous system tissue for a limited time during normal development. However, considering the relatively wide distribution reported for AB376 on other fetal and adult tissues, both of these suggestions seem inadequate for explaining the lack of the antigen on fetal and adult brain.

RESERVATIONS ON THE SPECIFICITY OF MONOCLONAL ANTIBODIES

Antigenic Heterogeneity Among Neuroblastoma Cells

Throughout this review the assumption has been made that a tumor of one cell type either expresses or does not express a particular antigenic determinant. Work with monoclonal antibodies has shown this not to be true, as considerable heterogeneity in antigen expression has been observed among different tumor cells of the same type. This was initially demonstrated for human neuroblastoma cell lines with the monoclonal antibody MIN1 (79). With a modified radioimmune assay, the cell line CHP 100 was shown to express approximately four times the amount of MIN1 antigen when compared to the cell line CHP 126 (Fig. 5).

Antigenic heterogeneity has also been demonstrated among fresh human neuroblastoma cells in three different ways: (a) by analysis of bone marrow aspirates taken from different patients, all of which showed massive infiltration of tumor cells by conventional histological techniques; (b) by comparisons of the antigenic profiles of tumor cells taken from two metastatic sites in one patient, for example, liver biopsy and bone marrow aspirate; and (c) by sequential studies on the antigenic status of tumor cells remaining in bone marrow over a 3-month period while the patient continued to receive low-dose chemotherapy (101).

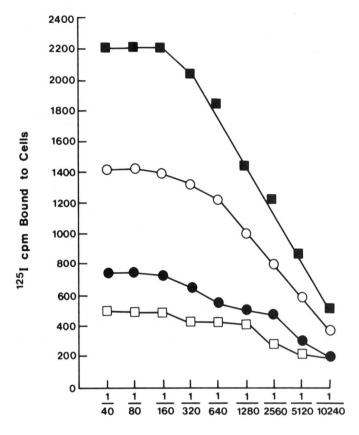

Figure 5 Binding of monoclonal MIN1 to different human neuroblastoma cell lines. A total of 2×10^5 exponentially growing, highly viable cells were incubated with different concentrations of monoclonal MIN1, followed by 100,000 cpm of $[^{125}I]$ goat anti-mouse immunoglobulin (■――――■, MIN1 binding to CHP 100; ○――――○, MIN1 binding to CHP 134; ●――――●, MIN1 binding to CHP 212; □――――□, MIN1 binding to CHP 126).

Whether the differences among tumor cells are the result of either qualitative and/or quantitative changes in antigenic expression is not known. Considering that many malignant cells have a grossly abnormal karyotype one might expect that they would lose control over the quantitative expression of certain gene products. Furthermore, lack of "visible" binding of a monoclonal antibody does not imply the total absence of an antigen. All that can be stated is that an insufficient density or concentration of the antigen exists to reach the threshold of detection, and that different assay techniques have different sensitivities for detecting antigen. For example, in Figure 5, all the neuroblastoma cell lines appear positive for MIN1 binding by modified radioimmune assay, but only CHP 100 and CHP 134 are positive in an indirect immunofluorescence assay. The question as to whether quantitative or qualitative differences in antigen expression occur among tumor cells is therefore not easy to answer.

If the simple concept that abnormal karyotypes lead to abnormal gene expression in malignant cells does not appeal as an idea to explain differential antigenic expression among tumor cells, then another hypothesis is to suggest that the heterogeneity is a reflection of normal cellular development. For example, the normal differentiation of neuroblasts possibly involves considerable antigenic modulation at the cell surface (16). If different tumors arise from maturation arrest during differentiation, they would be expected to express different patterns of membrane antigens. This has certainly been shown to be the case in lymphoid malignancies (102), and may be particularly relevant for neuroblastoma, as this tumor can show the unusual property of either spontaneous regression or maturation to a benign ganglioneuroma (11,16). In vitro studies using the human neuroblastoma cell line TR14 (37) suggest that antigenic modulation may occur during differentiation (J. T. Kemshead and T. Rupniak, unpublished observations).

Antibody Specificity and Avidity

Where a monoclonal antibody has been shown to bind to more than one cell type (e.g., neuroblasts and glial cells), the assumption has been made that the reagent is binding to the same molecule on each cell. This may not be the case, as it is possible that the same antigenic determinant is shared by two unrelated molecules. For example, Dulbecco et al. have suggested that certain monoclonal antibodies to Thy-1 also bind to intermediate filaments in cells (103). Also, the monoclonal antibody OKT 3, which binds specifically to a cell membrane protein present on T lymphocytes, also binds specifically to an intracellular protein in Purkinje cells (104). To confirm that a monoclonal antibody binds to the same molecule on two cell types, it is always necessary to biochemically characterize the antigen it recognizes. Unfortunately, in many cases this has not proved possible. Occasionally the antigen recognized by a monoclonal antibody can be shown to be shared between two or more cell types. For example, the antibody BA2 binds to the Ph[1] common acute lymphoblastic cell line, Nalm1 and to several human neuroblastoma cell lines (CHP 100, CHP212) (105). BA2 has been shown to bind to a 24,000 dalton protein isolated from both of these cell types (105,106).

By the nature of the interaction of antibody and antigen, a single antibody can bind to very similar but not identical antigenic sites. The avidity or strength of binding of an antibody will differ to slightly modified antigenic sites. It is again possible that two similar but nonidentical determinants could bind one antibody with different affinities and these moieties could be present on unrelated molecules.

One should therefore consider all of these reservations before claiming specificity of a monoclonal antibody. Furthermore, the fact that the specificity of many of the antibodies discussed in this review has been determined by different immunoassays (with different sensitivities) makes it difficult to compare reagents from different laboratories. Perhaps, with time, when the monoclonal antibodies become more freely available, it will become apparent that individual workers have made different antibodies to the same molecules in different fusions. This has already been shown to be true for monoclonal antibodies recognizing the transferrin receptor (107).

CLINICAL USE OF MONOCLONAL ANTIBODIES TO NEUROBLASTOMA

Autologous Bone Marrow Transplantation

As discussed in the Introduction, one of the major aims for acquiring monoclonal antibodies to neuroblastoma is to use them for the identification of metastatic spread of the malignancy to bone marrow. This becomes extremely important when autologous bone marrow transplantation is offered as a form of therapy, since it is desirable not to reinfuse tumor back into the patient. By using a panel of monoclonal antibodies, it is possible to identify neuroblastoma cells in bone marrow aspirates at a level of approximately 0.1% infiltration. Current analysis of bone marrow, before treatment of patients with high-dose melphalan, involves histological, cytological, and immunological analysis of 10 separate aspirates prior to the transplant (108). Even this analysis can be inadequate, as it is known that the tumor will localize to a particular area of marrow, and when bone marrow is removed for autografting, malignant cells can be detected even when earlier checks indicated the absence of neuroblasts (109). Furthermore, even with monoclonal antibodies, it is not possible to unequivocally identify metastatic spread of neuroblastoma to bone marrow at levels lower than 0.1%. This means that when approximately 5×10^9 nucleated hemopoietic cells are taken for autografting, it is potentially possible to reinfuse 5×10^6 tumor cell into the patient without knowledge of the event. In the human, no information exists as to the number of tumor cells needed to be infused into an individual to reseed a malignancy. If this number is 1, as it is in some animal models, then any known method used to "clean up bone marrow" prior to reinfusion to the patient will almost certainly fail. However, in the near future it may be possible to remove 99.9-99.99% of tumor cells from marrow prior to reinfusion, and this may be sufficient to ensure that any remaining malignant cells are insufficient to reseed a donor. Here I will discuss attempts to cleanse bone marrow from neuroblastoma cells using monoclonal antibodies.

Complement Killing: Using mixtures of monoclonal antibodies and different sources of complement (either rabbit or guinea pig), we have demonstrated poor killing of human neuroblastoma cell lines in vitro. Using either propidium iodide or ^{51}Cr release as a marker for cell death, only 35–50% of either cell line CHP 100 or CHP 212 were killed in a complement-mediated cytotoxicity assay. Little improvement in cell kill was detected, even when rabbit heteroantisera to human neuroblastoma cell lines and many different batches of complement were used. These results would suggest that human neuroblastoma cell lines are inherently insensitive to antibody and complement. Whether this is a peculiarity of the cell lines or an actual property of fresh neuroblastoma remains unknown, since it is extremely difficult to obtain sufficiently viable tumors to test this point.

Whether human complement would be more efficient at lysing neuroblastoma cells remains unknown, although in general it has been found that mouse antibodies do not efficiently fix human complement. It is also unknown whether cells coated but not killed by antibody may be opsonized if injected back into the patient. This has certainly been shown to be the case for T cells coated with the monoclonal OKT 3 (111). Opsonization is not an ideal method for removing tumor cells from marrow, since it is only possible to determine its effectiveness through long-term clinical trials.

Fluorescence-Activated Cell Sorter: By using mixtures of monoclonal antibodies directed to neuroblastoma cells but not normal bone marrow cells, it has been possible to separate neuroblasts from hemopoietic cells with high efficiency. In one model system, neuroblastoma cells (0.1–10%) were added to bone marrow and the mixture subsequently incubated with a panel of monoclonal antibodies. Following a washing step, fluorescein-conjugated goat anti-mouse immunoglobulin (preabsorbed against insolubilized human immunoglobulin) was added and after a further incubation period, cells were analyzed in a fluorescence-activated cell sorter (88). Analysis of the cells in the fluorescence-negative fraction showed that approximately 99% of the neuroblasts had been removed from the mixed cell population, irrespective of the initial level of tumor infiltration. Although it is not possible to determine the effect of the monoclonal antibodies on human hemopoietic stem cell function in marrow (112), CFUc (granulocytic cell precursor) and BFUc (erythroid progenitor) assays showed that the antibodies did not comprise hemopoietic cell development (113,114).

While the results of this model system are extremely encouraging, the technique is not currently open to exploitation for autografting because the rate of cell sorting is too slow to allow 5×10^9 cells to be analyzed in a reasonable period of time. Current cell sorters can analyze approximately 3000 cells per second, and the expense of the machine means banks of sorters cannot feasibly be supplied for the task of cleansing marrow of tumor cells.

Antibodies Tagged with Either Drugs or Toxins: Several reports have suggested that plant toxins (e.g., ricin) covalently coupled to either heteroantisera (115) or monoclonal antibodies (116) are highly effective at killing tumor cells in vitro. These studies have employed either whole ricin molecules coupled to antibody (117) (where the carbohydrate-binding specificity of the B chain is blocked by lactose) or the A chain of the molecule (the toxic part of the molecule) (118). We have attempted to selectively kill neuroblastoma cells using mixtures of monoclonal antibodies and rabbit anti-mouse immunoglobulin to which gelonin has been covalently coupled [gelonin is a natural plant product thought to be homologous to the A chain of ricin (119) and it was supplied by P. Thorpe, of the Imperial Cancer Research Fund Drug Targeting Laboratory, London]. These preliminary experiments suggest that the system may be useful for killing neuroblasts in bone marrow, but the high number of tumor cells killed (99.9%) observed with animal model systems, such as mouse leukemia, have not yet been obtained (110). Further experimentation is needed to determine if the indirect system of delivering toxins is more or less effective at killing tumor cells in vitro than a direct system, where the lethal agent is attached directly to the antibody. Also, the relative effectiveness of gelonin, ricin A chain, and ricin antibody conjugates has to be determined before the methodology can be used to kill tumor cells in bone marrow.

Conceptually, either ricin A chain or gelonin conjugates would appear to be considerably better reagents than ricin antibody conjugates, because there is theoretically no problem with the former agents binding to carbohydrate present in cell membranes (120). Certainly, free gelonin (not attached to antibody) does not appear toxic to the human neuroblastoma lines CHP 100 and CHP 212 at a level of 20 μg/ml (J. T. Kemshead, F. Gibson, and P. Thorpe, unpublished observations).

Many attempts have also been made to target drugs to tumor cells via antibodies (121). This conceptually has the effect of increasing drug concentrations around tumor cells to levels that would be lethal to normal cells if represented throughout the body fluids. Although many different drugs have been coupled to either heteroantisera or monoclonal antibodies, the literature remains inconclusive as to whether this may be a useful technique for killing tumor cells, either in vivo or in vitro.

Using the anti-neuroblastoma antibody UJ 13A, covalently coupled to the vinca alkaloid Vindesine (courtesy of G. Roelants at Eli Lilly Co.), we have attempted to selectively kill human neuroblastoma cell lines in vitro. The data are still very preliminary, but some effects of the reagent have been observed, although only at high levels of the antibody-drug conjugate (122). Like the toxin-antibody conjugates, it appears that cells have to be presented with relatively high concentrations of lethal agents to allow a small amount to pass through the membrane and have an effect on cellular metabolism. More work is necessary to fully evaluate drug-antibody conjugates for the potential of eradicating tumor cells from bone marrow used for autografting.

Isotopes Attached to Antibodies: Many attempts have been made to couple isotopes to antibodies and to use these conjugates to identify micrometastasis in patients with malignant disease (123,124). Currently this technology is being exploited in an attempt to improve diagnostic parameters for patients with neuroblastoma. A correlate to this work is to couple very short half-life isotopes (emitting high-energy irradiation) to antibodies and target these to tumor cells. The close proximity of the isotope to the malignant cell should result in a selective kill, leaving normal cells unaffected. We plan to evaluate this procedure to selectively kill (in vitro) neuroblasts metastizing to bone marrow.

Antibodies Attached to Immobilized Supports: We have also attempted to use monoclonal antibodies to target microspheres containing magnetite to tumor cells in bone marrow. When placed in a magnetic field, malignant cells will be attracted to the magnetic poles, leaving the normal hemopoietic cells in suspension (125). Microspheres of polystyrene containing magnetite (approximately 27% wt/vol) are made in uniform sizes from approximately 1 to 10 μm in diameter. Goat anti-mouse immunoglobulin (GMI) is then covalently coupled to the surface of these beads (supplied by J. Ugelstad of the University of Trondheim, Norway). By incubating bone marrow with a mixture of monoclonal anti-neuroblastoma antibodies, followed by GMI-coated microspheres, tumor cells could be removed from bone marrow when placed in a magnetic field. Up to 99.5% of tumor cells (neuroblastoma cell lines) were removed from bone marrow that had been seeded with up to 50% tumor cells. Currently work is continuing to scale our initial pilot experiments to a level where malignant cells can be removed from the 250-500 ml of marrow taken for autografting. At high levels of tumor infiltration to marrow, some nonspecific trapping of hemopoietic cells was observed in the aggregates of tumor cells bound to the magnetic poles. However, this should not be a problem when minimal infiltration is observed. Mixed cell colony assays for hemopoietic progenitors are being employed on marrow treated in this way to determine if the methodology is detrimental to hemopoietic cell development (112).

Current evaluation of all the methods of killing or removing tumor cells from bone marrow that will be used for autografts would suggest that this methodology may be the most effective and least toxic to normal cells. However, to obtain maximal tumor kill, it is envisaged that more than one separation procedure may have to be used. Ultimately the relative fragility of the hemopoietic stem cells may be the restraint with regards to the number of manipulations that can be tolerated before toxicity is obtained.

SUMMARY

A review of monoclonal antibodies to neuroblastoma cells is presented. None of these reagents are tumor specific. They have all been shown to cross-react with different neuroectodermally derived cell types. The antibodies have been useful in identifying metastatic spread of neuroblastoma to bone marrow. Similar to other solid tumors, considerable heterogeneity in antigen expression has been detected in neuroblastoma. To maximize the identification of neuroblasts in bone marrow, panels of monoclonal antibodies will be required. Considerable effort is being made to find ways of using the monoclonal antibodies to either selectively kill or remove tumor cells from bone marrow taken from patients receiving high-dose chemotherapy and autologous bone marrow transplantation therapy. Our experiences in this area are briefly reviewed in this chapter.

Within the group of malignancies defined as "small, round cell tumors," including leukemia, lymphoma, neuroblastoma, Ewing's tumor, and rhabdomysarcoma, it is often difficult to obtain an accurate differential diagnosis. Some 30 monoclonal anti-neuroblastoma antibodies (generated in our laboratory and others) can be used to distinguish all of these tumor types, quickly and easily, using an indirect immunofluorescence assay. These reagents are also being used to provide accurate differential diagnosis in neuropathology. The scope of using monoclonal antibodies as diagnostic tools for malignancy seems infinite. In the near future, they will almost certainly have a role in the identification of micrometastasis in patients with imaging techniques (123,124) and, in therapy, by cleansing tumor cells from marrow used for autografts. Whether monoclonal antibodies will fulfill their potential in targeting drugs or toxins to tumor cells in vivo remains inconclusive.

ACKNOWLEDGMENTS

I would like to thank J. Fritschy, F. Gibson, A. Goldman, J. Pritchard, and J. Garson for their advice in preparing this manuscript. Part of the work described here was supported by the Imperial Cancer Research Fund.

REFERENCES

1. R. Virchow, in *Die Krankhaften Geschwuste,* Vol. 2, August Herschwald, 1865.
2. J. F. Lingley, R. H. Sagerman, T. V. Santulli, and J. A. Wolff, *N. Engl. J. Med. 277*:1227 (1980).
3. J. Makinen, *Cancer 29*:1637 (1972).
4. H. R. Wahl, *J. Med. Res. 30*:205 (1914).
5. P. Ahdevaara, H. Kalimo, T. Torma, and M. Haltia, *Cancer 40*:784 (1977).
6. M. Bodian, *Arch. Dis. Child. 38*:606 (1963).
7. W. G. Thurman and M. H. Donaldson, in *Neoplasia in Childhood,* Chicago Year Book Medical, Chicago, 1967.
8. E. A. Evans, *Cancer 30*:1595 (1972).

9. K. E. Bore and A. J. McAdams, *N. Engl. J. Med. 292*:593 (1975).
10. C. E. Koop and J. R. Hernandez, *Surgery 56*:726 (1964).
11. N. Jaffe, *Cancer Treat. Rev. 3*:61 (1976).
12. J. Pritchard, T. J. McElwain, and J. Graham-Pole, *Br. J. Cancer 45*:86 (1982).
13. T. J. McElwain, D. W. Hedley, G. Burton, H. M. Clink, M. Y. Gordon, M. Jarman, C. A. Juttner, J. L. Millar, R. A. V. Milsted, G. Prentice, I. E. Smith, D. Spence, and M. Woods, *Br. J. Cancer 40*:72 (1979).
14. T. J. McElwain, D. W. Hedley, M. Y. Gordon, M. Jarman, and J. Pritchard, *Exp. Hematol. Suppl. 5*:360 (1979).
15. R. A. Abrams, D. Glaubiger, R. Simon, A. Lichter, and A. B. Deisseroth, *Lancet 2*:385 (1980).
16. J. T. Kemshead and J. Black, *Dev. Med. Child Neurol. 22*:816 (1980).
17. L. T. D. Sandoz, *Atlas of Haematology*, 2nd ed., Sandoz, Basel, Switzerland, 1973.
18. J. H. Wright, *J. Exp. Med. 12*:556 (1910).
19. M. L. Voorhess, *J. Pediatr. Surg. 3*:147 (1968).
20. M. L. Voorhess and I. S. Gardner, *J. Clin. Endocrinol. Metab. 21*:321 (1961).
21. Y. Nakano, S. Shinbo, Y. Nagayama, S. Manabe, and Y. Sugano, *Jpn. J. Clin. Med. 31*:1645 (1973).
22. M. A. Brewster and D. H. Berry, *Med. Pediatr. Oncol. 6*:93 (1979).
23. R. J. Begue, O. Bazerolle, J. Desgres, C. Lallemont, and P. Padieu, *Pathol. Biol. 19*:719 (1971).
24. T. Sato and K. Yoshinaga, *Tohoku J. Exp. Med. 110*:283 (1973).
25. R. Maurus, *Recent Results Cancer Res. 62*:210 (1977).
26. S. E. Gitlow, M. Mendlowitz, E. K. Wilk, S. Wilk, R. L. Wolf, and L. M. Botanie, *J. Lab. Clin. Med. 72*:612 (1973).
27. L. J. Grota and G. M. Brown, *Endocrinology 98*:615 (1975).
28. T. E. Williams and D. Donaldson, in *Clinical Pediatric Oncology* (W. Sutow, ed.), Mosby, St. Louis, 1973.
29. M. Ong and C. L. Dupont, *J. Pediatr. 86*:238 (1975).
30. S. Imashuku, E. H. La Brosse, E. M. Johnson, V. H. Morgenroth, and N. Zenker, *Biochem. Med. 5*:22 (1971).
31. M. Goldstein, L. S. Freedman, A. C. Bohuon, and F. Guerinot, *N. Engl. J. Med. 286*:1123 (1972).
32. B. Falck, N. A. Hillarp, G. Thieme, and A. Thorpe, *J. Histochem. Cytochem. 10*:348 (1962).
33. M. Ronsdahl and I. S. Cox, in *Proceedings of the Twentieth Annual Clinical Conference on Cancer,* University of Texas System Cancer Center, M. D. Anderson Hospital and Tumour Institute, Chicago Year Book Medical, Chicago, 1976, p. 251.
34. T. H. Joh, T. Shikimi, V. M. Pickel, and D. J. Reis, *Proc. Nat. Acad. Sci. U.S.A. 72*:3575 (1975).
35. V. Ulrich and W. Duppel, in *The Enzymes* Vol. 12 (P. D. Boyer, ed.), Academic, New York, 1974, p. 253.

36. A. A. Hakim, *Proc. Soc. Exp. Biol. Med. 168*:82 (1981).
37. H. T. Rupniak, G. Rein, J. Powell, T. Ryder, S. Carson, and B. T. Hill, *Cancer Res.* (in press).
38. H. T. Rupniak, B. T. Hill, J. T. Kemshead, P. H. Warne, D. C. Bicknell, G. Rein, and J. Pritchard, *Eur. J. Cell Biol. 22*:409 (1980).
39. B. W. Moore and V. J. Perez, in *Physiological and Biochemical Aspects of Nervous Integration* (F. D. Carlson, ed.), Prentice-Hall, Englewood Cliffs, N. J., 1968, p. 343.
40. D. Schmechel, P. J. Marangos, M. Brightman, and F. K. Goodwin, *Science 199*:313 (1978).
41. F. J. Tapia, A. J. A. Barbosa, P. J. Marangos, J. M. Polak, S. R. Bloom, C. Dermody, and A. G. E. Pearse, *Lancet 2*:808 (1981).
42. J. Wharton, J. M. Polak, G. A. Cole, P. J. Marangos, and A. G. E. Pearse, *J. Histochem. Cytochem. 29*:1359 (1981).
43. L. Odelstad, S. Pahlmas, K. Nilsson, E. Larsson, G. Lackgren, K. E. Johansson, S. Hjerten, and G. Grotte, *Brain Res.* (in press).
44. S. Pahlman, L. Odelstad, E. Larsson, G. Gunnar, and K. Nilson, *Int. J. Cancer 28*:583 (1981).
45. J. T. Kemshead, M. F. Greaves, J. Pritchard, and J. Graham-Pole, in *Differential Expression of Surface Antigens on Human Neuroblastoma Cells* (A. Evans, ed.), Academic, New York, 1980, p. 227.
46. J. D. Rowley, *Nature 243*:290 (1973).
47. J. L. Biedler, in *Advances in Neuroblastoma Research,* Vol. 12 (A. Evans, ed.), Academic, New York, 1980, p. 81.
48. J. L. Biedler, L. Helson, and B. A. Spengler, *Cancer Res. 33*:2643 (1973).
49. D. Cox, G. Yonken, and A. I. Spriggs, *Lancet 2*:55 (1965).
50. N. B. Atkin, in *Experimental Biology and Medicine,* Vol. 6, Karger, Basel, Switzerland, 1976, p. 110.
51. F. Gilbert, G. Balaban, and P. Moorhead, *Am. Soc. Hum. Gen. 314*:104A (1982).
52. L. J. Grota and G. M. Brown, *Endocrinology 98*:615 (1975).
53. S. Van Heyningen, *Biol. Rev. 52*:509 (1977).
54. T. G. Helting, O. Zwisler, and H. Wiegandt, *J. Biol. Chem. 252*:194 (1977).
55. W. Stallcup, J. Levine, and W. Rascake, in *Monoclonal Antibodies to Neural Antigens* (R. McKay, M. C. Raff, and L. F. Reichardt, eds.), Cold Spring Harbor Laboratory, 1981, p. 39.
56. B. R. Dasgupta and H. Sugiyama, *Biochem. Biophys. Res. Commun. 48*:108 (1972).
57. J. T. Kemshead, in *Immunology of the Brain* (M. Adinolphi, ed.), Marcel Dekker, New York (in press).
58. S. Fuchs, I. Schmidt-Hopfeld, G. Tridente, and R. Tarrab-Hazdai, *Nature 287*:162 (1980).
59. L. Svennerholm, in *Advances in Experimental Medicine and Biology,* Vol. 71, (G. Porcellati, B. Cellarelli, and G. Tettamani, eds.) Plenum, New York, 1975.

60. J. Hildebrand, P. A. Stryckmans, and E. Vanhouch, *Biochem. Biophys. Acta 260*:272 (1972).
61. J. T. Casper, L. Borella, and L. Sen, *Cancer Res. 37*:1750 (1977).
62. R. C. Seeger, P. M. Zeltzer, and S. A. Rayner, *J. Immunol. 122*:1548 (1979).
63. P. Wertheim and P. A. Voute, *J. Nat. Cancer Inst. 57*:701 (1976).
64. A. E. Reif and J. M. V. Allen, *J. Exp. Med. 120*:414 (1964).
65. R. T. Acton, R. J. Morris, and A. Williams, *Eur. J. Immunol. 4*:598 (1974).
66. A. N. Barclay and H. Hyden, *J. Neurochem. 31*:1357 (1978).
67. R. J. Morris, P. E. Mancini, and S. E. Pfeiffer, *Brain Res. 182*:119 (1980).
68. J. T. Kemshead, M. A. Ritter, S. F. Cotmore, and M. F. Greaves, *Brain Res. 236*:451 (1982).
69. S. F. Cotmore, S. A. Crowhurst, and M. D. Waterfield, *Eur. J. Biochem. 11*: 597 (1981).
70. R. J. Morris, S. Gower, and S. E. Pfeiffer, *Brain Res. 183*:145 (1980).
71. J. F. Lesley and V. A. Lennon, *Brain Res. 153*:109 (1978).
72. M. C. Raff, K. L. Fields, S. I. Hakomori, R. Mirsky, R. M. Pruss, and J. Winter, *Brain Res. 174*:283 (1979).
73. J. L. McKenzie and J. W. Fabre, *J. Immunol. 126*:843 (1981).
74. J. T. Kemshead, M. F. Greaves, F. Walsh, A. Chayen, and M. Parkhouse, in *American Society of Clinical Oncology Abstracts*, Vol. 22, Waverly, Baltimore, 1981.
75. J. L. McKenzie and J. W. Fabre, *J. Immunol 126*:843 (1981).
76. R. Dalchau and J. W. Fabre, *J. Exp. Med. 149*:576 (1979).
77. R. J. Morris and A. F. Williams, *Eur. J. Immunol. 5*:276 (1975).
78. R. H. Kennett and F. Gilbert, *Science 203*:1120 (1979).
79. J. T. Kemshead, D. Bicknell, and M. F. Greaves, *Pediatric Res. 15*:1282 (1981).
80. J. T. Kemshead, M. F. Greaves, J. Pritchard, F. Walsh, M. Parkhouse, A. Chayen, and R. Kennett, *Br. J. Cancer 43*:568 (1981).
81. M. F. Greaves, W. Verbi, J. T. Kemshead, and R. H. Kennett, *Blood 56*:1141 (1980).
82. R. H. Kennett, Z. Jonak, and K. B. Bechtol, in *Advances in Neuroblastoma Research*, Vol. 12, (A. E. Evans, ed.), Raven Press, New York, 1979, p. 209.
83. M. Momoi, R. H. Kennett, and M. C. Glick, *J. Biol. Chem. 255*:11914 (1980).
84. H. R. Schlesinger, J. M. Gerson, P. S. Moorhead, H. Maguire, and K. Hummeler, *Cancer Res. 36*:3094 (1976).
85. A. Mulder, The Immunological Characterization of Leukemia, Ph.D. thesis, Laboratory of Experimental and Clinical Immunology, University of Amsterdam, Amsterdam, 1982, p. 43.
86. J. T. Kemshead, J. G. Fritschy, U. Asser, S. Brown, and M. F. Greaves, in *Proceedings of the XIIIth Meeting of the International Society of Pediatric Oncology* (C. Raybaud, G. Clement, G. Lebreich, and J. L. Bernard, eds.), Excerpta Medica, Amsterdam, 1982, p. 85.

87. S. F. Cotmore, S. Crowhurst, and M. D. Waterfield, *Eur. J. Biochem. 11*: 597 (1981).
88. L. A. Herzenberg and L. A. Herzenberg, in *Handbook of Experimental Immunology*, Vol. 2 (D. M. Weir, ed.), Blackwell Scientific, Oxford, 1977, p. 22.
89. S. J. Collins, F. W. Ruscetti, R. E. Gallagher, and R. C. Gallo, *Proc. Nat. Acad. Sci. U.S.A. 75*:2458 (1978).
90. V. Solanki, T. J. Slaga, M. Callaham, and E. Huberman, *Proc. Nat. Acad. Sci. U.S.A. 78*:1722 (1981).
91. C. J. Wikstrand and D. D. Bigner, *Cancer Res. 42*:267 (1982).
92. H. B. Coakham and M. S. Lakshmi, *Oncology 31*:234 (1975).
93. J. Langman, in *Medical Embryology*, Livingstone, London, 1969, p. 290.
94. J. J. Marchalonis, R. E. Cone, and V. Santer, *Biochem. J. 124*:921 (1971).
95. R. O. Hynes, *Biochim. Biophys. Acta 458*:73 (1976).
96. A. E. Bolton, in *Radioiodination Techniques Review*, Vol. 18, Radiochemical Centre, Amersham, England, 1977.
97. C. P. Reynolds and R. G. Smith, in *American Society of Clinical Oncology*, Abstracts, Vol. 22, Waverly, Baltimore 1981.
98. G. S. Eisenbarth, F. S. Walsh, and M. Nirenberg, *Proc. Nat. Acad. Sci. U.S.A. 76*:4913 (1979).
99. J. T. Kemshead, F. Walsh, J. Pritchard, and M. F. Greaves, *Int. J. Cancer 27*: 447 (1981).
100. R. C. Seeger, H. M. Rosenblatt, K. Imai, and S. Ferrone, *Cancer Res. 41*:2714 (1981).
101. J. S. Malpas, J. T. Kemshead, J. Pritchard, and M. F. Greaves, in *Proceedings of the XIIIth Meeting of the International Society of Pediatric Oncology* (C. Raybaud, R. Clement, G. Lebreich, and J. L. Bernard, eds.), Excerpta Medica, Amsterdam, 1982, p. 90.
102. M. F. Greaves, G. Janossy, G. Francis, and J. Minowada, in *Differentiation of Normal and Neoplastic Haemopoetic Cells,* Cold Spring Harbor Laboratory, Boston, 1978, p. 823.
103. R. Dulbecco, M. Unger, M. Bologna, H. Battifora, P. Syka, and S. Okada, *Nature 292*:772 (1981).
104. J. A. Garson, P. C. L. Beverley, H. B. Coakham, and E. I. Harper, *Nature (Lond.) 298*:375–377 (1982).
105. J. T. Kemshead, J. Fritschy, U. Asser, D. R. Sutherland, and M. F. Greaves, *Hybridoma 1*:109 (1982).
106. R. A. Newman, D. R. Sutherland, T. W. LeBien, J. H. Kersey, and M. F. Greaves, *Biochim. Biophys. Acta 701*:318 (1982).
107. D. R. Sutherland, D. Delia, C. Schneider, R. Newman, J. T. Kemshead, and M. F. Greaves, *Proc. Nat. Acad. Sci. U.S.A. 78*:4515 (1981).
108. European Neuroblastoma Group Trial for the Effectiveness of High Dose Melphalan, Sec. J. Pritchard, Great Ormond St. Hospital for Sick Children, London.

109. O. Hartmann, European Neuroblastoma Group, Minutes of the Third Meeting, Brussels, December 1981.
110. K. A. Krolick, J. W. Uhr, and E. J. Vitetta, *Nature 295*, 604 (1982).
111. H. G. Prentice, G. Janossy, H. Blacklock, A. V. Hoffbrand, and G. Goldstein, submitted for publication.
112. H. A. Messner and A. A. Fauser, *Blut 41*:327 (1980).
113. B. L. Pike and W. A. Robinson, *J. Cell. Physiol. 76*:77 (1970).
114. A. D. Tepperman, J. E. Curtis, and E. A. McCulloch, *Blood 44*:659 (1976).
115. E. S. Vitetta, K. A. Krolick, and J. W. Uhr, *Immunol. Rev. 62*:159 (1982).
116. P. E. Thorpe, D. C. Edwards, A. J. S. Davies, and W. C. J. Ross, in *Monoclonal Antibodies: Clinical Medicine* (J. Fabre and A. McMichael, eds.), Academic, London, 1983, p. 167.
117. S. Olsnes and A. Pihl, in *Pharmacology of Bacterial Toxins* (J. Drew and F. Dorner, eds.) Pergamon (in press).
118. S. Olsnes and A. Pihl, in *Receptors and Recognition* (P. Cuatrecasas, ed.), Chapman and Hall, London, 1976, p. 129.
119. F. Stirpe, S. Olsnes, and A. Pihl, *J. Biol. Chem. 255*:6947 (1980).
120. G. Gregoriadis, *Nature 265*:407 (1977).
121. T. Ghose and A. H. Blair, *J. Nat. Cancer Inst. 61*:657 (1978).
122. G. F. Groeland, R. G. Simmonds, and J. R. F. Corvalan, *Protides of the Biological Fluids,* Vol. 30, Pergamon, London, 1982.
123. J. P. Mach, F. Buchegger, M. Forni, J. Ritschard, C. Berche, J. D. Lumbroso, M. Schreyer, C. Girardet, R. S. Accolla, and S. Carrel, *Immunol. Today 81*: 239 (1982).
124. D. M. Goldenberg, *Cancer Res. 40*:2953 (1980).
125. J. T. Kemshead, A. Rembaum, and J. Ugelstad, in *American Society of Chemical Oncology Abstracts,* Vol. 23, abstr. 143, 1983, p. 36.
126. P. M. Allan, J. A. Garson, E. I. Harper, U. Asser, H. B. Coakham, B. Brownell, and J. T. Kemshead, *Int J. Cancer 31*:591 (1983).
127. J. T. Kemshead, A. Goldman, J. Fritschy, J. S. Malpas, and J. Pritchard, *Lancet Jan 1/8*:12 (1983).

4 MONOCLONAL ANTIBODIES TO GLIOMA TUMOR ANTIGENS

Nicolas de Tribolet and Benoit de Muralt / Centre Hospitalier Universitaire Vaudois, Lausanne, Switzerland

Franz Buchegger / Institute of Biochemistry, University of Lausanne, Epalinges-sur-Lausanne, Switzerland

Jean-Pierre Mach, Magali Schreyer, and Stefan Carrel / Ludwig Institute for Cancer Research, Lausanne Branch, Epalinges-sur-Lausanne, Switzerland

INTRODUCTION

Definition of Gliomas

Gliomas are a group of tumors that arise mainly from neuroglial astrocytes, oligodendrocytes, and ependymal cells (1). Kernohan and Sayre's (2) system of grading glial tumors by increasing order of malignancy from I to IV is widely used; it is convenient to divide these tumors into benign gliomas (grades I and II) and malignant gliomas, glioblastomas (grades III and IV). Glioblastoma multiforme, the most malignant glioma, is thought to arise from anaplastic transformation of glial cells, mostly astrocytes, and represents 55% of all intracranial gliomas in all age groups. Mixed gliomas, composed of several gliogenous elements, are not uncommon (1). It thus appears that on morphological grounds gliomas represent a highly heterogeneous group. This heterogeneity of cells derived from individual gliomas has been demonstrated by Bigner et al. (3), who studied the phenotypic and genotypic characteristics of several human glioma cell lines.

Normal Brain Antigens Expressed by Gliomas

Gliomas share some antigens with normal brain cells. Glial fibrillary acidic protein is a specific marker for glial cells, especially astrocytes (4,5). This protein is found in gliomas of astrocytic origin and some ependymomas and is useful for their diagnosis (6). However, levels of glial fibrillary acidic protein decrease with increasing malignancy (7-9). This marker is almost absent from anaplastic glial cells and it also usually disappears from tumor cells after several passages in culture (10). Another marker called S100 protein is present in normal brain glial cells and Schwann cells of the peripheral nervous system (11,12), but S100 levels in glial tumor tissue are also inversely proportional to the degree of malignancy (13,14). In glioma cells maintained in vitro, the presence of S100 protein has been reported by some authors (15), but was not found by others (16). Recently S100 protein has also been found in large amounts in cultured human malignant melanomas (17), in malignant melanoma tissue (18), as well as in melanocytes and Langerhans cells of normal skin (19). Another protein found predominantly in oligodendrocytes (20) and associated with gliogenous tumors is α-2 glycoprotein; its concentration is also inversely correlated with the malignancy of the tumors (21).

The presence of myelin basic protein in gliomas is controversial. Myelin basic protein is known to provoke experimental allergic encephalomyelitis (EAE) when injected with complete Freund's adjuvant into animals or accidentally into man. Bigner et al. (22) induced lethal EAE by injecting human glioblastoma tissue with complete or incomplete Freund's adjuvant into nonhuman primates and guinea pigs. Similarly, rabbits immunized with glioblastoma tissue by Wahlström et al. (23) also developed EAE.

However, analysis by sodium dodecyl sulfate-polyacrylamide gel electrophoresis (SDS-PAGE) of extracts from glioblastoma tissue failed to demonstrate a detectable myelin basic protein band (22). On the other hand, cultured glioblastoma cells injected with complete Freund's adjuvant did not induce EAE (22).

Glioma-Associated Antigens Defined by Patient's Humoral or Cellular Immune Response

Evidence for the existence of glioma-associated antigens has been claimed by several authors who studied the cell-mediated response of patients with gliomas. Hitchcock et al. (24) reported on two tumor-associated antigens that produced a cell-mediated immune response in a glioblastoma patient with extracranial metastases who survived 18 years. The lymphocyte-mediated cytotoxicity of 66 patients was measured by Levy (25) against short-term cultured tumor cells. He found a specific tumor-directed lymphocyte-directed cytotoxicity in the sera of 85% of glioma patients and in 86% of patients with neurinomas and meningiomas. Specificity was assessed by testing the lymphocytes against 9-12 different target cell lines and by absorption studies. Two antigens, one common to gliomas regardless of anaplasia and the other present on anaplastic gliomas, melanomas, and fetal glial cells, could be defined. Sheikh et al. (26) studied the immune response of patients to glioma antigens, by a lymphocyte adherence inhibition assay. However, in addition to patient's with gliomas, control patients with cerebral trauma or aneurysms displayed some significant reactivity.

Several authors have studied the humoral immune response of glioma patients to autologous and allogeneic tumor cells. Trouillas (27) has immunized patients with crude extracts of their own tumor in complete Freund's adjuvant. Sera were collected before and after immunization and tested by immunodiffusion techniques with autologous and allogeneic tumor extracts, as well as with fetal brain extracts; normal sera and normal adult brain were used as controls. Glioblastomas, astrocytomas, and fetal brain were found to have a common antigen, an alpha-1 lipoprotein. The level of this antigen increased with increasing anaplasia of the tumor (28).

Solheid et al. (29) investigated the reactivity of glioma patients' sera with cultured glioma and normal glial cells using an immunofluorescence assay. He described two antigens: one common to glioblastomas, astrocytomas, and reactive normal glial tissue, and the other common to glioblastomas and reactive normal glial tissue only. Using a similar method on fresh cell suspensions and snap-frozen preparations from brain tumors, Sheikh et al. (30) claimed to have found common glioma-associated antigens. However, these studies were conducted without proper absorption procedures to remove anti-HLA antibodies. Using mixed hemadsorption, immune adherence, anti-C3 mixed hemadsorptions, and protein A assays, Pfreundschuh et al. (31) tested sera from 30 patients with astrocytomas for antibodies reacting with surface antigens of tumor cells. Absorption analysis of the reactive sera defined three types of antigens: (a) those restricted to autologous astrocytoma cells, (b) those shared by astrocytoma, neuroblastoma, sarcoma, and melanoma cells, and (c) those widely distributed on human and animal cells. Comparable results were reported by Coakham et al. (32), who studied the sera of 25 glioma patients by microcytotoxicity and immune adherence assays. Extensive absorption of one strongly reactive patient's serum allowed the detection of four antigens that were (a) glioma restricted, (b) common to gliomas, (c) present on glioma, neuroblastoma, and melanoma tissue, and (d) present on fetal brain and fibroblast tissue, respectively. Irie et al. (33) found antibodies in sera of melanoma patients that reacted with a so-called oncofetal antigen common to melanomas, other cancers, and skin, muscle, and brain tissue. Using the complement-dependent cytotoxicity assay, Kornblith et al. (34) detected antibodies against a glioblastoma cell line in 70% of over 100 sera from glioma patients, whereas Woosley et al. (35) reported a significant humoral response against autologous tumor cells in 8 of 38 serum samples from glioma patients. Martin-Achard et al. (36), in a critical reevaluation of the humoral response of glioma patients to a possible common tumor-associated antigen, found cytotoxic antibodies in sera from only 8 of 80 glioma patients (10%) as tested by complement-dependent cytotoxicity, while with the more sensitive antibody-dependent cell-mediated cytotoxicity assay, they found 20 positive sera (14%) from 143 glioma patients tested. The antibodies detected, however, did not seem to be directed against tumor-associated antigens, since the positive sera were found to have a similar antibody-dependent cell-mediated cytotoxicity reactivity against unrelated tumor cells and normal fibroblasts. Moreover, absorption of the positive sera with cells from unrelated tumor lines or with normal platelets abolished their reactivity with glioblastoma cells in all but one case. This particular serum was interesting, since its reactivity for glioma cells could be absorbed by 6 of 8 glioma lines and not by 10 of 11 nongliogenous cell lines. Its reactivity, however, was abolished by absorption with cells from an acute myeloid leukemia line, RPMI 6410.

From all the results reported, we conclude that the existence of immune responses in patients against autologous or common glioma-specific antigens has not yet been clearly demonstrated.

Glioma-Associated Antigens Defined by Heteroantisera

As early as 1936, Siris (37) immunized rabbits with antigen prepared from alcohol extracts of glioblastoma tissue. Using a complement fixation test and absorption with normal brain, he found that glioblastoma antigens do not differ from those of normal brain. Mahaley and Day (38) raised rabbit antisera against glioma tissue obtained at operation. After extensive absorption with normal brain and radiolabeling with ^{125}I, the antibodies were injected into patients. Biopsied tumor tissue obtained at reoperation had a higher antibody content than normal brain; however, no true specificity could be demonstrated.

In 1974, Coakham (39) studied the serum of a rabbit immunized with cultured astrocytoma cells by complement cytotoxicity, using short-term cultured astrocytoma cells as targets. After absorption with normal brain, the remaining activity was not further absorbed by cells from adult or fetal brain or from nonglial tumors, but it was absorbed by cells of seven astrocytomas and by extracts of astrocytoma tissue. This work suggested the existence of a glioma-associated antigen (40).

The same year, Wahlström et al. (23), using an immunofluorescence assay, found similar results with a rabbit anti-glioblastoma serum. All 15 established glioma cell lines tested gave a positive reaction, regardless of the age of the cell line. It is noteworthy that immunized rabbits developed severe EAE.

The existence of glioma-associated antigens defined by rabbit antisera was further supported by the work of Kehayov (41), who found two glioblastoma-associated antigens migrating in the beta and alpha-2 zones as determined by immunoelectrophoresis and one antigen shared by glioblastoma tissue and fetal brain of 8-10 weeks gestation. The latter appeared to be different from the carcinofetal glial antigen described by Trouillas (28). In contrast, Miyake and Kitamura (42) could not define any glioma-associated antigen when they used rabbit antiserum raised against glioblastoma tissue assayed in a mixed hemadsorption test; they did find a nonspecific reaction common to human tumors. With the same experimental model, Hass (43) and Delpech et al. (44) could not find glioma-restricted antigens. The most extensive work in this area has been done by Wikstrand et al. (45) and Wikstrand and Bigner (46). After extensive absorption with normal cells to remove anti-HLA activity, their antisera raised in nonhuman primates against glioblastoma tissue or cultured cell lines were tested in complement-dependent cytotoxicity and indirect membrane immunofluorescence against a large panel of cell lines from human malignant gliomas and nonglial tumors. When sera were further absorbed with an osteogenic sarcoma cell line, they still reacted with all eight gliomas tested but with none of the unrelated tumors (45). However, the activity against glioma cell lines of one anti-glioblastoma tissue serum was totally removed following absorption with normal human adult and fetal brain homogenate. On the other hand, two anti-glioma cell line sera, after similar absorption, retained some activity for 7 out of 11 and 3 out of 11 glioma lines, respectively (46). The expression of normal adult and fetal brain-associated antigens was shown to vary considerably from line to line. These results clearly demonstrated that normal brain antigens shared with glioma cells are strongly immunogenic in nonhuman primates and suggested the existence of glioma cell-associated specificities.

Our group immunized rabbits with membrane-enriched preparations from the human malignant glioma cell line LN-18 emulsified in complete Freund adjuvant (47). After extensive absorption, one antiserum reacted exclusively with antigenic determinants present on 7 out of 16 malignant glioma cell lines tested, as shown by complement-dependent cytotoxicity in a ^{51}Cr-release assay (Table 1). This glioma specificity could be further confirmed by quantitative absorption experiments where cells from a glioma line, LN-135, abolished the cytolytic activity of the antiserum against four other glioma lines (Fig. 1).

The results of the stepwise absorption of the antiserum are shown in Table 1. It consisted of the following steps:

Step 1—absorption with normal peripheral blood lymphocytes from 10 individual donors
Step 2—absorption with a pool of cells from four different lymphoblastoid cell lines and one endometrial carcinoma
Step 3—absorption with cells from a colon carcinoma
Step 4—absorption with cells from two different melanoma lines

Table 1 Reactivity of Rabbit Anti-Malignant Glioma Serum for Glioma Cell Lines

Cell line used as target	Step 1 (2 × 10⁷ PBL) 1:10	Step 2 (4 × 10⁷ Raji, Daudi, RPMI 6410, Nalm, End-1) 1:10	Complement-dependent cytotoxicity reactivity after absorption with			
			Step 3 (10^8 HT-29)		Step 4 (10^7 Mel-57, Mel-67)	
			1:80	1:20	1:40	1:80
LN-18	91[a]	75	92	73	72	69
U-118[b]	99	82	67	75	77	51
U-251[b]	92	62	45	55	18	18
U-343[b]	91	42	24	1	2	2
U-563[b]	93	85	45	0	4	4
U-1073[b]	87	75	54	33	43	25
LM[c]	90	65	44	4	5	4
LN-10	78	56	32	3	4	0
LN-40	88	81	52	5	5	5
LN-71	73	70	20	0	0	0
LN-94	96	93	75	1	2	0
LN-121	82	81	80	0	0	0
LN-135	88	80	80	89	86	63
LN-140	89	80	76	45	45	45
LN-215	72	62	50	35	12	7
LN-229	57	45	37	4	3	5

[a]Specific cytotoxicity of the antiserum 15% at a minimal dilution of 1:10.
[b]Malignant glioma line provided by J. Ponten.
[c]Malignant glioma line provided by P. Kornblith.

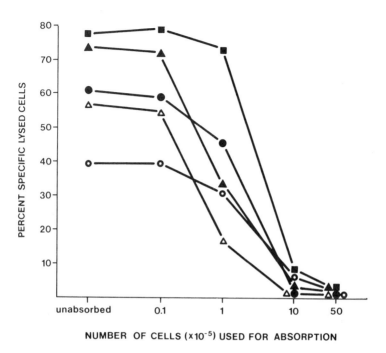

Figure 1 Quantitative absorption of rabbit anti-malignant glioma antiserum with malignant glioma cells LN-135. This cytotoxicity assay used ^{51}Cr-labeled target cells of five different malignant glioma cell lines: LN-135 (●), LN-18 (■), U-118 (△), U-1073 (○), LN-140 (▲). Each point represents the residual cytotoxicity of the antiserum after absorption of 250 μl of step 4 antiserum (1:50 diluted) with the number of cells indicated.

After each absorption step the antiserum was tested by complement-dependent cytotoxicity against a large panel of malignant glioma lines and control nonglioma cell lines. After the absorption from steps 1 and 2, the antiserum reacted with all cell lines tested, while after step 3 absorption, it reacted only with cells from malignant gliomas, melanomas, and fetal brain. Quantitative absorption experiments performed at this stage with fetal brain cells showed that the reactivity for fetal brain and melanoma cells could be abolished, while the antiserum was still cytolytic for malignant gliomas (Fig. 2). After the absorption from step 4, the antiserum reacted exclusively with seven malignant gliomas. After a further absorption with normal adult brain homogenate, the antiserum still reacted with four of the seven malignant glioma cell lines. Thus the antiserum described appears to recognize three types of antigens: antigens common to cells of neuroectodermal origin, antigens shared by malignant gliomas and adult brain, and antigens expressed only on some gliomas.

Glioma-Associated Antigens Defined by Monoclonal Antibodies

We have described monoclonal antibodies raised against human malignant glioma cells (48) and these will be analyzed in detail in the following sections.

Sikora and Phillips (49) have produced monoclonal antibodies first by fusing lymphocytes extracted from patient's brain glioma with the mouse myeloma P3-NS1-Ag4, and more recently by fusing lymphocytes extracted from several patient's gliomas with the human myeloma line LICR-LON-HMy^2 (50). The human monoclonal immunoglobulins produced by these two types of hybrids (human-mouse or human-human) reacted with cultured glioma cells (50), but the reactivity spectrum of these antibodies with other normal and neoplastic cells was too narrow to allow definite conclusions about their specificity. Recently Peng et al. (51) reported the generation of a monoclonal antibody against a rat glioma cell line (C-6) that cross-reacts with a human glioma cell line. However,

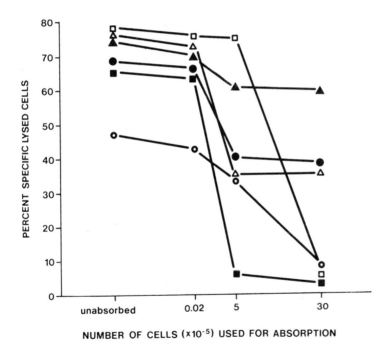

NUMBER OF CELLS (×10⁻⁵) USED FOR ABSORPTION

Figure 2 Quantitative absorption of rabbit anti-malignant glioma antiserum with fetal brain cells FB-243. This cytotoxicity assay used ^{51}Cr-labeled target cells of three different glioma cell lines, LN-18 (▲), U-118 (△), U1073 (●); one melanoma line, Mel-67 (■); and fetal brain cells, FB-243 (○). Each point represents the residual cytotoxicity of the antiserum after absorption of 250 μl of step 3 antiserum (diluted 1:80) with the number of cells indicated.

too few human cell lines and tissues were tested to evaluate the specificity of this antibody.

Neuroectodermal Antigens

Since gliomas, melanomas, and neuroblastomas are believed to be embryologically derived from the neuroectoderm, one may postulate that they share common differentiation antigens. This hypothesis was supported by the finding that a rabbit antiserum raised against a melanoma antigen reacted with an antigen present in the urine of patients with either melanoma or neuroblastoma (52).

More recently, Pfreundschuh et al. (31) and Coakham et al. (32) found antibodies in the serum of astrocytoma-bearing patients that cross-reacted with neuroblastomas and melanomas.

Kennett and Gilbert (53) produced a monoclonal antibody to neuroblastoma cell line IMR6 that reached with five other neuroblastomas, one retinoblastoma, and one glioma, as well as with fetal brain tissue. Carrel et al. (54,55) and Herlyn et al. (56) described several monoclonal antibodies against melanomas that cross-reacted with gliomas. Seeger et al. (57) raised monoclonal antibodies against melanoma that recognized antigenic determinants expressed by neuroectodermally derived neoplasms, including melanomas, gliomas, neuroblastomas, and sarcomas, but not expressed by normal adult or fetal brain.

Wikstrand and Bigner (58) have described monoclonal antibodies raised against second-trimester human fetal brain tissue. These antibodies reacted with cell lines derived from glioblastoma, melanoma, neuroblastoma, medulloblastoma, and fetal fibroblasts, as well as with fetal brain, liver, spleen, thymus, and adult spleen, suggesting the existence of shared fetal-neuroectodermal-lymphoid specificities.

Aim and Scope of the Present Chapter

In this chapter, we shall review and update the results concerning the characteristics of three monoclonal antibodies secreted by hybrids obtained from a fusion between mouse myeloma cells P3-x63-Ag8 and spleen cells from a mouse immunized with cells of the human glioma line LN-18 (59). Two of these antibodies have a preferential reactivity for cells from glioma lines, while the product from the third hybrid displays a cross-reactivity for melanomas and neuroblastoma cells (48). It will also be shown by immunochemical analysis that the first two antibodies react with two different antigenic determinants present on the same molecule of molecular weight 48,000. Furthermore, the reactivity of these antibodies on frozen tissue sections, using an indirect immunoperoxidase technique will be presented. We shall also review the reactivity of five monoclonal antibodies obtained from five fusions between two mouse myeloma cell lines, P3-NS1-Ag4 and P3-x63-Ag8, and spleen cells from mice immunized with membrane-enriched fractions from two melanoma cell lines, Me43 and IGR3. These antibodies react with

Table 2 Characteristics of the Glioma Cell Line Used for Immunization

Line:	Established 1978 (Diserens et al., 1981)
Origin:	Malignant glioma from a 61-year-old white male (grade IV according to Kernohan's classification)
Cells:	Grow as a monolayer in 10% fetal calf serum, glial fibrillary acidic protein absent, S100 negative, microfibrils present
Fibronectin:	Positive
Tumorigenicity in nude mice:	Yes
Ia-like antigen:	Present (DR3)
Marker chromosome:	Yes

melanoma cells, but also with structures present on gliomas and neuroblastomas. Finally, the expression of two antigens thought to be restricted to hematopoietic cells, HL-A-DR antigens and the common acute lymphoblastic leukemia antigen (CALLA), by glioma cells will be demonstrated and discussed.

PRODUCTION OF ANTIBODY-SECRETING HYBRIDS

Cell Lines

All human cell lines were grown in Dulbecco's minimal essential medium (DMEM) supplemented with 10% fetal calf serum. The characteristics of the malignant glioma line LN-18 used for immunization are summarized in Table 2. P3-x63-Ag8 myeloma cells were grown in the same medium, but supplemented with 10% gamma globulin-free horse serum (Gibco, Paisley, Scotland).

Immunization

BALB/c mice were given intraperitoneal injections of 10×10^6 whole cells of the established human glioma cell line LN-18 (59) suspended in 0.2 ml of DMEM. The mice were boosted intraperitoneally with the same number of cells 4 weeks later. Three days after the boost, one mouse was killed and the spleen cells were removed and used for fusion.

Cell Fusion

P3-x63-Ag8 (13) mouse myeloma cells (10×10^6) were incubated with 1×10^8 mouse spleen cells in 0.3 ml of 40% polyethylene glycol, mol wt 1000; Merck,

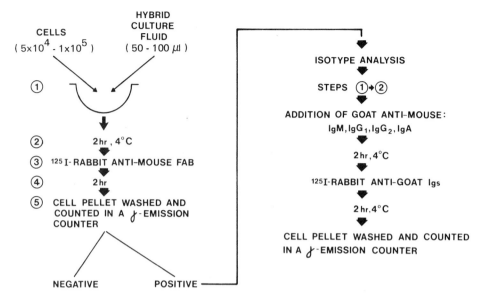

Figure 3 Schematic representation of the indirect binding radioimmunoassay used for the detection of monoclonal antibodies.

Darmstadt, West Germany) for 3 min at 37° (48). Cells were centrifuged for 5 min at 2000 × g, and then 5 ml of serum-free DMEM were added dropwise to dilute the polyethylene glycol. After fusion, the cells were washed; resuspended in 80 ml of DMEM containing 10^{-4} M hypoxanthine, 5×10^{-7} M aminopterin, and 1.6×10^{-5} M thymidine (HAT), and 10% gamma globulin-free horse serum, gentamicin, and 2 mM glutamine; and distributed in four 96-well plates of diameter 0.6 cm (Costar, Cambridge, Mass.).

Antibody Detection Radioimmunoassay

The production of specific antibodies by hybrids that grew in selective HAT medium was detected by antibody-binding assay essentially as described by Williams (60). Briefly, 4×10^5 target cells in µl of phosphate-buffered saline (PBS) were incubated for 2 hr at room temperature in U-bottom microtest plates with 50 µl of culture fluid from the different hybrids. The plates were centrifuged at 200 × g for 3 min, and the supernatants were removed. After three washings with 150 µl of PBS, 100 µl of ^{125}I-labeled purified rabbit anti-mouse F(ab)$_2$ antibody (10 ng of protein corresponding to 100,000 cpm) were added and incubated for 1 hr. Cells were then washed three times with PBS and transferred to tubes for gamma counting (Fig. 3). Positive hybrids detected by this method were then cloned by a limiting dilution system (61) in 96-well plates and a representative clone of each specificity was chosen for further studies.

SPECIFICITY ANALYSIS

Screening of Antibody-Secreting Hybrids

A total of 345 hybrid colonies was obtained from a single fusion between P3-x63-Ag8 myeloma cells and spleen cells from a mouse immunized with whole human malignant glioma cells (LN-18); 36 hybrids secreted antibodies binding to the immunizing glioma cells. As a first screening for specificity, culture fluids from these 36 hybrids were tested against two nonglial cell lines, a myeloid line, K562 (62), and an endometrial carcinoma line, End-1, known to express Ia antigens (63). Of 36 hybrid products, 33 reacted with either one of the two control cell lines. The three hybrids secreting antibodies that did not react with these two control cell lines were cloned by limiting dilution, and a representative clone for each hybrid was chosen for further specificity analysis.

Testing of Anti-Glioma Antibodies

The three monoclonal antibodies were designated BF7, GE2, and CG12. Table 3 summarizes the radioimmunoassay (RIA) results obtained with these reagents on 47 different malignant glioma cell lines. The results are expressed as a binding ratio (BR), which represents the total number of cell-bound counts divided by the number of cell-bound counts obtained with culture fluid of the mouse myeloma P3-x63-Ag8 which produces an IgG_1 (κ) immunoglobulin of unknown specificity. The background counts varied for each cell line tested, ranging between 70 and 500 cpm. Table 4 summarizes the RIA results obtained with the same antibodies on 12 cell lines from nongliogenous tumors, including endometrial carcinoma, cervical carcinoma, breast carcinoma, four colon carcinomas, rhabdomyosarcoma, and four lymphoid cell lines. The three monoclonal antibodies were further tested on normal skin fibroblasts, peripheral blood lymphocytes (from a pool of five healthy donors), and normal spermatozoids (from a pool of seven donors). The results presented in Tables 3 and 4 show that the BF7 antibody gives a BR of 3 or more on 38 of 47 glioma lines tested and on only 1 nongliogenous line (colon carcinoma line, Lovo). Similarly, GE2 gives a BR of more than 3 with 43 of 47 glioma cell lines tested, while a BR of 4 is also obtained with the same nongliogenous line (colon carcinoma line Lovo). CG12 antibody binds to 22 of 47 glioma lines and shows no significant binding with nongliogenous cells, except for 8 of 9 melanomas and 2 of 3 neuroblastomas (Table 5). This cross-reactivity with neuroectodermally derived tumors will be described in detail later.

Table 3 Binding of Monoclonal Anti-Glioma Antibodies to Glioma Cells

	Number of passage	Hybridoma product[a]			Number of counts per minute bound using P-x63-Ag8 culture fluid
		BF7	GE2	CG12	
Long-term glioma cell lines					
Cl-18	203	19	22	11	120
CL-71	113	30	26	9	245
Cl-215	52	10	10	5	150
Cl-235	23	11	15	2	180
Cl-40	170	8	10	6	250
Cl-140	78	7	8	3	150
Cl-229	45	3	8	3	100
Cl-94	95	4	6	5	170
Cl-135	100	2	5	1	230
Cl-121	50	2	4	2	250
LN-10	120	3	4	2	120
UCSF-167[b]	14	9	14	6	200
UCSF-168[b]	10	8	14	6	90
MG-343[c]	170	18	16	5	240
MG-251[c]	287	6	4	2	170
MG-118[c]	239	4	2	12	100
MG-1073[c]	144	5	5	3	150
MG-563[c]	267	2	6	2	200
LM[d]	320	3	4	1	220
UCSF-160[b]	10	9	14	4	250
LN-273	3	9	18	7	80
LN-282	1	8	15	4	190
LN-272	3	5	17	5	100
LN-247	7	12	17	2	140
LN-249	5	5	10	2	110
LN-284	1	5	9	2	170
LN-255	5	5	8	3	400

Table 3 (continued)

LN-253	2	4	5	2	160
LN-258	1	4	6	2	70
LN-263	1	3	8	1	70
LN-295	2	3	5	3	190
LN-297	4	3	5	2	110
LN-299	3	3	5	2	150
LN-245	3	2	6	1	180
LN-278	2	2	5	1	160
LN-286	1	2	3	1	400
LN-248	2	1	1	1	500
UCSF-188[b]	5	15	22	5	180
UCSF-159[b]	9	3	6	3	140
LN-291	2	7	16	2	190
LN-292	4	8	12	3	140
LN-283	4	9	13	5	110
UCSF-181[b]	4	10	4	2	150
LN-275	3	5	9	1	80
LN-264	1	3	6	1	300
LN-266	1	2	2	1	70
LN-302	3	1	2	1	270

[a]Results are expressed as the binding ratio (BR), which is the total number of cell-bound counts divided by the number of cell-bound counts using P-x63-Ag8 culture fluid: BR $\geqslant 3$ is considered as positive.
[b]Malignant glioma line provided by M. Rosenblum.
[c]Malignant glioma line provided by J. Ponten.
[d]Malignant glioma line provided by P. Kornblith.

Quantitative Absorption Experiments

In order to further study the specificity of the three hybrid products (BF7, GE2, and CG12) for malignant gliomas, two series of quantitative absorption experiments were performed. For BF7 and GE2 antibodies an increasing number of cells from three different malignant gliomas (LN-18, LN-215, LN-140) and from two control lines (End-1, Nalm-1) were added to 200 μl of culture fluid at a 1:10 dilution. The remaining binding activity in the supernatant for LN-140 malignant glioma cells was then tested by RIA. Figure 4 demonstrates that cells from the three glioma lines absorbed the binding activity of GE2, while endometrial carcinoma cells (End-1) or lymphoid cells (Nalm-1) gave no significant inhibition.

Table 4 Binding of Monoclonal Anti-Glioma Antibodies to Various Nongliogenous Cells

Cell line used as target	Hybridoma product[a]			Number of counts per minute bound using P-x63-Ag8
	BF7	GE2	CG12	
Tumor cells				
End-1[b]	2	1	1	50
Me180[c]	1	2	2	120
Br-3 [d]	1	1	2	100
HT-29[e]	1	1	1	170
Co-125[e]	1	1	1	120
Co-115[e]	1	2	2	150
Lovo	3	4	1	230
RD[f]	2	1	1	190
K562[g]	1	2	1	250
Jurkat[g]	2	2	2	100
Raji[g]	1	1	1	200
Nalm-1[g]	1	1	1	190
Normal cells				
Fbl·239[h]	2	2	2	220
PBL[i]	2	1	1	100
Sp[j]	1	1	1	110

[a] Results are expressed as the binding ration (BR), which is the total number of cell-bound counts divided by the number of cell-bound counts using P-x63-Ag8 culture fluid: BR $\geqslant 4$ is considered as positive.
[b] Endometrial carcinoma.
[c] Cervical carcinoma.
[d] Breast carcinoma.
[e] Colon carcinoma.
[f] Rhabdomyosarcoma.
[g] Hemopoietic cell line.
[h] Normal skin fibroblasts.
[i] Peripheral blood lymphocytes (pool of five donors).
[j] Normal spermatozoids (pool of seven donors).

Table 5 Binding of Monoclonal Anti-Glioma Antibodies to Nongliogenous Tumors Derived from the Neuroectoderm

Tumor cell lines	Hybridoma product[a]			Number of counts per minute using P-x63-Ag8 culture fluid
	BF7	GE2	CG12	
Melanomas				
Me43	1	1	15	110
MP-6	2	5	15	170
IGR3	2	2	8	240
MP-8	6	3	4	140
Mel-57	2	2	4	250
Mel-67	2	2	5	250
Mel-2-am	2	1	3	240
Me8	1	1	3	150
SK-Mel-1	2	2	1	70
Neuroblastomas				
IMR32	1	1	5	140
SK-N-SH	1	1	3	90
SK-N-SM	1	2	2	100
Medulloblastomas				
LN-260	2	4	5	1700
337/76	1	1	1	150
Schwannomas				
LN-242	3	4	6	260
LN-277	3	5	1	100
Retinoblastomas				
LN-257	2	4	1	620
Weri-Rbl	1	1	1	80

[a]Results are expressed as the binding ratio (BR), which is the total number of cell-bound counts divided by the number of cell-bound counts using P-x63-Ag8 culture fluid: BR $\geqslant 4$ is considered as positive.

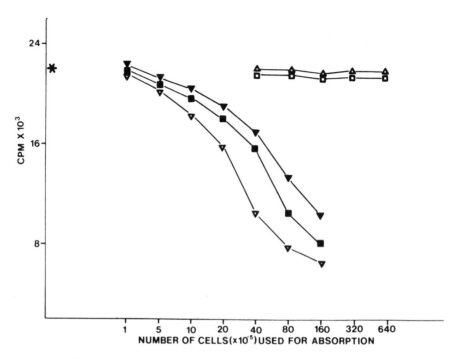

Figure 4 Quantitative absorption of GE2 antibodies. This binding assay used LN-140 glioma cells as targets. Each point represents the number of counts per minute bound by GE2 culture fluid after absorption of 200 μl (1:10) with the number of cells indicated (*, cpm of ^{125}I-labeled rabbit anti-mouse antibodies b bound by the unabsorbed culture fluid; ▼, malignant glioma LN-215; ■, LN-18; ▽, LN-140 cells; □, endometrial carcinoma End-1; △, c-ALL leukemia Nalm-1 cells).

Similar results were obtained with BF7 culture fluid (data not shown). For CG12 antibodies increasing numbers of cells from two different gliomas (LN-18, MG-118), two melanomas (ME143, IGR3), and control lines (End-1, Nalm-1) were used. The remaining binding activity in the supernatant was tested on MG-119 glioma cells (Fig. 5A) and on Me43 melanoma cells (Fig. 5B). Malignant glioma cells and melanoma cells both absorbed the binding activity of CG12 for malignant glioma cells MG-118(Fig. 5A), as well as for melanoma cells ME43. No inhibition was observed with the control cells used. The reactivity of the monoclonal antibodies after absorption with human adult and fetal brain was also investigated. The whole brain of a 21-cm fetus was obtained 0.5 hr after delivery of a prostaglandin-induced abortion. Adult brain was obtained 8 hr after death of a 56-year-old woman with no history of neurological disease. The whole fetal brain and the white

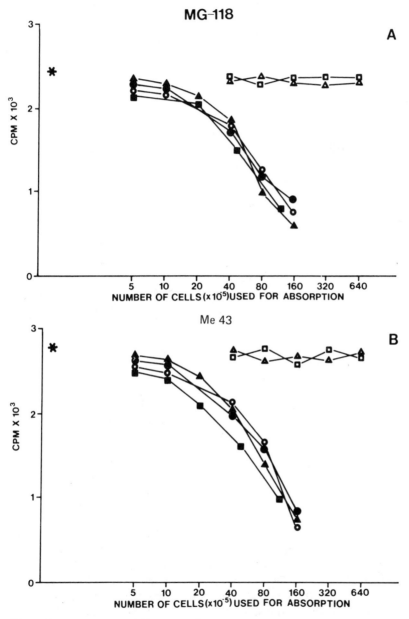

Figure 5 Quantitative absorption of CG12 antibodies. This binding assay used (A) MG-118 malignant glioma and (B) Me43 melanoma cells as targets. Each point represents the number of counts per minute bound by CG12 culture fluid after absorption of 200 μg (1:10) with the number of cells indicated (*, cpm of ^{125}I-labeled rabbit anti-mouse antibodies bound by the unabsorbed culture fluid; ■, malignant glioma LN-18; ▲, MG-118 cells; ○, melanoma IGR3; ●, Me43 cells; □, endometrial carcinoma End-1; △, c-ALL leukemia Nalm-1 cells).

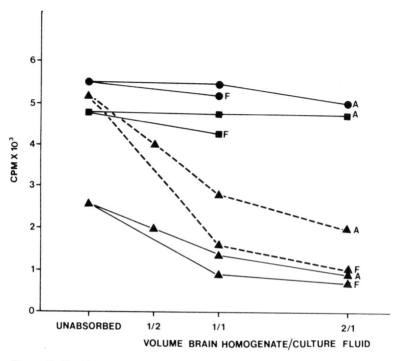

Figure 6 Residual binding activity of the three monoclonal antibodies (BF7, GE2, CG12) specific for gliomas after absorption with adult (A) and fetal (F) brain preparations. Binding assay was carried out using LN-18 glioma cells (——) and Me43 melanoma cells (- - -) as targets. Each point represents the number of counts per minute bound by the monoclonal antibodies after absorption of 500 μl of culture fluid with 250, 500, and 1000 μl of brain homogenates; (■, BF7; ●, GE2; ▲, CG12).

matter of the adult brain were mechanically homogenized in Hanks' solution, centrifuged for 5 min, and washed four times in Hanks' solution. The pellets were used for absorption assays as follows. Culture fluid (500 μl) was added to different volumes (250-1000 μl) of crude brain homogenates and incubated for 1 hr at room temperature. The mixtures were then centrifuged, and the remaining binding activity of the supernatant was tested by RIA as described above. The binding activity of BF7 and GE2 antibodies with LN-18 glioma cells was not modified after absorption with normal adult (white matter) or fetal brain (Fig. 6). In contrast, the reactivity of CG12 antibody with glioma LN-18 and melanoma Me43 cells was inhibited after absorption. The amount of tissue necessary to inhibit 50% of the binding to either melanoma or glioma cells was higher for adult than for fetal brain, indicating that the detected antigen is quantitatively more expressed on fetal brain.

Binding Assay to Fibronectin

Since the LN-18 cells used for immunization were shown to produce fibronectin (59), it was important to determine if one of the monoclonal antibodies was directed against this protein. The results are shown in Figure 7. Using a solid-phase RIA as described by Zardi et al. (64), it can be seen that none of the three anti-malignant glioma antibodies bound to fibronectin. (The monoclonal anti-fibronectin antibodies and the purified fibronectin used in this assay were kindly given by Dr. Zardi.)

CHARACTERIZATION OF MONOCLONAL ANTIBODIES AND ANTIGENS

Isotype Analysis

The isotype of hybridoma products was determined by the following binding radioimmunoassay: 4×10^5 target cells were incubated with culture fluid in

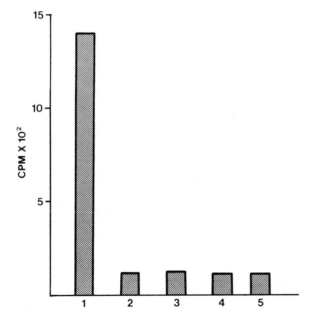

Figure 7 Solid-phase RIA for fibronectin. Unlabeled fibronectin (0.01 mg per well) was absorbed to wells of a polyvinyl plate. Culture fluid was then incubated for 2 hr before adding ^{125}I-labeled rabbit anti-mouse antibodies (1, positive control monoclonal anti-fibronectin; 2, BF7; 3, GE2; 4, CG12 antibodies; 5, negative control P3-x63 culture fluid).

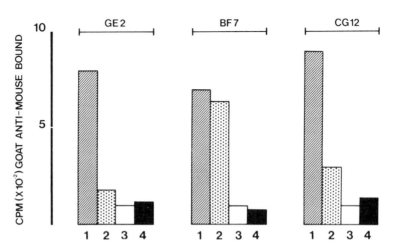

Figure 8 Determination of the immunoglobulin classes and subclasses (isotype) of the three monoclonal anti-glioma antibodies (GE2, BF7, CG12) using LN-18 glioma cells as targets. First the mouse monoclonal antibodies were incubated with the cells, then goat antisera specific for either IgG_1, IgG_2, IgA, or IgM (100 μl, diluted 1:500), and as a third layer ^{125}I-labeled rabbit antibodies against goat IgG. The results are expressed as the number of counts per minute bound to the cells.

U-bottom plates. After centrifugation and washing, 100 μl of the appropriate dilution (1:100-1:1000) of goat antisera specific for either IgM, IgG_1, IgG_2 or IgA (Meloy, Springfield, Va.) were added. After washing, ^{125}I-labeled rabbit anti-goat IgG was added. The cells were washed again and their bound radioactivity counted. All incubation steps, lasting 2 hr each, were done at 4°C. The results obtained from the isotype analysis of three anti-glioma antibodies are summarized in Figure 8. The isotype of two anti-glioma antibodies GE2 and CG12 was IgG_1, while the third anti-glioma antibody BF7 was reacting with both IgG_1 and IgG_2 antisera, indicating that it contains two heavy chains of different IgG subclasses.

Reciprocal Binding Inhibition Tests

These experiments were performed to determine whether the two monoclonal antibodies BF7 and GE2, which appeared to be directed against common antigens expressed on the majority of malignant glioma cell lines tested, bound to identical or different antigenic determinants. [3H] Leucine-labeled antibodies from these two clones were tested for their binding capacity to LN-18 malignant glioma cells in the presence of an excess of unlabeled antibodies from various clones. Antibodies from the selected clones were internally labeled by the addition of 10 μCi of [^{3}H] leucine to cultures of 1 X 10^6 hybrid cells in 1 ml of leucine-free DMEM. After 36 hr of incubation, culture fluids were harvested and dialyzed in PBS for 24 hr. The ^{3}H-labeled antibody solution (75 μl, diluted 1:3) was incubated with 4 X 10^5 cells; after 1 hr, cells were centrifuged and counted in a beta-liquid scintillation counter. For competition analysis, 50 μl of unlabeled antibodies of the various hybridomas were incubated for 0.5 hr with the target cells before addition of 25 μl of ^{3}H-labeled antibodies from each hybrid. After 1 hr, cells were washed and counted. Figure 9a shows that the binding of unlabeled GE2 antibodies was inhibited by unlabeled antibodies from the same clone, but not by BF7 antibodies. As a control, unlabeled CG12 antibodies were

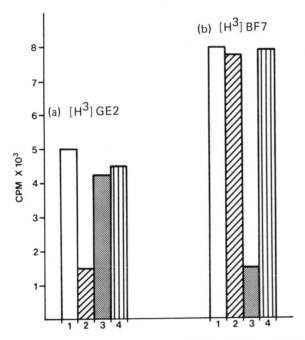

Figure 9 Competition between GE2 and BF7 antibodies for binding to LN-18 glioma cells. Antibodies from both clones (GE2, BF7) were internally labeled with [^{3}H] leucine: (a) labeled GE2–1, without unlabeled culture fluid; 2, after preincubation with unlabeled GE2; 3, after preincubation with BF7; 4, after preincubation with CG12; (b) labeled BF7–1, without unlabeled culture fluid; 2, after preincubation with unlabeled GE2; 3, after preincubation with BF7; 4, after preincubation with CG12.

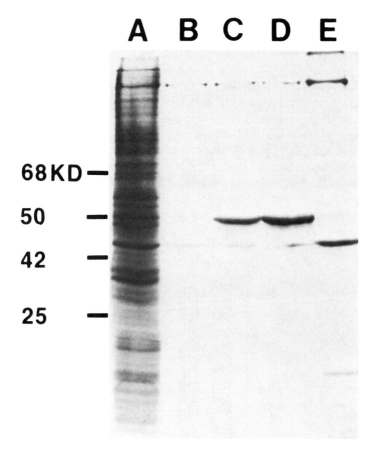

Figure 10 Immunoprecipitations performed with monoclonal antibodies GE2 (C), BF7 (D), and control IgG$_1$ from myeloma P3-x63 (B) on [^{35}S] methionine-labeled C1-71 glioma cells lysed in 0.5% Nonidet P40. (A) shows the total cell lysate and (E) the material nonspecifically bound to protein A-Sepharose during a preadsorption procedure. Electrophoresis was performed in 0.1% SDS-polyacrylamide slab gel with a concentration gradient of 7.5–13%, after reduction of the labeled proteins by 0.1 M dithiothreitol in 10% SDS. Fluorography of the dried gel was obtained by exposure for 15 days at 70°C.

also tested and found to be ineffective in inhibiting the binding of GE2. Figure 9b shows the reciprocal experiment, where the binding of labeled BF7 antibodies was inhibited only by unlabeled BF7, but not by GE2 and CG12 antibodies. These results clearly indicate that the antibodies from these two clones, GE2 and BF7, are reacting with different antigenic determinants.

Preliminary Immunochemical Characterization of a Glioma-Associated Antigen

Cells from glioma lines were labeled either with ^{125}I by the lactoperoxidase method or with [^{35}S]methionine biosynthetically. Radiolabeled cell lysates were immunoprecipitated with the three monoclonal anti-glioma antibodies (BF7, GE2, and CG12), using protein A-Sepharose to bind the antigen-antibody complexes, followed by analysis in SDS-PAGE and autoradiography or fluorography. Both BF7 and GE2 antibodies gave a major protein band with an apparent molecular weight of 48,000 with glioma cell lysate labeled by either of the two isotopes, whereas CG12 did not precipitate any definite protein band in this molecular weight range.

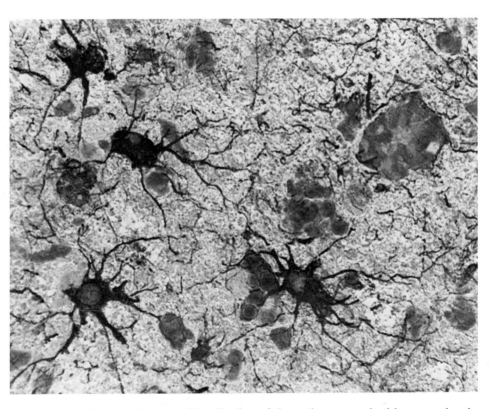

Figure 11 Immunohistological localization of the antigen recognized by monoclonal antibodies GE2 and BF7 on resected glioma. Shown here is a frozen section of a malignant glioma (×1000). Indirect immunoperoxidase used the biotin-avidin system with amino-ethyl-carboxyl as chromogen. Large, rather well-differentiated astrocytes are stained throughout the cytoplasm. Anaplastic cells are stained with less intensity.

Figure 10 shows the fluorography of a representative immunoprecipitation experiment obtained with [^{35}S]methionine-labeled Cl-71 glioma cell lysate. Lane A shows the total cell lysate; lane B the material bound to a control IgG$_1$, secreted by the parent myeloma P3-x63; lanes C and D the material precipitated by antibody GE2 and BF7, respectively; and lane E the material nonspecifically bound to protein A-Sepharose during a preabsorption step. It is evident that only the two anti-glioma monoclonal antibodies precipitated a major protein band (lanes C and D) with an identical apparent molecular weight of 48,000 suggesting that the two antibodies react with the same protein. In view of the results from Figure 9, our tentative conclusion is that antibodies BF7 and GE2 react with two different antigenic determinants present on the same polypeptide chain. Control experiments with [^{35}S]methionine-labeled lysates from Raji cells and myeloma cells (IGR3 and Me43) showed that the 48-kilodalton protein was absent from Raji cells, but detectable in melanoma cells.

Use of Monoclonal Antibodies for the Immunohistological Localization of Glioma-Associated Antigen on Fresh Tumor Material

The three-stage biotin-avidin-peroxidase system (65) was used for staining fresh tumor tissue with the anti-glioma monoclonal antibodies GE2 and BF7. The monoclonal antibodies were used at the first stage, at the second stage biotinylated horse anti-mouse antiserum was added, and avidin-peroxidase conjugate was added in the third stage. Figure 11 is a section of a grade IV malignant glioma stained with monoclonal antibody GE2. An intense staining of rather well-differentiated neoplastic astrocytes can be seen. The astrocytic processes are clearly visible. Undifferentiated multinucleated cells are also stained, but with less intensity. The pattern of staining throughout the cellular body indicates that the antigen is present in large amounts in the cytoplasm and not restricted to the membrane.

NEUROECTODERMAL ANTIGENS

Monoclonal Anti-Glioma Antibodies Binding to Melanomas and Neuroblastomas

Table 5 summarizes the results obtained on nine melanoma and three neuroblasttoma cell lines, as well as two medulloblastoma, two schwannoma, and two retinoblastoma cell lines with the three anti-glioma antibodies. Antibodies GE2 and BF7 bind to two and one, respectively, of the nine melanomas tested and to none of the three neuroblastomas, while antibody CG12 binds to eight out of nine melanomas, as well as to two of three neuroblastomas. BF7 binds to two of two schwannomas, but to none of two medulloblastomas and two retinoblastomas, while GE2 binds to the two schwannomas, one of two medulloblastomas, and one of two retinoblastomas.

Table 6 Binding of Monoclonal Anti-Glioma Antibodies to Meningioma Cells

Meningioma cells	Number of passages	Hybridoma product[a]			Number of counts per minute bound using P-x63-Ag8 culture fluid
		BF7	GE2	CG12	
Men-279	3	11	11	7	180
Men-246	1	2	2	1	250
Men-250	1	2	2	1	820
Men-267	1	2	2	1	160
Men-285	1	3	2	2	300
Men-288	2	2	4	3	280
Men-296	2	2	4	1	240
Men-303	2	2	2	1	300
Men-309	2	2	3	1	190
Men-1	0	2	2	1	290

[a]Results are expressed as the binding ratio (BR), which is the total number of cell-bound counts divided by the number of cell-bound counts using P-x63-Ag8 culture fluid: BR $\geqslant 4$ (underscored) is considered as positive.

and CG12 binds to one of two schwannomas, one of two medulloblastomas, and one of two retinoblastomas. Thus BF7 and GE2 seem to react preferentially to gliomas, with some exceptions to a few tumors derived from the neuroectoderm, whereas CG12 shows a much broader cross-reactivity for tumors of neuroectodermal origin. The three anti-glioma antibodies were also tested on a panel of 10 meningioma lines (Table 6). All three anti-glioma antibodies showed some binding activity with two to four meningioma lines.

Monoclonal Anti-Melanoma Antibodies Binding to Gliomas and Neuroblastomas

The specificity analysis of five different anti-melanoma monoclonal antibodies was performed on a large number of melanoma cell lines as well as other neural crest-derived tumors, such as gliomas and neuroblastomas (Table 7). Antibodies from clone Mel-5 bound to five out of seven gliomas and to three out of three neuroblastomas. Antibodies from clone Mel-14 bound also to five out of seven gliomas, but only to one neuroblastoma. A similar but not identical cross-reactivity with these glioma and neuroblastoma cell lines was observed with antibodies from three other anti-melanoma clones, Me3-TB7, Me4-F8, Me5-D5. None of these anti-melanoma monoclonal antibodies reacted significantly with any of the 33 nonmelanoma

Table 7 Binding of Hybridoma Anti-Melanoma Antibodies to Melanomas, Gliomas, and Neuroblastomas

Target cell used	Hybridoma product				
	Mel-5	Mel-14	Me3-TB7	Me4-F8	Me5-D5
Melanomas					
IGR3	2760[a]	2450	1920	1200	720
Me43	2400	2700	2650	1680	1200
MP-6	1560	1600	550	210[b]	600
MP-8	480	600	800	1950	850
Mel-67	1100	1850	1500	1550	240[b]
Daudel	940	1400	2480	740	850
Mel-57	1250	1080	800	800	1050
Mel-2-am	1440	1800	2200	1200	680
Mel-Ei78	3000	2800	360	500	810
Me8	980	1560	1080	740	750
SK-Mel-1	1080	840	240[b]	850	960
Gliomas					
LN-229	1800	3400	950	130[b]	510
LN-18	1080	1560	140[b]	170[b]	200[b]
LN-121	1900	1690	1100	930	750
LN-215	1450	950	1080	1140	800
MG-1073	210[b]	200[b]	1000	130[b]	180[b]
LN-71	180[b]	220[b]	210[b]	210[b]	500
LN-135	1840	1400	1200	100[b]	680
Neuroblastomas					
IMR32	1000	1740	1050	670	1320
SK-N-SM	1150	180[b]	500	420	710
SK-N-SH	980	220[b]	470	380	1080

[a]Results are expressed as the cpm bound of ^{125}I-labeled rabbit anti-mouse $F(ab')_2$ antibodies to 5×10^4 target cells incubated with the various culture fluids.
[b]Value considered as background (cpm $\leqslant 240$).

and nongliogenous control cell lines tested, including colon carcinomas, cervical carcinomas, breast carcinomas, normal skin fibroblasts, as well as T and B cells (data not shown). The specificity of these five hybridoma products was further demonstrated by quantitative absorption experiments. Two representative experiments are shown in Figure 12. Increasing numbers of cells from two glioma lines (LN-215, LN-121) and one neuroblastoma line (IMR32) absorbed the binding activity of Me3-TB7 and Me4-F8 culture fluids for IGR3 melanoma target cells, while as many as 16×10^6 colon carcinoma cells (Co-115) or endometrial carcinoma cells (End-1) gave no significant binding inhibition.

Cross-Reactivity of the Monoclonal Antibodies for Neuroectodermal Antigens

The reactivity spectrum of five monoclonal anti-melanoma antibodies and of the monoclonal anti-glioma antibody CG12 on five melanoma cell lines, five glioma lines, and three neuroblastoma lines is summarized in Figure 13. From this study, it can be concluded that these six monoclonal antibodies are not directed against the same antigenic molecule, since in no instance was there a complete homology between the reactivity spectrum of each of these different antibodies for the cell lines tested. The binding activity of ascitic fluids from four anti-melanoma hybridomas (Me1-5, Me1-14, Me3-TB7, and Me4-G8) for IGR3 melanoma cells was not modified after absorption with fetal brain homogenate, in contrast to the anti-glioma antibody CG12, whose activity was abolished by absorption with adult and fetal brain.

EXPRESSION OF LYMPHOID DIFFERENTIATION ANTIGENS ON GLIOMAS

Reactivity of Monoclonal Anti-HLA-DR Antibodies

Monoclonal antibodies against Ia-like antigens were obtained from a fusion of spleen cells from a mouse immunized with Daudi cell membranes and mouse myeloma cells P3-x63-Ag8 and were characterized as described previously (66). The monoclonal antibody D1-12 reacts with a monomorphic determinant present on the small (β) subunit of the Ia molecule. As shown in Table 8, D1-12 antibody lysed 33-88% of three out of eight glioma cell lines, as tested in complement-dependent cytotoxicity using ^{51}Cr-labeled target cells. As expected, this antibody was also cytolytic for the two control cell lines, known to express HLA-DR antigens, End-1 and IGR3.

Reactivity of Rabbit Anti-CALLA Antiserum

Antiserum against CALLA was obtained by immunization of a rabbit with membrane-enriched fractions from the permanent cell line Nalm-1, established

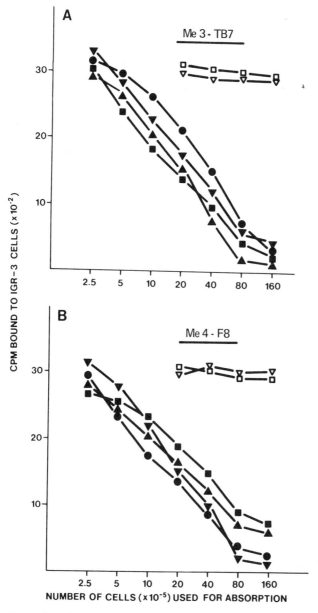

Figure 12 Quantitative absorption of monoclonal anti-melanoma antibodies from hybridoma (A) Me3-TB7 and (B) Me4-F8. Binding RIA used IGR3 melanoma cells as target. Each point represents the number of counts per minute bound by $50\,\mu l$ of the culture fluids from the two hybridomas after absorption with the number of cells indicated on the abscissa. The cells used for absorption were the following: gliomas (LN-215, ●- - -●; LN-121, $\triangle$ - - - $\triangle$), neuroblastoma (IMR32, ■ - - - ■) melanoma (Me43, ▼ - - - ▼), colon carcinoma (Co-115, □ - - - □), and endometrial carcinoma (End-1, ▽ - - - ▽).

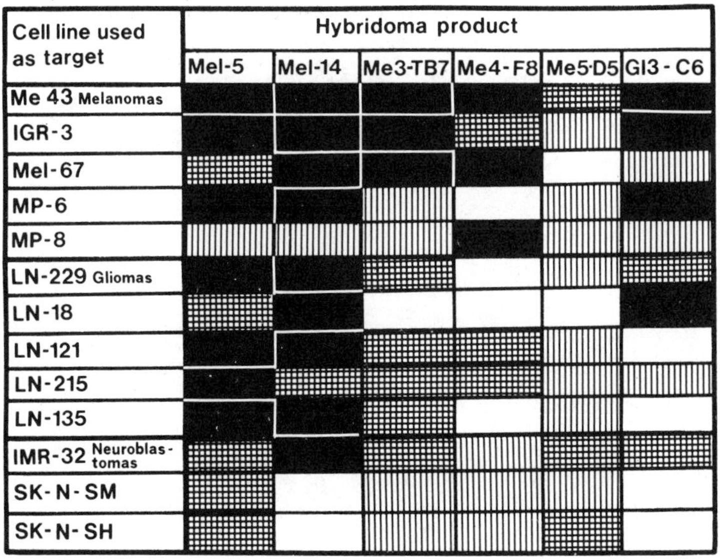

Cell line used as target	Hybridoma product					
	Mel-5	Mel-14	Me3-TB7	Me4-F8	Me5-D5	Gl3-C6
Me 43 Melanomas						
IGR-3						
Mel-67						
MP-6						
MP-8						
LN-229 Gliomas						
LN-18						
LN-121						
LN-215						
LN-135						
IMR-32 Neuroblastomas						
SK-N-SM						
SK-N-SH						

Figure 13 Cross-reactivity of monoclonal anti-melanoma and anti-glioma antibodies for neuroectodermal antigens (■, very strong reactivity, > 1500 CPM; ▦, strong reactivity, 900–1490 cpm; ▥, positive reactivity, 300–890 cpm; □ no reactivity, < 300 cpm).

from a patient with chronic myeloid leukemia in blast crisis (67, 70-72). This antiserum lysed 53-81% of the ^{51}Cr-labeled target cells from six different glioma cell lines in a 3-hr complement-dependent cytotoxicity assay. No significant lysis was obtained with rabbit anti-CALLA serum for five nongliogenous control cell lines consisting of one endometrial carcinoma, End-1, one breast carcinoma, SK-BR-3, two melanomas, Me43 and IGR, and one cervical carcinoma, M3-180 (Table 8). These results were confirmed by using the monoclonal anti-CALLA antibody J-5 (68). Absorption of anti-CALLA serum and anti-Ia antibodies by glioma cells abolished their cytotoxicity against blasts isolated from a common acute lymphoblastic leukemia (68). Immunoprecipitation experiments with rabbit anti-CALLA serum and monoclonal anti-DR antibodies confirmed the presence of CALLA and HLA-DR antigens on the surface of some of the glioma cells tested. From solubilized labeled LN-229 cells, rabbit anti-CALLA serum precipitated a single polypeptide chain with an apparent molecular weight of 100,000, characteristic for CALLA (Fig. 14a). Monoclonal anti-DR antibodies precipitated two polypeptide chains characteristic of the HLA-DR antigens with an apparent molecular weight of 28,000 and 33,000 (Fig. 14b). From LN-215 cells, anti-CALLA serum precipitated a similar single polypeptide chain of approximately 100 kilodaltons as with LN-229 cells (Fig. 14c). No precipitation was obtained with anti-DR antibodies

Table 8 Reactivity of Anti-CALLA and Anti-DR Antibodies for Glioma Cell Lines

Target cell line	Rabbit anti-CALLA (% lysed cells)	Monoclonal anti-DR (% lysed cells)	DR phenotype[a]
Gliomas			
LN-229	81[b]	76	1,7
LN-121	66	88	2,4
LN-135	53	34	2,8
LN-215	74	0	
LN-71	57	0	
LN-140	72	0	
LN-343	0	0	
LN-40	0	0	
Controls			
End-1[c]	0	89	2,0
SK-BR-3[d]	0	0	
Me43[e]	0	0	
IGR3[e]	0	82	1,7
Me180[f]	0	0	

[a]The DR phenotype was determined by Dr. M. Jeannet (University Hospital, Geneva).
[b]Measured by complement-dependent cytotoxicity using ^{51}Cr-labeled target cells (69).
[c]Endometrial carcinoma.
[d]Breast carcinoma.
[e]Melanoma.
[f]Cervical carcinoma.

(Fig. 14d), confirming the absence of detectable HLA-DR antigens on this cell line as determined by complement-dependent cytotoxicity. As a positive control, immunoprecipitates obtained with solubilized Nalm-1 cells, demonstrated the specificity of the two reagents anti-CALLA and anti-DR (Fig. 14e,f). Absorption of anti-CALLA serum with LN-229 glioma cells abolished its capacity to precipitate the 100-kilodalton polypeptide chain from Nalm-1 cells (Fig. 14g). Taken together, these experiments show that anti-CALLA serum recognized a very similar, if not identical, 100-kilodalton polypeptide chain on both glioma and Nalm-1 cells. The functional role of these antigens on glioma cells is unknown. Since not all glioma cell lines tested express HLA-DR antigens or CALLA, it will be important to determine whether these antigenic differences could help in the classification of gliogenous tumors.

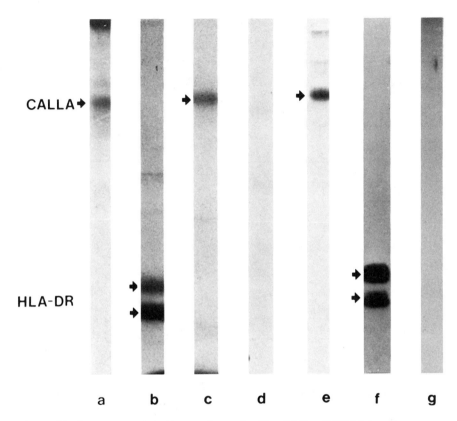

CALLA→

HLA-DR

a   b   c   d   e   f   g

Figure 14 Immunoprecipitation performed with rabbit anti-CALLA and monoclonal anti-DR antibodies: (a) anti-CALLA tested on LN-229, (b) anti-DR tested on LN-229, (c) anti-CALLA tested on LN-215, (d) anti-DR tested on LN-215, (e) anti-CALLA tested on Nalm-1, (f) anti-DR tested on Nalm-1, (g) anti-CALLA absorbed with LN-229 tested on Nalm-1. Cells from the two glioma lines (LN-229 and LN-215) and one non-T, non-B line (Nalm-1) were surface labeled with ^{125}I by the lactoperoxidase method, and extracted with 0.5% Nonidet P40. Cell-surface proteins were isolated by a two-step immunoprecipitation procedure using Sepharose-protein A to bind the antigen-antibody complexes formed upon addition of rabbit anti-CALLA serum or monoclonal anti-DR antibodies to the cell lysates. The bound antigens were eluted and applied to 10% SDS-PAGE. Autoradiographs of dried gels were obtained by exposure for 2-7 days at 70°C.

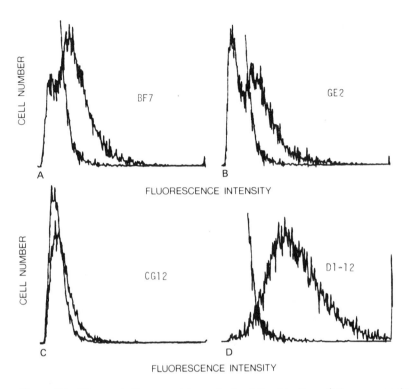

Figure 15 Flow cytofluorometric analysis of the binding of three monoclonal anti-glioma antibodies (GE2, BF7, CG12) and one monoclonal anti-Ia antibody (D1-12) on LN-8 glioma cells.

FLUORESCENCE-ACTIVATED CELL SORTER ANALYSIS OF GLIOMA ANTIGENS

The cellular expression of the antigenic determinants recognized by monoclonal antibodies BF7, GE2, and CG12 has been analyzed by fluorescence-activated cell sorter (FACS II, Becton Dickinson, Los Angeles, Calif.) Figure 15A shows the fluorescence pattern obtained after reacting C1-121 glioma cells in suspension with BF7 monoclonal antibodies and a fluorescein-labeled goat anti-mouse immunoglobulin. A typical bimodal distribution is seen, suggesting that about 50% of the cells from C1-121 line express the antigenic determinant recognized by BF7. A similar distribution was observed with GE2 antibodies (Fig. 15B). Figure 15C shows that the antigen defined by CG12 is expressed on only a minority of the cells. The expression of Ia antigens on cells of the same line has been analyzed using anti-Ia monoclonal antibody D1-12. No negative cell population was detected, suggesting that all cells of this line express Ia antigens (Fig. 15D).

DISCUSSION

The identification of tumor-associated antigens by means of heteroantisera is extremely difficult because of the large number of contaminating antibodies directed against antigens present on normal cells that must be removed by extensive absorption before any tumor specificity can be demonstrated.

Our results show that the hybridoma technology can be used to identify glioma tumor-associated antigens as well as differentiation antigens on glioma cells. The malignant glioma specificity of the two antibodies BF7 and GE2 directed against a putative common glioma-associated antigen was studied by a series of quantitative absorption experiments. Our first results showed that incubation with malignant glioma cells abolished the reactivity of BF7 and GE2 antibodies to malignant glioma cells, whereas nongliogenous cells were unable to reduce the binding capacity of BF7 and GE2 for glioma. Absorptions with normal and fetal brain homogenates were also unable to reduce the binding capacity of these two monoclonal antibodies for malignant glioma. From these experiments, we tentatively concluded that the antigenic determinants recognized by BF7 and GE2 antibodies were not expressed on normal and fetal brain cells, or at least not in an amount detectable by these absorption experiments. However, further extensive analysis of the reactivity of these antibodies on a vast panel of cell lines has revealed that BF7 and GE2 antibodies are not strictly specific for gliomas, since they reacted with a few melanomas, some meningiomas, and a colon carcinoma. Furthermore, immunoperoxidase analysis of the cellular distribution of the antigen recognized by BF7 and GE2 on frozen tissue sections has shown that it is present not only on tumor astrocytes, but also on reactive astrocytes in normal brain surrounding the tumor. In addition, immunocytochemistry results have shown that the antigen is present in the cytoplasm of astrocytic cells and not only on their surface as demonstrated by binding assays.

Although it has been shown by binding inhibition that BF7 and GE2 recognize two different antigenic determinants, the immunoprecipitation of radiolabeled cell lysate demonstrated that both monoclonal antibodies reacted with a similar if not identical polypeptide chain with an apparent molecular weight of 48,000. The question then arises as to why these two monoclonal antibodies have different binding activities on many of the individual glioma cell lines tested, GE2 being usually more active than BF7. A possible explanation is that the determinant recognized by BF7 may be situated deeper in the cell membrane than the one recognized by GE2 and is therefore less accessible to the antibodies. The cellular distribution and molecular weight of this molecule are very similar to those of glial fibrillary acidic protein (GFAP). It seems, however, unlikely that the 48-kilodalton protein immunoprecipitated by GE2 and BF7 is GFAP, since the glioma cell line (C1-71) used for these experiments did not express GFAP. Furthermore, the glioma cell line (LN-18) used for immunization of the mouse that provided the lymphocytes for our fusions was also GFAP-negative.

Analysis by fluorescence-activated cell sorter of the antigen identified by GE2 and BF7 antibodies showed that it was expressed on a fraction (45-55%) of the cells from the glioma line C1-121. It will be interesting to sort and subclone such cell lines in order to determine if one can obtain stable clones with 100% reactivity with GE2 and BF7 antibodies. Furthermore, the tumorigenicity in nude mice and cell division characteristics in vitro of putative positive or negative clones should be studied.

The existence of common antigens shared by tumors derived from the neuroectoderm was further demonstrated both by monoclonal antibody CG12 raised against glioma cells and cross-reacting with melanoma cells, and a series of monoclonal antibodies raised against melanoma cells and cross-reacting with glioma cells. Absorption of antibody CG12 with melanoma cells or adult and fetal brain abolished its reactivity with glioma and neuroblastoma cells, confirming that this antibody reacted with a common antigenic determinant. Furthermore, absorption of the anti-melanoma monoclonal antibodies with glioma cells abolished their reactivity with melanoma cells, whereas absorption of the same antibodies with fetal brain homogenates did not modify their binding capacity. Similar patterns of reactivity have recently been reported by other groups working with monoclonal antibodies to melanomas (56,57,73). A special analysis of the six cross-reactive monoclonal antibodies on a panel of melanoma, glioma, and neuroblastoma cell lines suggested the existence of six different cross-reacting antigens, since each antibody had a different reactivity pattern. However, precise immunochemical studies are necessary to identify each of these antigens.

The expression on several established human glioma cell lines and on resected glioma tissue of two well-defined lymphoid differentiation antigens, HLA-DR and the common acute lymphoblastic leukemia antigen (CALLA), is of special interest. The presence of such antigens on gliomas may suggest a common embryonic origin between brain and lymphoid tissue. However, it has been shown that CALLA is also present on a number of nonlymphoid tissues (74). It should be underlined that the levels of CALLA and Ia-like antigens expressed on the different glioma lines tested showed wide variations even within a single line, as observed by fluorescence-activated cell sorter analysis, and that not all glioma lines tested expressed Ia-like antigens or CALLA. The functional role of these antigens on glioma cells is unknown. The expression of common surface antigens by brain and lymphoid tissue was first described in the mouse with the Thy-1 antigen (75). Recently Seeger et al. (76) have demonstrated with a monoclonal antibody against human Thy-1 that this antigen is present on neuroblastoma, glioma, sarcoma, teratoma cells, as well as on normal brain.

In conclusion, our results and those of other investigators show that monoclonal antibodies can identify several antigenic systems associated with human gliomas: A first class of antigens appears to be preferentially expressed by gliomas and is common to most of them. A second class of antigens is expressed by gliomas, melanomas, and neuroblastomas. These antigens appear to be linked to the neuroectodermal origin of these tumors. A third class includes antigens shared by tissues derived from the neuroectoderm and by the lymphoid system, such as HLA-DR antigens, CALLA, and Thy-1 antigens. The qualitative and quantitative expression of these antigens is highly variable among different cell lines of the same tumor type and even among the cells from a single tumor line, confirming the marked heterogeneity of glioma cells. Thus a panel of monoclonal antibodies recognizing tumor-associated as well as differentiation antigens should be tested on histological sections or cultured cells from each glioma in order to determine if any of these markers have a qualitative or quantitative correlation with the degree of malignancy. Although monoclonal antibodies have not yet defined a glioma-specific antigen, they are valuable reagents for the precise identification of subpopulations of cells present in gliomas and therefore they may help in understanding the development of tumors of the central nervous system.

REFERENCES

1. L. J. Rubinstein, in *Tumors of the Central Nervous System* (H. I. Firminger, ed.), Armed Forces Institute of Pathology, Washington, D.C., 1972, p. 7.
2. J. W. Kernohan and F. P. Sayre, in *Tumors of the Central Nervous System,* Armed Forces Institute of Pathology, Washington, D.C., 1952.
3. D. D. Bigner, S. H. Bigner, J. Ponten, B. Westermark, M. S. Mahaley, E. Ruoslahti, H. Herschman, L. F. Eng, and C. J. Wikstrand, *J. Neuropathol. Exp. Neurol. 40*:201 (1981).
4. L. F. Eng, in *Proteins of the Nervous System,* Raven Press, New York, 1980, p. 85.
5. L. F. Eng, J. J. Vanderhaegen, A. Bignami, and B. Gerstk, *Brain Res. 28*:351 (1971).
6. L. F. Eng and L. J. Rubinstein, *J. Histochem. Cytochem. 26*:513 (1978).
7. C. M. Jacque, C. Vinner, M. Kujas, M. Raoul, J. Racadot, and N. A. Baumann, *J. Neurol. Sci. 35*:147 (1978).
8. J. W. Palfreyman, D. G. T. Thomas, J. G. Ratcliffe, and D. I. Graham, *J. Neurol. Sci. 41*:101 (1979).

de Tribolet et al.

9. J. D. M. Van der Meulen, H. J. Houthoff, and E. J. Ebels, *Neuropathol. Appl. Neurobiol.* 4:177 (1978).
10. M. N. Vidard, N. Girard, C. Chauzy, B. Delpech, A. Delpech, R. Maunoury, and R. Laumonier, *C. R. Acad. Sci. D* 286:1837 (1978).
11. B. W. Moore, Biochem. *Biophys. Res. Commun.* 19:739 (1965).
12. L. F. Eng, J. L. Kosek, L. Forno, J. Deck, and J. Bigbee, *Trans. Am. Soc. Neurochem.* 7:211 (1976).
13. L. Dittmann, N. H. Axelsen, B. Norgaard-Pedersen, and E. Bock, *Br. J. Cancer* 35:135 (1977).
14. K. G. Haglid, D. Stavrou, L. Rönnbäck, C. A. Carlsson, and W. Weidenback, *J. Neurol. Sci.* 20:103 (1973).
15. F. C. Dohan, P. L. Kornblith, G. R. Wellum, S. E. Pfeiffer, and L. Levine, *Acta Neuropathol.* 40:123 (1977).
16. D. D. Bigner, D. Bullard, S. Clifford, S. H. Preissig, and C. J. Wikstrand, in *Multidisciplinary Aspects of Brain Tumor Therapy* (P. Paoletti, M. D. Walker, P. Butti, et al., eds.), Elsevier/North-Holland, Amsterdam, 1979, p.329.
17. R. Gaynor, R. Irie, D. Morton, and H. R. Herschman, *Nature* 286:400 (1980).
18. R. Gaynor, R. Irie, D. Morton, H. R. Herschman, P. Jones, and A. Cochran, *Lancet* 1:869 (1981).
19. D. Cocchia, F. Michetti, and R. Donato, *Nature* 294:85 (1981).
20. D. Warecka, H. G. Moller, H. M. Vogel, and I. Tripatzis, *J. Neurochem.* 19: 719 (1972).
21. K. Warecka, *J. Neurol. Sci.* 26:511 (1975).
22. D. D. Bigner, O. M. Pitts, and C. J. Wikstrand, *J. Neurosurg.* 55:32 (1981).
23. T. Wahlström, E. Linder, E. Saksela, and B. Westermark, *Cancer* 34:272 (1974).
24. M. H. Hitchcock, A. C. Hollinshead, P. Chretien, and H. V. Rizzoli, *Cancer* 40:660 (1977).
25. N. L. Levy, *J. Immunol.* 121:903 (1978).
26 K. M. A. Sheikh, M. L. J. Apuzzo, and M. H. Weiss, *Cancer Res.* 39:1733 (1979).
27. P. Trouillas, *Lancet* 2:552 (1971).
28. P. Trouillas, *Ann. Inst. Pasteur. Lille* 122:819 (1972).
29. C. Solheid, G. Lauro, and G. Palladini, *J. Neurol. Sci.* 30:55 (1976).
30. K. M. A. Sheikh, M. L. J. Apuzzo, K. R. Kochsiek, and M. H. Weiss, *Yale J. Biol. Med.* 50:397 (1977).
31. M. Pfreundschuh, H. Shick, T. Takahashi, R. Ueda, J. Ransohoff, H. F. Oettgen, and L. J. Old, *Proc. Nat. Acad. Sci. U.S.A.* 75:5122 (1978).
32. H. B. Coakham, P. L. Kornblith, E. A. Quindlen, L. A. Pollock, W. C. Wood, and L. C. Hartnett, *J. Nat. Cancer Inst.* 64:223 (1980).
33. R. F. Irie, K. Irie, and D. L. Morton, *Cancer Res.* 36:3510 (1976).
34. P. L. Kornblith, F. C. Dohan, W. Wood, and B. O. Whitman, *Cancer* 33:1512 (1974).
35. R. E. Woosley, S. Mahaley, J. L. Mahaley, G. M. Miller, and W. H. Brooks, *J. Neurosurg.* 47:871 (1977).

36. A. Martin-Achard, A. C. Diserens, N. de Tribolet, and S. Carrel, *Int. J. Cancer 25*:219 (1980).
37. J. H. Siris, *Bull. Neurol. N.Y. 4*:597 (1936).
38. M. S. Mahaley and E. D. Day, *J. Neurosurg. 23*:363 (1965).
39. H. B. Coakham, *Nature 250*:328 (1974).
40. H. B. Coakham and M. S. Lakshmi, *Oncology 31*:233 (1975).
41. I. R. Kehayov, *Ann. Immunol. 127*:703 (1976).
42. E. Miyake and K. Kitamura, *Acta Neuropathol. 37*:27 (1977).
43. W. K. Hass, *Arch. Neurol. 14*:443 (1966).
44. B. Delpech, A. Delpech, J. Clement, and R. Laumonier, *Int. J. Cancer 9*: 374 (1972).
45. C. J. Wikstrand, M. S. Mahaley, and D. D. Bigner, *Cancer Res. 37*:4267 (1977).
46. C. J. Wikstrand and D. D. Bigner, *Cancer Res. 39*:3235 (1979).
47. J. F. Schnegg, N. de Tribolet, A. C. Diserens, A. Martin-Achard, and S. Carrel, *Int. J. Cancer 28*:265 (1981).
48. J. F. Schnegg, A. C. Diserens, S. Carrel, R. S. Accolla, and N. de Tribolet, *Cancer Res. 41*:1209 (1981).
49. K. Sikora and J. Phillips, *Br. J. Cancer 43*:105 (1981).
50. K. Sikora, T. Alderson, J. Phillips, and J. V. Watson, *Lancet 1*:11 (1982).
51. W. W. Peng, J. P. Bressler, E. Tiffany-Castiglioni, and J. De Vellis, *Science 215*:1102 (1982).
52. S. Carrel and L. Theilkaes, *Nature 242*:609 (1973).
53. R. H. Kennett and F. Gilbert, *Science 203*:1120 (1979).
54. S. Carrel, R. S. Accolla, A. L. Carmagnola, and J. P. Mach, *Cancer Res. 40*: 2523 (1980).
55. S. Carrel, N. de Tribolet, and J. P. Mach, *Acta Neuropathol. 57*:158 (1982).
56. M. Herlyn, W. H. Clark, M. J. Mastrangelo, G. Du Pont, D. E. Elder, D. La Rossa, R. Hamilton, E. Bondi, R. Tuthill, Z. Steplewski, and H. Koprowski, *Cancer Res. 40*:3602 (1980).
57. R. C. Seeger, H. M. Rosenblatt, K. Imai, and S. Ferrone, *Cancer Res. 41*:2714 (1981).
58. C. J. Wikstrand and D. D. Bigner, *Cancer Res. 42*:267 (1982).
59. A. C. Diserens, N. de Tribolet, A. A. Martin, A. C. Gaide, J. F. Schnegg, and S. Carrel, *Acta Neuropathol. 53*:21 (1981).
60. A. F. Williams, *Mol. Immunol. 6*:93 (1977).
61. R. S. Accolla, S. Carrel, and J. P. Mach, *Proc. Nat. Acad. Sci. U.S.A. 77*:563 (1980).
62. C. B. Lozzio and B. B. Lozzio, *Blood 45*:321 (1975).
63. S. Carrel, N. Gross, D. Heumann, and J. P. Mach, *Transplantation 27*:431 (1979).
64. L. Zardi, B. Carnemolla, A. Siri, L. Santi, and R. S. Accolla, *Int. J. Cancer 25*:325 (1980).
65. J. L. Guesdin, T. H. Ternynck, and A. Stratis, *J. Histochem. Cytochem. 27*: 1131 (1979).

66. S. Carrel, R. Tosi, N. Gross, N. Tanigaki, A. L. Carmagnola, and R. S. Accolla, *Mol. Immunol. 18*:403 (1981).

67. J. Minowada, T. Tsubota, M. F. Greaves, and T. R. Walters, *J. Nat. Cancer Inst. 59*:83 (1977).

68. S. Carrel, N. de Tribolet, and N. Gross, *Eur. J. Immunol. 12*:354 (1982).

69. S. Carrel, N. Gross, and J. P. Mach, *Cancer Res. 39*:5171 (1979).

70. A. Böyum, *Scand. J. Clin. Lab. Invest. 21*:77 (1968).

71. N. Gross and C. Bron, *Eur. J. Immunol. 10*:417 (1980).

72. S. Carrel, N. Gross, D. Heumann, R. P. Sekaly, A. Morell, and V. von Fliedner, in *Leukemia Markers* (W. Knapp, ed.), Academic, London, 1981, p. 56.

73. S. K. Liao, B. J. Clarke, P. C. Kwong, A. Brickenden, B. L. Gallie, and P. B. Dent, *Eur. J. Immunol. 11*:450 (1981).

74. R. S. Metzgar, M. J. Borowitz, N. H. Jones, and L. B. Dowell, *J. Exp. Med. 154*:1249 (1981).

75. A. E. Reif and J. M. V. Allen, *J. Exp. Med. 120*:413 (1964).

76. R. C. Seeger, Y. L. Danon, S. A. Rayner, and F. Hoover, *J. Immunol. 128*: 983 (1982).

5 POTENTIAL DIAGNOSTIC AND PROGNOSTIC APPLICATIONS OF MONOCLONAL ANTIBODIES TO HUMAN MAMMARY CARCINOMAS

David Colcher, Patricia Horan Hand, David Wunderlich, Marianna Nuti, Yoshio A. Teramoto, Donald Kufe,* and Jeffrey Schlom / Laboratory of Tumor Immunology and Biology, National Cancer Institute, National Institutes of Health, Bethesda, Maryland

INTRODUCTION

Numerous investigators have reported the existence of human mammary tumor-associated antigens (1-9). These studies, all conducted with conventional hyper-immune polyclonal sera, however, were hampered with regard to the heterogeneity of the antibody populations employed and the amount of specific immunoglobulin that could be generated. Since the advent of hybridoma technology, monoclonal antibodies of predefined specificity and virtually unlimited quantity, can now be generated against a variety of antigenic determinants present on normal and/or neoplastic cells.

---

* Also affiliated with Dana-Farber Cancer Institute, Boston, Massachusetts.

Monoclonal antibodies reactive with human mammary tissue have been generated by a number of laboratories using a variety of immunogens. Several groups have generated monoclonal antibodies against human milk fat globule membranes (10-14). These antibodies react strongly with lactating breast tissues and to a lesser extent with normal resting breast. Monoclonal antibodies have also been generated to estrogen receptors from the MCF-7 human breast tumor cell line (15). These antibodies bind to a variety of estrogen receptors, including those purified from monkey endometrium, and they can be used to detect estrogen receptor-positive human mammary tumors by immunofluorescence of frozen sections and immunoperoxidase of fixed sections. Human mammary tumor cell lines have been used as immunogens by several laboratories (16-18). The antibody generated against the ZR-75-1 cell line reacts with approximately half of the malignant mammary tumors tested and to over 80% of the benign mammary tumors tested (18). Monoclonal antibodies have also been generated against human breast fibroblasts with some reported reactivity to the MCF-7 cell line (19).

Studies previously reported from our laboratory have demonstrated that lymphocytes, obtained from lymph nodes of mastectomy patients, may be fused with murine non-immunoglobulin-secreting myeloma cells to generate human-mouse hybridomas secreting human monoclonal antibodies (20,21). One of these monoclonals (22) has been shown to be selectively reactive with human breast carcinoma and selected nonbreast carcinoma cells, but it is of the IgM isotype. Further studies to generate human monoclonals of the IgG isotype are in progress.

A number of laboratories have also generated monoclonal antibodies to a variety of tumors that cross-react with breast tumors. Antibodies prepared using melanomas (23-25), lung carcinomas (26,27), renal carcinomas (28), and prostate carcinomas (29) as immunogens bind to a variety of breast tumor cell lines or sections of breast tumors. Antibodies to antigens found on normal human cells have shown reactivity with human breast carcinomas (30).

The rationale of the studies overviewed here was to utilize membrane-enriched extracts of human metastatic mammary tumor cells as immunogens in an attempt to generate and characterize monoclonal antibodies reactive with determinants that would be maintained on metastatic, as well as primary, human mammary carcinoma cells. Multiple assays using tumor cell extracts, tissue sections, and live cells in culture have been employed to reveal the diversity of the monoclonal antibodies generated (31-36).

RESULTS AND DISCUSSION

Generation of Monoclonal Antibodies

Mice were immunized with membrane-enriched fractions of human metastatic mammary carcinoma cells from either of two involved livers (designated Met-1

Table 1 Reactivity of Monoclonal Antibodies in Solid-Phase RIAs

Monoclonal antibody	Isotype	Cell extracts[a]			Live cells[b]				
					Mammary carcinoma			Melanoma, sarcoma[c]	Normal[d]
		Met-1	Met-2	Liver	BT-20	MCF-7	ZR-75-1		
B6.2	IgG_1	+++	++	-	++	+++	++	-	-
B14.2	IgG_1	+++	++	-	+	++	+	-	-
B39.1	IgG_1	+++	++	-	++	++	++	-	-
F64.5	IgG_{2a}	+++	++	-	++	++	+	-	-
F25.2	IgG_1	+++	++	-	+	+	+	-	-
B84.1	IgG_1	+++	++	-	+	+	+	-	-
B50.4	IgG_1	++	+	-	-	+	-	-	-
B50.1	IgG_1	++	+	-	-	+	-	-	-
B25.2	IgM	-	+++	-	-	-	-	-	-
B72.3	IgG_1	+++	-	-	-	+	-	-	-
B38.1	IgG_1	+	+	-	+++	++	+++	-	-
W6/32	IgG_{2a}	-	-	-	+	+	-	++	++
B139	IgG_1	+++	++	++	++	++	++	++	++

[a]Solid-phase RIAs (-, <500; +, 500-2000 cpm; ++, 2001-5000 cpm; +++, >5000 cpm).
[b]The live cell immunoassay was performed on human cells (-, <300 cpm; +, 300-1000 cpm; ++, 1001-2000 cpm; +++, >2000 cpm).
[c]Rhabdomyosarcoma (A204), fibrosarcoma (HT-1080), and melanoma (A375, A101D, A875, A3875).
[d]Human cell lines were derived from apparently normal breast (HSo584Bst, HSo578Bst), embryonic skin (D550, D551), fetal lung (WI-38, MRC-5), fetal testis (HSo181Tes), fetal thymus (HSo208Th), fetal bone marrow (HSo074BM), embryonic kidney (Flow-4000), fetal spleen (HSo203Sp), and uterus (HSo769Ut).

and Met-2) of two different patients. Spleens of immunized mice were fused with non-immunoglobulin-secreting NS-1 murine myeloma cells to generate 4250 primary hybridoma cultures. All hybridoma methodology and assay methods employed have been described previously (37,38). Supernatant fluids from hybridoma cultures were first screened in solid-phase radioimmunoassays (RIAs) for the presence of immunoglobulin reactive with extracts of metastatic mammary tumor cells from involved livers and not reactive with extracts of apparently normal human liver. Following passage and double-cloning by endpoint dilution of cultures secreting immunoglobulins demonstrating preferential reactivity with breast carcinoma cells, the monoclonal antibodies from 11 hybridoma cell lines were chosen for further study. The isotypes of all 11 antibodies were determined; 10 were IgG of various subclasses and 1 was an IgM (Table 1).

The 11 monoclonal antibodies could immediately be divided into three major groups based on their differential reactivity to Met-1 versus Met-2 in solid-phase RIA (Fig. 1). It is interesting to note that the immunogen used in the generation of monoclonal B72.3 was Met-1, while the immunogen used for the generation of monoclonal B25.2 was Met-2. All 11 antibodies were negative when tested against similar extracts from normal human liver, a rhabdomyosarcoma cell line, the HBL100 cell line derived from cultures of human milk, mouse mammary tumor and fibroblast cell lines, disrupted mouse mammary tumor virus and mouse leukemia virus, purified carcinoembryonic antigen (CEA), and ferritin. Two monoclonal antibodies were used as positive controls in all these studies: (a) W6/32, an anti-human histocompatibility antigen (39), and (b) B139, which was generated against a human breast tumor metastasis but which showed reactivity to all human cells tested (Table 1).

To determine if the monoclonals bind cell-surface determinants, each antibody was tested for binding to live cells in culture, that is, established cell lines of human mammary carcinomas. The nine monoclonals grouped together on the basis of their binding to both metastatic cell extracts could be further separated into three different groups on the basis of their differential binding to cell-surface determinants (Table 1). Some of the monoclonals bound to the surface of selected nonbreast carcinoma cell lines. None of the 11 monoclonal antibodies, however, bound to the surface of sarcoma or melanoma cell lines, or to the surface of a variety of cell lines derived from apparently normal human tissues (Table 1). Control monoclonals W6/32 or B139, however, did bind all of these cells (Table 1).

Monoclonal antibody B6.2 was further analyzed by Kufe et al. (40) for surface binding to a panel of human cell lines using fluorescence-activated cell sorter analyses. Antibody B6.2 was reactive with five of six breast carcinoma cell lines, but was unreactive with most other carcinomas. Cell lines derived from melanomas, sarcomas, and lymphoid tumors were uniformly unreactive. There

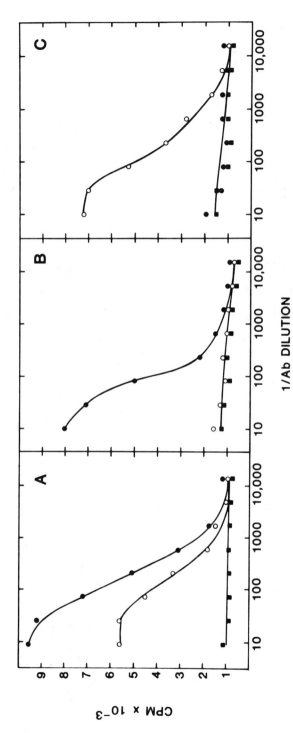

Figure 1 Reactivity of monoclonal antibodies with extracts of metastatic breast tumors to the liver, and normal liver, in solid-phase RIA: (A) Monoclonal B6.2, (B) monoclonal B72.3, (C) monoclonal B25.2 (metastases from patients 1, ●, and 2, ○, and normal liver, ■).

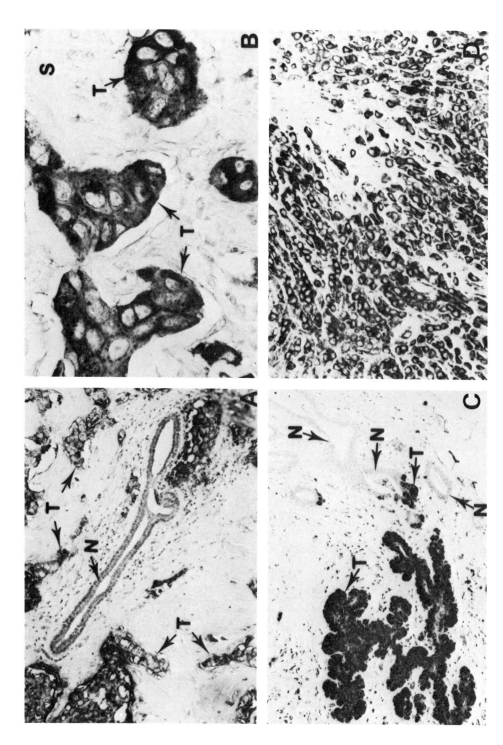

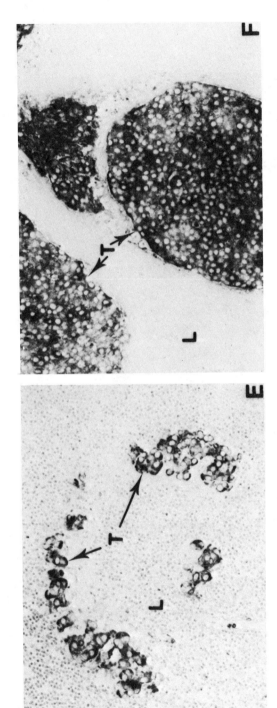

Figure 2 Immunoperoxidase staining of fixed tissue sections of primary and metastatic mammary carcinomas with monoclonal antibody B6.2. (A) Infiltrating duct carcinoma. At the center of the field is a negative normal duct (N) surrounded by positively stained tumor cells (T) (X 130). (B) Higher magnification of tumor cells (T) and stroma (S) from same tissue section shown in (A) (X 540). (C) Cancerization of a mammary lobule. Note the positively stained tumor cells (T) and the unstained normal mammary cells (N) (X 130). (D) Infiltrating lobular carcinoma (X 220). (E) Breast tumor metastasis of the lymph node: tumor cells (T) and lymphocytes (L) (X 220). (F) Breast tumor metastasis of the lymph node from another patient: tumor cells (T) and lymphocytes (L) (X 220).

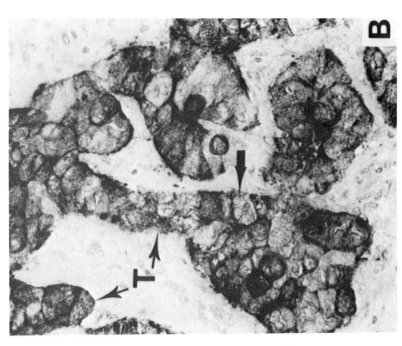

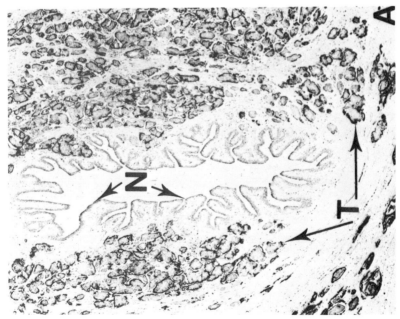

Figure 3 Immunoperoxidase staining of fixed tissue sections of primary and metastatic mammary carcinomas of four different patients with monoclonal antibody B72.3. (A) Infiltrating duct carcinoma. At the center of the field is a large, negative normal duct (N) surrounded by positively stained infiltrating tumor cells (T) (X 54). (B) Infiltrating duct carcinoma. Note the intense membrane and faint cytoplasmic staining of the tumor cells (T). The broad arrow indicates a negative tumor cell flanked by positive tumor cells (X 540). (C) In situ element (T) of an infiltrating duct carcinoma. Note the stroma and lymphocytes (L), which are negative (X 130). (D) Breast tumor metastasis in the pleura. This is an example of the focal pattern of staining: Intense stain is concentrated in the cytoplasm of tumor cells (T); the stroma (S) is negative (X 330).

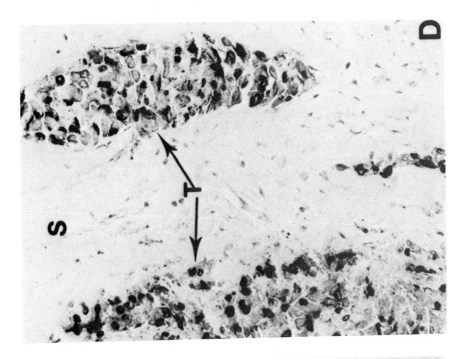

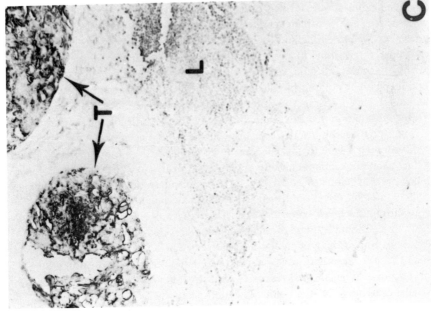

was complete agreement in assay results when the same cell lines were tested in live cell RIA and by cell sorter analysis. A variety of tissues obtained directly from biopsy were also evaluated via fluorescence-activated cell sorter analyses. Breast carcinoma cells were examined from patients with malignant pleural effusions. Tumor cells from three of six patients were positive with B6.2. Single cell suspensions derived from normal lymphoid tissue including bone marrow, lymph node, spleen, and tonsil demonstrated no reactivity.

To further define the specificity and range of reactivity of each of the 11 monoclonal antibodies, the immunoperoxidase technique was employed on tissue sections. All the monoclonals reacted with mammary carcinoma cells of primary mammary carcinomas, both infiltrating ductal (Fig. 2A,B) and lobular Fig. 2D). Formalin-fixed and frozen section tissue preparations gave comparable results. The percentage of primary mammary tumors that were reactive varied for the different monoclonals; this point will be discussed in detail later on. In many of the positive primary and metastatic mammary carcinomas, not all tumor cells stained. In certain tumor masses, furthermore, heterogeneity of tumor cell staining was observed in different areas of a tumor, and even within a given area, as will be discussed in detail below. A high degree of selective reactivity with mammary tumor cells, and not with apparently normal mammary epithelium, stroma, blood vessels, or lymphocytes of the breast, was also observed. This is exemplified with monoclonals B6.2 in Figure 2A and C. A dark reddish-brown stain (the result of the immunoperoxidase reaction with the diaminobenzidine substrate) was observed only on mammary carcinoma cells, whereas only the light-blue hematoxylin counterstain was observed on adjacent normal mammary epithelium, stroma, and lymphocytes. Occasionally a few of the apparently normal mammary epithelial cells immediately adjacent to the mammary tumor did stain weakly with the same pattern of staining seen in the tumor cells. The polymorphonuclear leukocytes and histiocytes in the stroma within the area of mammary tumor also showed positive cytoplasmic staining. This would suggest that this reactivity may be due to antigen shed by the tumor and phagocytized by reactive cells in the immediate proximity.

Experiments were then carried out to determine if the 11 monoclonals could detect mammary carcinoma cell populations at distal sites, that is, in metastases. Since the monoclonals were all generated using metastatic mammary carcinoma cells as antigens, it was not unexpected that the monoclonals all reacted, but with different degrees, to various metastases (Figs. 2E,F and 3D). As exemplified in Fig. 2E and F, none of the monoclonals reacted with normal lymphocytes or stroma from any involved or uninvolved nodes. The monoclonals were then tested for reactivity to normal and neoplastic nonmammary tissues. Some of the monoclonals showed reactivity with selected nonbreast carcinomas such as adenocarcinoma of the colon. These observations are currently being extended. Other neoplasms tested, which showed no staining, were sarcomas, lymphomas, glioblastomas, and melanomas. All 11 monoclonals were negative for cellular reactivity with apparently normal tissues of the following organs: thyroid, intestine, kidney, liver, bladder, tonsils, and prostate.

A factor in the potential utility of any monoclonal antibody is its selective reactivity. The immunoperoxidase method of staining of fixed tissue sections with antibody has the advantage of screening large amounts of tissues in a relatively short period of time. Moreover, it permits the testing of antibody reactivity with tissues that would otherwise be inaccessible. For example, to date there are no cell lines available from in situ breast carcinoma. A major drawback of using fixed tissue sections in the immunoperoxidase technique, however, is that this procedure makes it extremely difficult to define cell-surface reactivities; one must therefore employ techniques using live cells to determine surface binding. One example of this is the observation that antibody B6.2 has shown some reactivity with subpopulations of polymorphonuclear leukocytes in fixed tissue sections of spleens of some patients using the immunoperoxidase technique. Antibody B6.2, however, has shown no binding to the surface of unfixed bone marrow, spleen, lymph node, and tonsil cell preparations from a variety of patients using fluorescence-activated cell sorter analyses (40). This antibody is unreactive with the surface of all normal cells tested thus far. Since it is cell-surface binding that is of clinical importance, one must distinguish between potential reactivity of an antibody with a cross-reactive internal antigen, and cell-surface binding.

Of the 11 monoclonals described above, B72.3 (an IgG_1) displayed the most restricted range of reactivity for human mammary tumor versus normal cells. Monoclonal B72.3 was used at various concentrations in immunoperoxidase assays of tissue sections to determine the effect of antibody dose on the staining intensity and the percentage of tumor cells stained. Since one cannot titrate antigen in the fixed tissue section, an antibody dilution experiment was performed to give an indication of the relative titer of reactive antigen within a given tissue. A range of antibody concentrations, varying from 0.02 to 10 μg of purified immunoglobulin (per 200 μl) per tissue section, was used on each of four mammary carcinomas from different patients. The results (Table 2) demonstrate that (a) different mammary tumors may vary in the amount of the antigen detected by B72.3, (b) a given mammary tumor may contain tumor cell populations that vary in antigen density, and (c) some mammary tumors may score positive or negative, depending on the dose of antibody employed.

To further characterize the range of reactivity of B72.3, the immunoperoxidase technique was used to test a variety of malignant, benign, and normal mammary tissues. Using 4 μg of monoclonal per slide, the percentage of positive primary breast tumors was 46% (19/41); 62% (13/21) of the metastatic lesions scored positive. Several histological types of primary mammary tumors scored positive: these were infiltrating duct (Fig. 3A,B), infiltrating lobular, and

Table 2 Dose of Monoclonal Antibody B72.3 versus Reactivity of Human Mammary Carcinoma Cells in Immunoperoxidase Assay

Micrograms of B72.3[b]	Tumor staining intensity[a] (% reactive tumor cells)			
	Tumor 1	Tumor 2	Tumor 3	Tumor 4
10	1+(90) 2+(10)	3+(100)	3+(80)	—
4	1+(5)	2+(100)	3+(80)	—
2	—	1+(80)	3+(70)	—
1	—	—	3+(70)	—
0.2	—	—	2+(50)	—
0.02	—	—	2+(30)	—

[a]Staining intensity: 1+, weak; 2+, moderate; 3+, strong.
[b]Here 0.02 μg of B72.3 is equivalent to a 1:100,000 dilution of B72.3 produced in mouse ascites fluid.

comedo carcinomas. Many of the in situ elements present in the above lesions also stained (Fig. 3C). None of the six medullary carcinomas tested were positive. Approximately 66% of the tumors that showed a positive reactivity demonstrated a cell-associated membrane and/or diffuse cytoplasmic staining (Fig. 3B), approximately 5% showed discrete focal staining of the cytoplasm (Fig. 3D), and approximately 25% of the reactive tumors showed an apical or marginal staining pattern. Metastatic breast carcinoma lesions that were positive were in axillary lymph nodes and at the distal sites of skin, liver, lung, pleura (Fig. 3D), and mesentery. A total of 15 benign breast lesions were also tested; these included fibrocystic disease, fibroadenomas, and sclerosing adenosis. Two specimens showed positive staining: one case of fibrocystic disease where a few cells in some ducts were faintly positive and a case of intraductal papillomatosis and sclerosing adenosis, with the majority of cells staining strongly. Monoclonal B72.3 was also tested against normal breast tissue and normal lactating breast from noncancer patients and showed no reactivity. A variety of nonbreast cells and tissues were tested and were negative; these included two uteri, two livers, two spleens, three lungs, two bone marrows, five colons, one stomach, one salivary gland, five lymph nodes, and one kidney.

Differential Binding to Human Mammary and Nonmammary Tumors of Monoclonal Antibodies Reactive with Carcinoembryonic Antigen

The presence of high plasma levels of CEA (41) has been reported to be an indicator of the possible presence of metastatic disease in patients with cancers of the digestive system, breast, lung, as well as other sites (42-44). Using assays based on antibodies to colonic CEA, elevated plasma levels of CEA (above 2.5 ng/ml) have been reported in 38-79% of patients with mammary carcinomas (42,45-51). There have been several reports (52-56), however, indicating that "CEA" is a heterogeneous family of glycoproteins, some of which demonstrate cross-reactivity with each other as well as with so called "CEA-related" proteins. One issue that has not yet been clearly resolved is the possibility that different tumor cell types may produce, or maintain on their cell surface, a CEA that is only partially related to CEAs associated with other malignancies. Monoclonal antibodies should be a valuable reagent toward resolving this point. To date, several monoclonal antibodies have been generated and characterized using CEA from colon carcinomas as the immunogen (57-62). In the studies reported here, monoclonal antibodies were generated to membrane-enriched fractions of human mammary carcinoma metastases and screened for reactivity with purified CEA. The differential binding properties of two of these antibodies (B1.1 and F5.5) to CEA and to breast and nonbreast tumors was investigated. Monoclonal B1.1 is an IgG_{2a}, while F5.5 is an IgG_1.

Both B1.1 and F5.5 precipitated iodinated CEA, resulting in a radiolabeled peak at approximately 180,000 daltons. No precipitation of purified CEA was obtained using monoclonal antibody B6.2 or with any of the monoclonals described above. Cross-reactivities have been reported (63) between determinants on CEA and an antigen expressed in normal spleens termed normal cross-reacting antigen. Monoclonals B1.1 and F5.5 did not react, however, with a normal spleen extract rich in normal cross-reacting antigen. Purified immunoglobulin preparations of monoclonals B1.1 and F5.5 were then titered for binding to five CEAs purified from five different patients with colon cancer. As can be seen in Figure 4, significant binding was observed with both antibodies to all five CEAs. Monoclonals B1.1 and F5.5 are clearly reactive with different epitopes on the CEA molecule, however, as evidenced by their differential binding to the various CEA preparations. Specifically, monoclonal F5.5 reacted similarly with all five CEA preparations, whereas B1.1 exhibited preferential binding to different CEA preparations. Monoclonals B1.1 and F5.5 were tested for binding to live cells in culture to further define their range of reactivities and to ascertain if they bind to antigenic determinants that are present on the cell surface. As seen in Table 3, both monoclonals bound to the same three of six established human mammary carcinoma cell lines and to the two colon carcinoma cell lines, but not to the lung carcinoma or vulva carcinoma cell lines. No surface binding was observed with either antibody to normal breast cell lines or to a variety of cell lines derived from apparently normal human tissues (Table 3). The two monoclonals could be distinguished, however, by their differential reactivity to the surface of melanoma cell lines. B1.1 bound to three of four melanoma cell lines tested, while F5.5 did not bind to any of the four (Table 3). Reactivity with B1.1 was

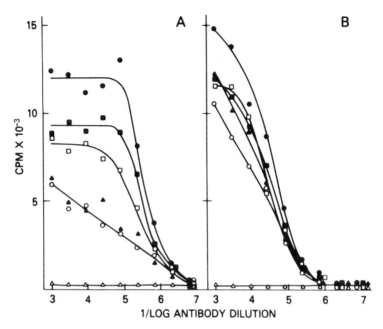

Figure 4 Titration of monoclonal antibodies B1.1 and F5.5 against five preparations of CEA from different patients. A total of 30 ng of purified CEA from five
different patients were utilized in a solid-phase RIA: CEA DH3B (●), CEA
BP160 (○), CEA DH2-3 (■), CEA HCA3B (□), CEA JFII (▲), bovine serum albumin (△). Ascitic fluid from mice containing monoclonal antibodies (A) B1.1 or
(B) F5.5 were titered against the different CEAs in a solid-phase RIA as described (34).

repeatedly observed with late passages (greater than passage 80) of the A204
rhabdomyosarcoma cell line (Table 3). These findings are further substantiated
by a comparative titration of monoclonals B1.1 and F5.5 against breast carcinoma, colon carcinoma, and melanoma cell lines. As seen in Figure 5A, B1.1
binds the melanoma, colon, and breast tumor cell lines comparably. There is a
clear preferential binding of monoclonal F5.5, however, with the mammary
tumor line as compared to the colon tumor or melanoma cell lines (Fig. 5B).

To further identify the range of reactivities of monoclonals B1.1 and F5.5
with human mammary carcinomas, the immunoperoxidase technique was used
on formalin-fixed tumor sections. Positive staining with both B1.1 and F5.5 was
observed with three colon carcinomas and three lung carcinomas. Monoclonals
F5.5 and B1.1 reacted positively with 55 and 66%, respectively, of the mammary carcinomas tested. The positive mammary tumors included infiltrating

Table 3 Reactivity of Monoclonal Antibodies in Live Cell RIAs[a]

Cell type	Cell line	B1.1	F5.5	B139[b]
Mammary carcinoma	MCF-7	2391	2239	1343
	ZR-75-1	1350	1331	605
	BT-20	1899	1563	1818
	MDA-MB-231	–	–	2800
	ZR-75-31A	–	–	3219
	T47D	–	–	2501
Carcinoma				
Colon	WIDR	1959	506	2110
Colon	HT-29	2683	1463	2646
Lung	A549	–	–	3060
Vulva	A431	–	–	2250
Melanoma	A3827	2840	–	3780
	A101D	1453	–	4482
	A875	876	–	3747
	A375	–	–	4813
Sarcoma				
Rhabdomyosarcoma	A204,P18-79[c]	–	–	4456
	A204,P80-90[c]	1024	–	4673
Fibrosarcoma	HT-1080	–	–	3688
Normal				
Breast	HSo584Bst	–	–	1481
Breast	HSo578Bst	–	–	1360
Embryonic skin	D550	–	–	2100
Embryonic skin	D551	–	–	2296
Embryonic kidney	Flow-4000	–	–	2256
Fetal lung	MRC-5	–	–	3210
Fetal lung	WI-38	–	–	2331
Fetal testis	HSo181Tes	–	–	2298
Fetal thymus	HSo208Th	–	–	3391
Fetal bone marrow	HSo074BM	–	–	1062
Fetal spleen	HSo203Sp	–	–	2500
Fetal kidney	HSo807K	–	–	3682
Uterus	HSo769Ut	–	–	1647

[a]Live cell immunoassays were performed as described (31). The minus sign indicates less than 300 cpm above background (approximately 200 cpm).
[b]B139 is a monoclonal antibody that binds to all human cell lines tested.
[c]At different passage (P) levels within our laboratory the reactivity with B1.1 was altered. At passage levels below 80, B1.1 was negative; at passage levels above 80, there was significant binding of B1.1.

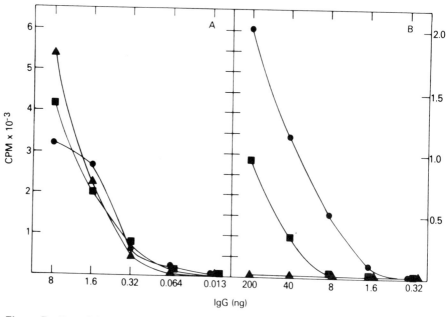

Figure 5 Reactivity of monoclonal antibodies B1.1 and F5.5 in live cell RIA. Increasing amounts of purified IgG of (A) B1.1 and (B) F5.5 were reacted in a live cell RIA with 5 × 10⁴ cells of the following established human cell lines: MCF-7, mammary adenocarcinoma (●); HT-29, colon adenocarcinoma (■); and A3827, melanoma (▲).

ductal, in situ, and medullary carcinomas. Monoclonals B1.1 and F5.5 also reacted positively with metastatic mammary tumor cells in lymph nodes and at distal sites.

It is anticipated that studies can now be undertaken to determine if the presence, intensity, or cellular localization of these reactions, using either or both of these monoclonals with tissue sections of primary breast lesions, is of any prognostic value. A previous study (64), performed using heterologous antisera and small cell carcinomas of the lung, has indicated that CEA reactivity of tissue sections may have prognostic significance. Since radiolabeled immunoglobulin preparations of heterologous sera to CEA (derived from colon carcinoma) have already been used (65,66) for binding metastatic breast carcinoma lesions in situ, appropriately labeled immunoglobulin or antibody fragment preparations of monoclonals F5.5 and B1.1 may also eventually prove useful toward this end.

Identification and Purification of Mammary Tumor-Associated Antigens

As a first step in the identification of the best source of antigens reactive with the monoclonal antibodies described, monoclonal antibodies were screened by solid-phase RIA for reactivity with a variety of mammary tumor extracts, including primary and metastatic tumors and established cell lines. Monoclonals B1.1 and B6.2 reacted similarly with tissue extracts and extracts of cell lines. Antibody B72.3, however, showed very strong reactivity with some human tumor extracts, but reacted poorly with mammary tumor cell lines. Two breast tumor metastases to the liver were chosen as the prime sources for antigen identification and purification on the basis of their broad immunoreactivity to all the monoclonal antibodies and the quantity of tumor tissue available.

Immunoprecipitation studies were initiated to determine the molecular weights of the tumor-associated antigens (TAAs) reactive with the monoclonal antibodies described. Purified CEA was iodinated and was used as antigen source for the binding of B1.1 and F5.5. Sodium dodecyl sulfate-polyacrylamide gel electrophoresis (SDS-PAGE) of the immunoprecipitates showed that the polypeptide precipitated by both monoclonal antibodies is a heterogeneous protein with an average molecular weight of 180,000. An extract of a breast tumor metastasis to the liver was used as the antigen source for the other monoclonal antibodies described. Initial attempts to identify the various reactive antigens in radioiodinated extracts of the metastasis were unsuccessful. The limiting factor appeared to be either an inability to label the desired antigen and/or an inability to detect an antigen that may constitute a very small percentage of the total tumor mass. To determine which hypothesis was correct, experiments were undertaken to determine if CEA could be immunoprecipitated in "CEA-spiked" extracts of the mammary tumor metastasis. Purified CEA was iodinated and added to an extract of the breast tumor metastasis at a final concentration of 0.2%; monoclonal antibody B1.1 was able to precipitate the CEA in this extract. However, a similar amount of unlabeled CEA added to the extract prior to labeling was not detected by similar immunoprecipitation procedures. It appeared, therefore, that there was a preferential labeling of proteins other than CEA in this extract. In order to overcome this problem, experiments were undertaken to increase the relative antigen concentration by partial purification of the extract. The metastatic liver extract was detergent disrupted and separated using molecular sieving on Ultrogel AcA34. The column fractions were assayed for reactivity with monoclonals B1.1, B6.2, and B72.3 by solid-phase RIA (Fig. 6). The appropriate immunoreactive fractions were then pooled and labeled with [125]I. SDS-PAGE analyses of the immunoprecipitates generated are seen in Figure 7. Monoclonal antibody B72.3 immunoprecipitated a complex of four bands with

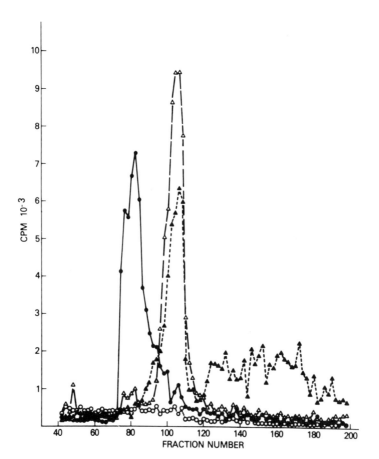

Figure 6 Gel filtration of an extract of a breast tumor on Ultrogel AcA34.
Immunoreactivity of fractions was determined in a solid-phase RIA: B72.3
(●), B6.2 (△), B1.1 (▲), phosphate-buffered saline (○).

estimated molecular weights of approximately 220,000, 250,000, 285,000, and
340,000; B1.1 immunoprecipitated a heterogeneous component with an average
estimated molecular weight of 180,000; and B6.2 immunoprecipitated a 90,000
dalton component, as did several other monoclonal antibodies.

Extracts of a breast tumor metastasis to the liver, normal liver, and the MCF-
7 breast tumor cell line were disrupted and run on an SDS-polyacrylamide gel.
The polypeptides were electrophoretically transferred to nitrocellulose filters,
and the filters were incubated with IgG from B1.1, B6.2, or B72.3. The filters
were washed, and the remaining antibodies were detected with rabbit anti-

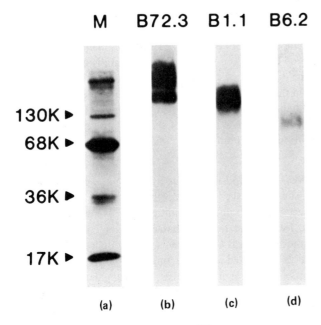

Figure 7 Immunoprecipitation of [125I]-labeled partially purified extract of a human breast tumor: lane a, molecular weight markers (M); lanes b-d, immunoprecipitation by monoclonal antibodies B72.3, B1.1, and B6.2, respectively.

murine IgG and [125I] protein A. Antibody B72.3 bound to a high molecular weight complex of approximately 220-400 kilodaltons in the extract from the metastasis, B1.1 bound to a 180,000-dalton polypeptide, and B6.2 bound to a 90,000-dalton polypeptide in extracts of both the breast tumor metastasis and the MCF-7 cell line. These data demonstrate that the immunoreactivity of the antigenic determinants is not destroyed by SDS and mercaptoethanol, and that molecular weights of the polypeptides in the crude extracts are consistent with those obtained by the immunoprecipitations from semipurified extracts as described above.

Five of the monoclonal antibodies, including B6.2, were reactive with an antigen of approximately 90,000 daltons. To determine whether these antibodies reacted with the same determinants, a competitive binding assay was established. Purified monoclonal antibody B6.2 was labeled with [125I]. Increasing amounts of unlabeled monoclonal antibodies were added to a breast tumor extract followed by the addition of [125I]-labeled B6.2 IgG. As little as 10 ng of B6.2 IgG was able to inhibit the binding of the labeled antibody by greater than 90%. Various degrees of competition were also observed with other antibodies (B39.1, B14.2, B50.4, F25.2, B84.1). The ability of some of these monoclonal antibodies to compete for the binding of B6.2 to the breast tumor metastasis extract indicates that these antibodies react to the same antigen. The differences in the slope of the competition curve and the amount of antibody needed to achieve the competition may be due to differences in the affinities of the antibodies to the same epitope. Another possibility may be the existence of spatially close epitopes, which may result in steric inhibition of the binding of ^{125}I-labeled B6.2 to a nearby epitope.

Purification of the 220,000-Dalton High Molecular Weight Complex: Monoclonal antibody B72.3 has been shown to have highly selective reactivity to tumor versus normal tissues. We thus attempted to purify the antigen reactive with B72.3 first, so that further immunological and biochemical characterization could be made. An extract of a breast tumor metastasis to the liver, which contained the highest immunoreactivity with B72.3, was used as the starting material for purification of the 220,000-dalton high molecular weight complex. Following detergent disruption and high-speed centrifugation, the supernatant was subjected to molecular sieving using Ultrogel AcA34. Immunoreactive fractions were then passed through a B72.3 antibody affinity column and eluted with 3 M KCN. Radiolabeled aliquots from the various purification steps were analyzed by SDS-PAGE (Fig. 8). Only minimal radioactivity in the high molecular weight range was seen in gel patterns of the AcA34 pool, whereas the affinity column eluant demonstrated the four distinct bands of the 220,000-dalton complex. ^{125}I-Labeled B72.3 affinity-purified antigen was tested for immunoreactivity by solid-phase RIA. Approximately 70% of the purified ^{125}I-labeled antigen was bound in B72.3 antibody excess. The identical method of purification was used with a normal human liver extract as the starting tissue, and at no step within the purification scheme was any reactivity with B72.3 detected.

Heterogeneity Among Human Mammary Carcinoma Cell Populations

In 1954 Foulds (67) documented the existence of distinct morphologies in different areas of a single mammary tumor. Since then, several investigators have reported the occurrence of heterogeneity in a variety of tumor cell populations (68,69). By a variety of methods and reagents, including heterologous antisera, heterogeneity has also been observed with respect to the antigenic properties of tumor cell populations (69-73). Consistent with this finding, we have observed antigenic heterogeneity, as defined by the expression of TAAs detected by monoclonal antibodies, among and within murine mammary tumor masses (37). The objectives of the studies described below were to use the monoclonal antibodies to (a) determine the extent of antigenic heterogeneity of specific TAAs that exist

Extract (100,000xg)	AcA-34 (Pool-B)	Affinity (B72.3)

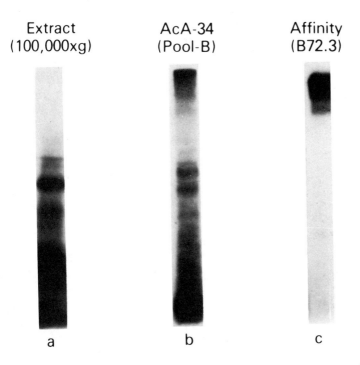

a   b   c

Figure 8 Purification of mammary tumor-associated antigen reactive with monoclonal B72.3. Sodium dodecyl sulfate-PAGE of ^{125}I-labeled extract from a breast tumor metastasis is shown for various purification steps. An equal amount of each ^{125}I-labeled sample was loaded onto the gel: (a) crude extract, (b) pool of AcA34 fractions reactive with B72.3, (c) pool of affinity column fractions reactive with B72.3.

among human mammary tumors as well as within a given mammary tumor population, (b) determine some of the parameters that mediate the expression of various antigenic phenotypes, and (c) develop model systems in which to study and perhaps eventually control these phenomena.

Formalin-fixed tissue sections of human mammary tumors were examined, using the immunoperoxidase method, in an attempt to determine the range of expression of TAAs reactive with monoclonal antibodies (31). Although some mammary tumors reacted with all monoclonal antibodies tested, other mammary tumors reacted with none. Both fixed and frozen sections gave similar results. Some mammary tumors showed a differential expression of one antigen versus another. As shown in Figure 9, an infiltrating duct mammary carcinoma contains the 90,000-dalton TAA reactive with monoclonal antibody B6.2 (Fig. 9a), but

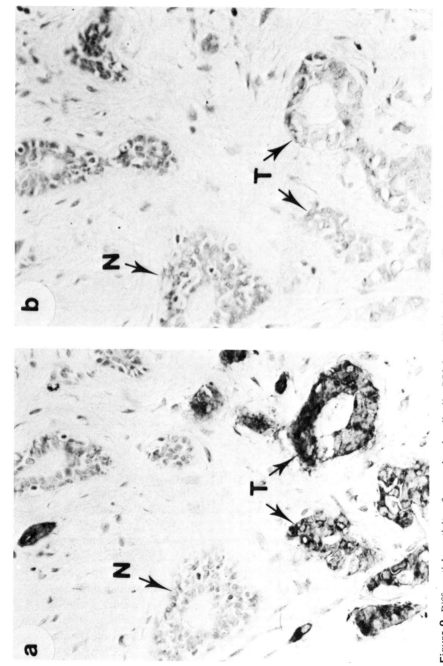

Figure 9 Differential reactivity of monoclonal antibodies B72.3 and B6.2 with two different human mammary adenocarcinomas using the immunoperoxidase technique. Serial tissue sections in (a) and (b) are from an infiltrating duct carcinoma; in (c) and (d) serial sections are from an infiltrating duct carcinoma from another patient. Panels (a) and (c) are reacted with monoclonal antibody B6.2. Panels (b) and (d) are stained with monoclonal antibody B72.3. Note the stained tumor cells (T) and unstained normal mammary cells (N) (a–c, × 220; d × 330).

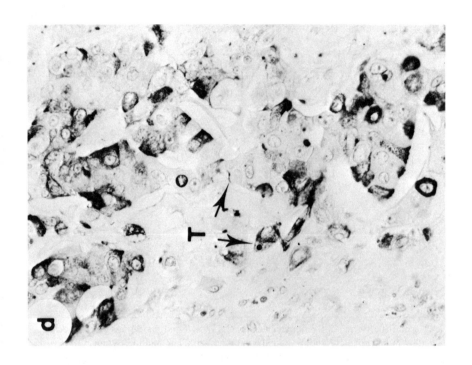

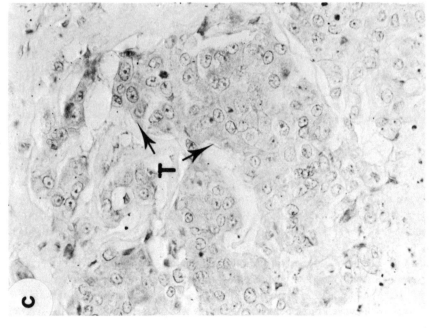

Table 4 Differential Reactivity of Monoclonal Antibodies with Different Human Mammary Tumors[a]

Tumor phenotype	Number of patients[b]	Monoclonal antibody				
		B72.3	B1.1	B6.2	F25.2	B38.1
Group A	6	+	+	+	+	+
Group B	1	+	−	+	+	+
Group C	2	+	+	+	+	−
Group D	10	−	+	+	+	+
Group E	4	−	+	+	+	−
Group F	3	+	−	+	−	−
Group G	1	−	+	−	+	−
Group H	2	−	−	−	+	+
Group I	1	−	+	+	−	−
Group J	1	−	+	−	−	−
Group K	2	−	−	+	−	−
Group L	3	−	−	−	−	+
Group M	9	−	−	−	−	−
Total	45					

[a]Serial sections of formalin-fixed mammary tumors were tested for expression of TAAs detected by monoclonal antibodies using the immunoperoxidase method. Tumors were scored positive if antigen was present on 5% or more of carcinoma cells.
[b]Number of patients with tumor specimens displaying the indicated pattern of reactivity with the monoclonal antibodies.

not the 220,000-dalton TAA reactive with monoclonal B72.3 (Fig. 9b). Conversely, an infiltrating duct mammary carcinoma from another patient expresses the TAA detected only by B72.3 (Fig. 9c,d). To exclude the possibility of variation due to location of tissue within the tumor, several alternate serial sections of the tumors were used in these experiments with identical results.

The immunoperoxidase method was then used to test the reactivity of fixed sections of primary infiltrating duct mammary carcinomas from 45 different patients to a panel of five monoclonal antibodies (Table 4). What emerges is a variety of antigenic phenotypes of the 45 mammary tumors that can be placed into several distinct groups. Reactivity to all five monoclonal antibodies, including B1.1, which is directed against CEA, was demonstrated by the presence of antigens in 6 of 45 (13.3%) of the mammary tumors, while 9 of 45 (20.0%) contained none of these TAAs (Table 4). The remaining 30 tumors displayed a variety of immunological phenotypes with the five monoclonal antibodies. What emerges from these studies is a demonstration of the wide range of antigenic phenotypes present in human mammary tumors. Tumors also differed in their pattern of staining with a given monoclonal antibody. These patterns included focal staining (representing dense foci of TAA in the cytoplasm), diffuse cytoplasmic staining, membrane staining, and apical or luminal staining (representing a concentration of TAA on the luminal borders of cells).

Phenotypic variation was also observed in the expression of TAAs within a given mammary tumor. One pattern repeatedly observed was that one area of a mammary tumor contained TAAs reactive with a particular monoclonal antibody, while another area of the same tumor was not reactive with the identical antibody (Fig. 10A). Another type of antigenic heterogeneity was observed among cells in a given area of a tumor mass. This type of antigenic diversity, termed "patchwork," is demonstrated by the presence of tumor cells expressing a specific TAA directly adjacent to tumor cells negative for the same antigen (Fig. 9b). Patterns of reactivity with a specific monoclonal antibody were also observed to vary within a given tumor mass; that is, antigen was detected in the cytoplasm of cells in one part of the tumor mass and on the luminal edge of differentiated structures in a different part of the same mass.

Heterogeneity of TAA Expression in Human Mammary Tumor Cell Lines: In an attempt to elucidate the phenomenon of variation of antigenic phenotypes in primary human mammary tumors, model systems were examined. Human mammary tumor cell lines, transplanted in athymic mice, demonstrated antigenic heterogeneity. To determine if this phenomenon also exists in human mammary tumor cell lines grown in vitro, MCF-7 cells were tested for the presence of TAAs using the cytospin-immunoperoxidase method (32,36). As seen in Figure 10B, the MCF-7 cell line contained various subpopulations of cells as defined by variability in expression of TAA reactive with monoclonal antibody B6.2. Positive MCF-7 cells are seen adjacent to cells that scored negative.

Antigenic Drift of Mammary Tumor Cell Populations: Studies were then undertaken to determine if any change in antigenic phenotype occurs during extended passage of cells in culture. The BT-20 cell line, obtained at passage 288, was serially passaged and assayed at each passage level during logarithmic growth. As seen in Table 5, a cell-surface HLA antigen, detected by monoclonal antibody W6/32 (39), was present at all passage levels, as was the antigen detected by monoclonal antibody B38.1. The antigen detected by monoclonal antibody B6.2 was expressed on the BT-20 cell surface up to passage 319, but was not evident after this passage level. Similarly, monoclonal B14.2 reacted with BT-20 cells only up to passage 317. This phenomenon was repeatedly observed in several separate experiments, at approximately the same passage levels. Antigenic drift was also observed with the MCF-7 cell line.

As a result of the phenotypic changes observed after passage in culture, MCF-7 cell lines obtained from four sources were examined for the presence of several cell-surface TAAs. Karyotype profiles of the four cell lines were tested and were

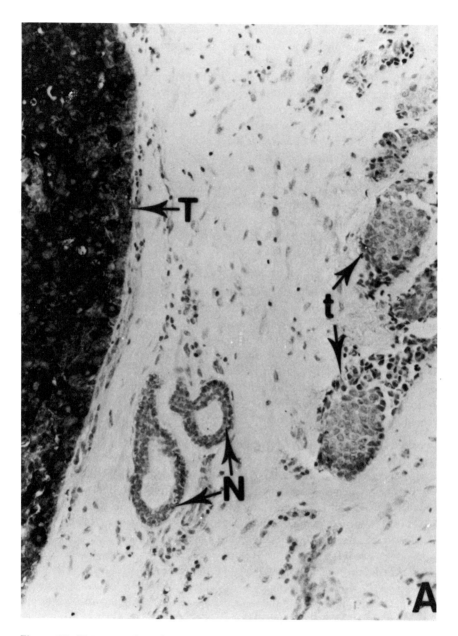

Figure 10 Heterogeneity of antigenic expression of TAAs. (A) An infiltrating duct mammary carcinoma was reacted with monoclonal antibody B6.2 using the immunoperoxidase technique. Note the stained (T) and unstained (t) tumor cells.

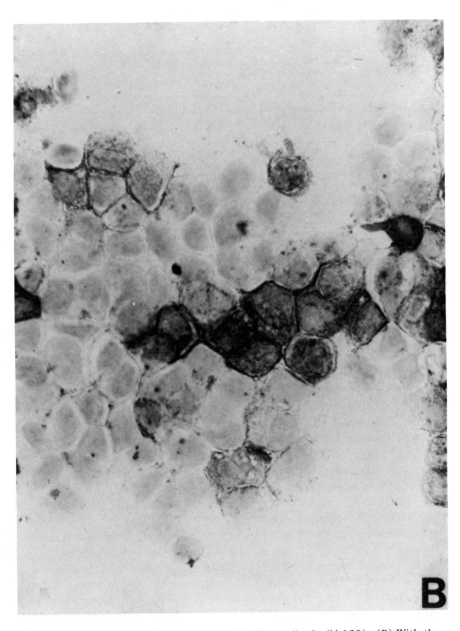

Normal mammary cells (N) do not react with the antibody (X 130). (B) With the cytospin-immunoperoxidase technique as described in Refs. 32 and 36, MCF-7 cells were stained with monoclonal antibody B6.2 (X 540).

Table 5 Differential Expression of Tumor-Associated Antigens in BT-20 Cells Upon Passage[a]

Monoclonal antibody	Passage number					
	316	317	318	319	320	323
W6/32	690[b]	1620	750	620	700	500
B38.1	2560	2280	1380	1640	1550	1320
B6.2	1620	2910	560	710	−[c]	−
B14.2	1600	1380	−	−	−	−

[a]Monoclonal antibodies were tested for binding to the surface of BT-20 mammary tumor cells in a live cell RIA.
[b]Values are expressed as the number of counts per minute above background.
[c]−, < 200 cpm.

all identical and characteristic of the MCF-7 cell line. A single lactate dehydrogenase band, characteristic of only a few breast tumor cell lines, including MCF-7, was also supportive evidence that these cell lines were indeed MCF-7. Using a live cell RIA, which detects the reactivity of antigens at the cell surface, antigenic profiles of the four MCF-7 cell lines were determined. Using three monoclonal antibodies (B1.1, B6.2, and B50.4), four different antigenic phenotypes emerged.

To further understand the nature of antigenic heterogeneity of human mammary tumor cell populations, MCF-7 cells were cloned by end-point dilution and 10 different clones were obtained and assayed for cell-surface TAAs. As seen in Figure 11, the parent MCF-7 culture reacts most strongly with monoclonal antibody B1.1 and least with monoclonal B72.3. Clone 6F1 (Fig. 11B) exhibits a similar phenotype to that of the parent. At least three additional major phenotypes were observed among the other clones. For example, clone 10B5 is devoid of detectable expression of any of the antigens assayed (Fig. 11C), although it does contain HLA and human antigens detected by monoclonal antibodies W6/32 and B139, respectively.

Studies were then undertaken to determine the stability of the cell-surface phenotype of the MCF-7 clones. These cell lines have been monitored through a 4-month period, and assayed during log phase at approximately every other passage. A dramatic change in antigenic phenotype was observed in some of the clones, while other MCF-7 clones maintained a stable antigenic phenotype throughout the same observation period.

Antigenic variability of TAAs among and within human mammary tumor cell populations presents a potential problem in the development and optimization of immunodiagnostic and therapeutic procedures for breast cancer. Knowledge about the nature of this antigenic heterogeneity may be helpful in the prediction or

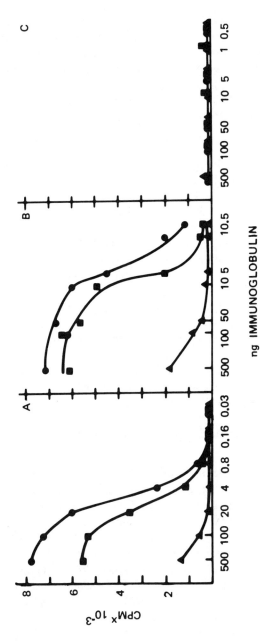

Figure 11 Reactivity of monoclonal antibodies with the surfaces of the parent MCF-7 mammary adenocarcinoma cell line and cloned MCF-7 cell populations. Using a live cell radioimmunoassay, increasing amounts of monoclonal antibodies B1.1 (●), B6.2 (■), and B72.3 (▲) were tested for binding to (A) the parent MCF-7 cell line, (B) MCF-7 clone 6F1, and (C) MCF-7 clone 10B5.

control of the expression of specific antigenic phenotypes. The studies described
have enabled us to demonstrate the extent of specific antigenic variability in vivo
among and within human mammary tumor cell populations. Heterogeneity was
observed not only within a given mammary tumor cell line, but also among the
"same" mammary tumor cell line obtained from four different laboratories. This
observation should serve as a caveat to investigators who are utilizing established
cell lines in their studies and attempting to correlate their results with those of
other laboratories.

In collaboration with Dr. D. Kufe and colleagues (Sidney Farber Cancer Institute, Boston, Mass), other studies, using fluorescence-activated cell sorter analyses,
have shown that at least two of the monoclonal antibodies developed (B6.2 and
B38.1) are most reactive with the surface of MCF-7 cells during S phase of the
cell cycle (40). For this reason, all the experiments using cell lines described above
were performed with cells in the log phase of growth.

With model systems, including the monoclonal antibodies and the cloned human
mammary tumor cell lines described here, determinations of the parameters associated with a distinct change in antigenic phenotype are now feasible. Studies may
now be undertaken to examine the relationship between the expression of specific
antigenic phenotypes and such variables as morphology, tumorigenicity, drug susceptibility, growth rate, and the presence of specific hormone receptors in cloned
mammary tumor cell lines. In view of the widespread variation of antigenic phenotypes among and within human mammary tumors and its implications for the immunodiagnosis and therapy of breast cancer, it would also be of importance to determine which compounds, that could potentially be used clinically, will enhance
the expression of specific TAAs on the surface of human mammary tumor cells.

Radiolocalization of Human Mammary Tumors in Athymic Mice by a Monoclonal Antibody

Radioactively labeled antibodies to a variety of TAAs have been used to detect
the presence of tumors in both experimental animals and humans by gamma scintigraphy. The majority of the antibodies used for clinical trials were constituents
of goat or rabbit antisera, and were directed against antigens such as CEA (65,66,
74), alpha-fetoprotein (75-77), ferritin (78), and human chorionic gonadotropin
(79,80); the studies using anti-CEA demonstrated the localization of malignant
breast tumors (65,66). In some of these studies (65,66,74,79-81) the immunoglobulins have been partially purified using affinity chromatography with an increase in immunoreactivity of the IgG (81). With the development of the hybridoma technology, homogeneous populations of monoclonal antibodies (82,83) to
TAAs can now be utilized to this end. In the studies described below, monoclonal
B6.2 IgG was purified and $F(ab')_2$ and Fab' fragments were generated by pepsin
digestion. These three forms of the antibody were radiolabeled and used to

determine their utility in the radioimmunolocalization of human mammary tumor masses.

Monoclonal antibody B6.2 IgG, obtained from ascitic fluid, was precipitated with ammonium sulfate, dialyzed, and purified by ion exchange chromatography. The IgG was further purified by molecular sieving using an Ultrogel AcA 34 column to remove low molecular weight contaminants with a similar charge as the IgG. Some of the purified IgG was used to generate $F(ab')_2$ and Fab' fragments. The fragments were purified by molecular sieving and retained all their immunoreactivity to mammary tumor extracts and not to normal liver in solid-phase RIAs, when compared on a molar basis to the intact IgG. The IgG and its fragments were labeled with ^{125}I using the iodogen method, and specific activities of 15-50 $\mu Ci/\mu g$ of protein were easily obtained. The labeled antibody was shown to bind to the surface of live MCF-7 cells and retained the same specificity as the unlabeled antibody. Better than 70% of the antibody remained immunoreactive in sequential saturation solid-phase RIAs after labeling.

Athymic mice were implanted with 1-2 mm^3 pieces of the transplantable Clouser human mammary tumor. After approximately 10-20 days the tumors grew to detectable nodules and continued to grow until they obtained diameters of 2.5 cm or more. Some tumors grew rapidly, while others, from the same inoculum, stopped growing at various times, yielding stable tumors as small as 0.6 cm in diameter. This variation in growth rate and ultimate tumor size, even arising from different aliquots of the same mammary tumor, is important in view of subsequent variations observed among different tumors in the amount of radiolabeled antibody bound per milligram of tumor tissue. Athymic mice bearing the Clouser human mammary tumor were injected with 0.1 μg of B6.2 IgG labeled with ^{125}I to a specific activity of approximately 15 $\mu Ci/\mu g$. The radioactivity per milligram in the tumor compared to that of various tissues rose over a 4-day period (Fig. 12A-E) and then fell at 7 days. The tumor-to-tissue ratios were 10:1 or greater in the liver, spleen, and kidney at day 4. Ratios of the counts in the tumor to that found in the brain and muscle were greater than 50:1 and as high as 110:1. Lower tumor-to-tissue ratios were obtained when compared to blood and to the lungs with their large blood pool. The activity found in the lungs was probably not a consequence of trapping of particulates, as evidenced by the low uptake in the liver and spleen.

When the Clouser mammary tumor-bearing mice were injected with $[^{125}I]$ $F(ab')_2$ fragments of B6.2, higher tumor-to-tissue ratios were obtained (Fig. 12F-J). The tumor-to-tissue ratios in the liver and spleen were 15-20:1 at 96 hr. The tumor-to-tissue ratios were somewhat lower with blood and lungs, but were still higher than those obtained using IgG. This is probably due to the faster clearance of the $F(ab')_2$ fragments as compared to the IgG. The tumor-to-kidney ratio was relatively low and was probably due to the more rapid clearance of Fab' fragments, which may have been generated from the $F(ab')_2$ in vivo by the breakage of the cross-linking disulfide bonds.

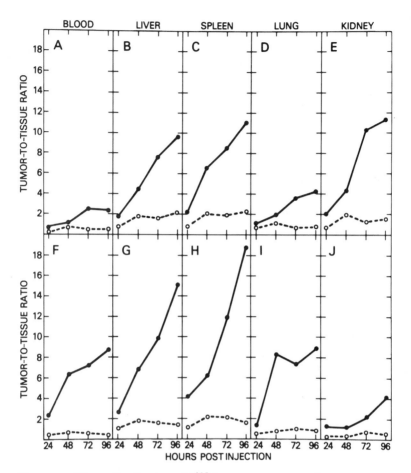

Figure 12 Tissue distribution of [^{125}I] B6.2 IgG and F(ab')$_2$ in athymic mice bearing human tumor transplants. Athymic mice bearing a transplantable human mammary tumor (Clouser, ●) or a human melanoma (A375, ○) were inoculated with [^{125}I] B6.2. Approximately 1.5 μCi of (A-E) IgG or (F-J) F(ab')$_2$ were injected intravenously and the mice were sacrificed at daily intervals. The radioactivity per milligram of tumor was determined and compared to that of various tissues; the averages of 2-20 mice per group are shown.

Athymic mice bearing a human melanoma (A375), a tumor that shows no surface reactivity with B6.2 in live cell RIAs, were used as controls for nonspecific binding of the labeled antibody or antibody fragments to tumor tissue. As shown in Figure 12 (open circles), no preferential localization of the monoclonal antibody was observed in the tumor; in fact, the number of counts per milligram in the tumor was lower than that found in many organs resulting in ratios of less than 1. Similarly, no localization was observed when either normal murine IgG or MOPC-21 IgG_1 (the same isotype as B6.2) from a murine myeloma, or their $F(ab')_2$ fragments, were inoculated into athymic mice bearing Clouser mammary tumors or melanomas, with tumor-to-blood ratios less than or equal to 0.5:1. Athymic mice bearing human mammary tumors derived from tissue culture cell lines were also injected with labeled B6.2 antibody and fragments. Tumor-to-spleen and liver ratios of 6-8:1 were obtained using B6.2 $F(ab')_2$ in mice bearing tumors derived from MCF-7 cells and BT-20 cells.

Athymic mice bearing Clouser mammary tumors were also injected with ^{125}I-labeled B6.2 Fab'. The clearance rate of the Fab' fragment was considerably faster than the larger $F(ab')_2$ fragment and the intact IgG. Acceptable tumor-to-tissue ratios were obtained, but the fast clearance rate resulted in a large amount of the labeled Fab' being found in the kidney and bladder, resulting in low tumor-to-kidney ratios. These studies therefore indicate that $F(ab')_2$ fragments are superior to Fab' or intact IgG in the radiolocalization studies in mice with monoclonal antibody B6.2.

Scanning of Athymic Mice Bearing Human Tumors: Studies were undertaken to determine whether the localization of the ^{125}I-labeled antibody and fragments in the tumors was sufficient to detect using a gamma camera. Athymic mice bearing the Clouser mammary tumor or the A375 melanoma were injected intravenously with approximately 30 μCi of $[^{125}I]$ B6.2 IgG. The mice were scanned and then sacrificed at 24-hr intervals. The Clouser tumors were easily detected at 24 hrs (Fig. 13A, Plate 1, facing page 154) using B6.2 IgG, with a small amount of activity detectable in the blood pool. The tumor remained strongly positive over the 4-day period, with the background activity decreasing to the point where it was barely detectable at 96 hr (Fig. 13B, Plate 1). The 0.5-cm diameter tumors localized in Figures A and B appear bigger than their actual size; this may be due to the dispersion of rays through the pinhole collimator. No tumor localization was observed using radiolabeled B6.2 IgG in mice bearing the control human melanoma transplants (Fig. 13C, Plate 1).

Mice were also injected with $[^{125}I]$ B6.2 $F(ab')_2$ fragments. The mice cleared the fragments faster than the intact IgG and a significant amount of activity was observed in the two kidneys and bladder at 24 hr [Fig. 14A (Plate 1)], but tumors were clearly positive for localization of the $[^{125}I]$ B6.2 $F(ab')_2$ fragments. The activity was cleared from the kidneys and bladder by 48 hr and the tumor-to-background ratio increased over the 4-day period of scanning, with little background and good tumor localization observed at 96 hr [Fig. 14B (Plate 1)]. No localization of activity was observed with the radiolabeled B6.2 $F(ab')_2$ fragments in the athymic mice bearing the A375 melanoma [Fig. 14C (Plate 1)].

The utility of radiolabeled antibodies for the in vivo localization of tumors in humans has been shown with heterologous polyclonal antibodies to a number of different antigens. Human mammary tumors have been localized using antibodies to CEA (65,66) that have been affinity purified. Murine mammary tumors have been localized using antibodies to murine mammary epithelial antigens generated in rabbits (84). These studies required computer-aided background subtraction (employing a second radiolabeled immunoglobulin or other protein) and are thus limited in use to institutions with such sophisticated equipment. The use of monoclonal antibodies with defined specificities should eliminate such additional manipulations, and should also thus reduce radiation dose to the patients.

Monoclonal antibodies to murine Thy-1.1 antigens (85), Rauscher leukemia virus gp70 (using ^{111}In; see Ref. 86) and a stage-specific embryonic antigen (87) have been used to show localization of tissues in mice. The study by Houston et al. (85) using ^{125}I-labeled anti-Thy-1.1 showed selective localization of the antibody to lymphatic tissues in mice containing the antigen. Scheinberg et al. (86) were able to show the localization of radioactivity in leukemic spleens of mice injected with the Rauscher leukemia virus. This work has been extended with the successful localization of human colon carcinomas in athymic mice and in patients with monoclonal antibodies to CEA (88) and in athymic mice bearing a human germ cell tumor using monoclonal antibodies generated against the tumor (89). Attempts to localize human tumors in mice with monoclonal antibodies to HLA were unsuccessful (90).

The studies described here demonstrate the ability of radiolabeled monoclonal antibody to detect human breast tumor xenografts in athymic mice. The ^{125}I-labeled antibody and fragments all successfully localized tumors with the F(ab')$_2$ fragment giving the overall highest tumor-to-tissue ratios. The F(ab')$_2$ fragments may be the best form of the antibody to use because of the potential problem of Fc receptors on a variety of cells binding the labeled IgG and yielding a higher nonspecific distribution of the antibody. The use of an antibody without the Fc portion should also reduce its immunoreactivity in patients and thus minimize an immune response. The smaller fragments also clear the body faster than intact immunoglobulin and should thus result in a lower whole body radiation absorbed dose to the host.

Radiolabeled monoclonal antibodies that are reactive with the surface of human mammary carcinoma cells may eventually prove useful in several areas in the management of human breast cancer. The detection of occult metastatic lesions at distal sites via gamma scanning could serve as an adjunct in determining which patients should receive adjuvant therapy, and subsequent scanning may reveal which tumors are responding to therapy. At present, only axillary lymph nodes, removed at mastectomy, are examined for tumor involvement for use in staging; the extent of nodal tumor involvement in the internal mammary chain is not determined.

Plate 1

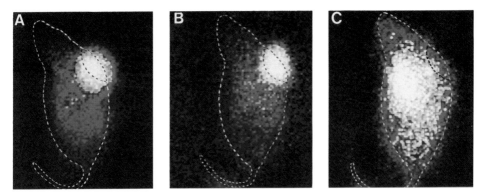

Figure 13 Gamma camera scanning with B6.2 IgG of athymic mice bearing transplanted human tumors. Athymic mice bearing (A, B) a transplantable human mammary tumor (Clouser) or (C) a human melanoma (A375) were inoculated with approximately 30 μCi of [^{125}I] B6.2 IgG. The mice were scanned after various time intervals (A and C, 24 hr; B, 96 hr) until an equal number of counts were detected in each field.

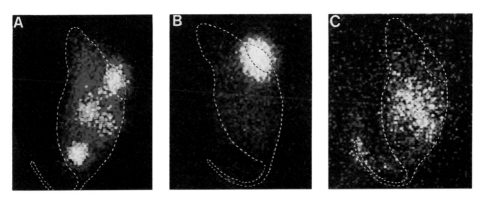

Figure 14 Gamma camera scanning with B6.2 F(ab')$_2$ of athymic mice bearing transplanted human tumors. Athymic mice bearing (A, B) a transplantable human mammary tumor (Clouser) or (C) a human melanoma (A375) were inoculated with approximately 30 μCi of [^{125}I] B6.2 F(ab')$_2$. The mice were scanned after various time intervals (A, 24 hr; B and C, 96 hr) until an equal number of counts were detected in each field.

The use of radiolabeled monoclonal antibodies in lymphangiography of the internal mammary chain may thus eventually increase the reliability of staging of nodal involvement (both axillary and internal chain) as a prognostic indicator. Along with their potential in the diagnosis and prognosis of breast cancer, monoclonal antibodies coupled with isotopes decaying via high-energy transfer with short-range radiation may eventually prove useful as radiotherapeutic agents. This approach, however, is obviously quite complex and would require extensive studies in an experimental model. The system described here of a radiolabeled monoclonal antibody that is selectively reactive with the surface of human mammary tumor cells in vivo may provide an excellent experimental system for such therapy studies.

SUMMARY

Murine monoclonal antibodies reactive with human mammary tumor-associated antigens have been generated and characterized. The immunogens used in these studies were membrane-enriched fractions of human metastatic mammary carcinoma lesions. The 13 monoclonal antibodies characterized could be divided into five major groups based on differential reactivity to various mammary carcinoma lesions, binding to the surface of carcinoma cell lines, and the molecular weight of the reactive antigen precipitated. Two monoclonals (B1.1 and F5.5) were reactive with purified carcinoembryonic antigen and showed differential binding to the surface of various nonbreast tumor cells. Monoclonals B6.2 and B72.3 were extensively characterized as to their range of reactivities and were shown to immunoprecipitate a 90,000-dalton protein and a 200-400 kilodalton high molecular weight protein complex, respectively. The monoclonals were used to demonstrate a wide range of differential expression of several tumor-associated antigens among various mammary carcinomas, and even within a given tumor mass. Purified immunoglobulin, $F(ab')_2$, and Fab' fragments of monoclonal B6.2 were radiolabeled and used in gamma scanning studies to successfully localize human mammary tumor transplants in athymic mice. These monoclonal antibodies may aid in the development of a firm understanding of the dynamics of mammary carcinoma cell populations and may potentially have clinical applications.

ACKNOWLEDGMENTS

We wish to thank D. Poole, D. Simpson, J. Howell, J. Collins, J. Crowley, R. Fitzgerald, and A. Sloan for expert technical assistance in these studies. We also thank Dr. D. Stramignoni for many helpful discussions. Some of these studies were supported in part by a contract from the National Cancer Institute, National Institutes of Health, Bethesda, Md.

REFERENCES

1. A. C. Hollinshead, W. T. Jaffurs, L. K. Alpert, J. E. Harris, and R. B. Herberman, *Cancer Res. 34*:2961 (1974).

2. F. Avis, I. Avis, J. F. Newsome, and G. Haughton, *J. Nat. Cancer Inst. 56*:17 (1976).

3. R. Mesa-Tejada, I. Keydar, M. Ramanarayanan, T. Ohno, C. Feoglio, and S. Spiegelman, *Proc. Nat. Acad. Sci. U.S.A. 75*:1529 (1978).

4. M. M. Black, R. E. Zachrau, B. Shore, A. S. Dion, and H. P. Leis, *Cancer Res. 38*:2068 (1978).

5. G. F. Springer, P. R. Desai, M. S. Murthy, and E. F. Scanlon, *J. Surg. Oncol. 11*:95 (1979).

6. J. P. Leung, G. M. Borden, R. M. Nakamura, D. H. Delteer, and T. S. Edington, *Cancer Res. 39*:2057 (1979).

7. D. R. Howard and C. R. Taylor, *Cancer 43*:2279 (1979).

8. K. M. A. Shekh, F. A. Quismorio, G. J. Friou, and Y. Lee, *Cancer 44*:2083 (1979).

9. G. S. M. Yu, A. S. Kadish, A. B. Johnson, and D. M. Marcus, *Am. J. Clin. Pathol. 74*:453 (1980).

10. J. Arklie, J. Taylor-Papadimitriou, W. Bodmer, M. Egan, and R. Millis, *Int. J. Cancer 28*:23 (1981).

11. J. Hilgers, J. Hilkens, F. Buijis, P. Hageman, A. Sonnenberg, U. Koldovsky, K. Karande, R. P. van Hoeven, C. Feltkamp, and J. M. van de Rijn, in *Monoclonal Antibodies and Breast Cancer*, Breast Cancer Task Force Committee, Bethesda (1981).

12. J. Taylor-Papadimitriou, J. A. Peterson, J. Arklie, J. Burchell, and R. L. Ceriani, *Int. J. Cancer 28*:17 (1981).

13. C. S. Foster, E. A. Dinsdale, P. A. W. Edwards, and A. M. Neville, *Virchows Arch. 394*:295 (1982).

14. C. S. Foster, P. A. W. Edwards, E.A. Dinsdale, and A. M. Neville, *Virchows Arch. 394*:279 (1982).

15. G. L. Greene, C. Nolan, J. P. Engler, and E. V. Jensen, *Proc. Nat. Acad. Sci. U.S.A. 77*:5115 (1980).

16. K. Grzyb, D. R. Ciocca, S. R. Murthy, R. J. Bjercke, and W. L. McGuire, in *Monoclonal Antibodies and Breast Cancer*, Breast Cancer Task Force Committee, Bethesda (1981).

17. K. A. Krolick, D. Yuan, and E. S. Vitetta, *Cancer Immunol. Immunother. 12*: 39 (1981).

18. D. Yuan, F. J. Hendler, and E. S. Vitetta, *J. Nat. Cancer Inst. 68*:719 (1982).

19. P. A. W. Edwards, C. S. Foster, and R. A. J. McIlhinney, *Transplant. Proc. 12*: 398 (1980).

20. J. Schlom, D. Wunderlich, and Y. A. Teramoto, *Proc. Nat. Acad. Sci. U.S.A. 77*:6841 (1980).

21. D. Wunderlich, Y. A. Teramoto, C. Alford, and J. Schlom, *Eur. J. Cancer Clin. Oncol. 17*:719 (1981).

22. Y. A. Teramoto, R. Mariani, D. Wunderlich, and R. Schlom, *Cancer 50*:241 (1982).
23. R. G. Woodbury, J. P. Brown, M. Y. Yeh, I. Hellström, and K. E. Hellström, *Proc. Nat. Acad. Sci. U.S.A. 77*:2183 (1980).
24. S. M. Loop, K. Nishiyama, I. Hellström, R. G. Woodbury, J. P. Brown, and K. E. Hellström, *Int. J. Cancer 27*:775 (1981).
25. P. G. Natali, B. S. Wilson, K. Imai, A. Bigotti, and S. Ferrone, *Cancer Res. 42*:583 (1982).
26. F. Cuttitta, S. Rosen, A. F. Gazdar, and J. D. Minna, *Proc. Nat. Acad. Sci. U.S.A. 78*:4591 (1981).
27. T. Mazauric, K. F. Mitchell, G. J. Letchworth III, H. Koprowski, and Z. Steplewski, *Cancer Res. 42*:150 (1982).
28. R. Ueda, S. Ogata, D. M. Morrissey, C. L. Finstad, J. Szkudlarek, W. F. Whitmore, H. F. Oettgen, K. O. Lloyd, and L. J. Old, *Proc. Nat. Acad. Sci. U.S.A. 78*:5122 (1981).
29. A. E. Frankel, R. V. Rouse, and L. A. Herzenberg, *Proc. Nat. Acad. Sci. U.S.A. 79*:903 (1982).
30. A. S. Daar and J. W. Fabre, *Lancet 2*:434 (1981).
31. D. Colcher, P. Horan Hand, M. Nuti, and J. Schlom, *Proc. Nat. Acad. Sci. U.S.A. 73*:3199 (1981).
32. M. Nuti, Y. A. Teramoto, R. Mariani-Costantini, P. Horan Hand, D. Colcher, and J. Schlom, *Int. J. Cancer 29*:539 (1982).
33. M. Nuti, D. Colcher, P. Horan Hand, F. Austin, and J. Schlom, in *Monoclonal Antibodies and Development in Immunoassay* (A. Albertini and R. Ekins, eds.), Elsevier/North-Holland, Amsterdam, 1981, p. 87.
34. D. Colcher, P. Horan Hand, M. Nuti, and J. Schlom, *Cancer Invest. 1*:127 (1983).
35. D. Colcher, M. Zalutsky, W. Kaplan, D. Kufe, F. Austin, and J. Schlom, *Cancer Res. 43*:736 (1983).
36. P. Horan Hand, M. Nuti, D. Colcher, and J. Schlom, *Cancer Res. 43*:728 (1983).
37. D. Colcher, P. Horan Hand, Y. A. Teramoto, D. Wunderlich, and J. Schlom, *Cancer Res. 41*:1451 (1981).
38. L. A. Herzenberg, L. A. Herzenberg, and C. Milstein, in *Handbook of Experimental Immunology* (D. M. Weir, ed.), Blackwell Scientific, London, 1979, p. 25.1.
39. C. J. Barnstable, W. F. Bodmer, G. Brown, G. Galfré, C. Milstein, A. F. Williams, and A. Ziegler, *Cell 14*:9 (1978).
40. D. W. Kufe, L. Nadler, L. Sargent, H. Shapiro, P. Horan Hand, F. Austin, D. Colcher, and J. Schlom, *Cancer Res. 43*:851 (1983).
41. P. Gold and S. O. Freedman, *J. Exp. Med. 121*:439 (1964).
42. H. J. Hansen, J. J. Snyder, E. Miller, J. P. Vandevoorde, O. N. Miller, L. R. Hines, and J. J. Burns, *Hum. Pathol. 5*:139 (1974).
43. B. P. Krebs, C. M. Lalanne, and M. Schneider, *Proceedings of a Symposium, Nice, France,* Excerpta Medica, Amsterdam, 1978.

44. P. Gold, S. O. Freedman, and J. Shuster, in *Immunodiagnosis of Cancer* (R. B. Herberman and K. R. McIntire, eds.), Marcel Dekker, New York, 1979, p. 147.
45. T. M. Chu and T. Nemoto, *J. Nat. Cancer Inst. 51*:1119 (1973).
46. A. M. Steward, D. Nixon, N. Zamcheck, and A. Aisenberg, *Cancer 33*:1246 (1974).
47. C. J. Menendez-Botet, J. S. Nisselbaum, M. Fleisher, P. P. Rosen, A. Fracchia, G. Robbins, J. A. Urban, and M. K. Schwartz, *Clin. Chem. 22*:1366 (1976).
48. J. J. Lokich, N. Zamcheck, and M. Lowenstein, *Ann. Intern. Med. 89*:902 (1978).
49. T. P. Waalkes, C. W. Gehrke, D. C. Tormey, K. B. Woo, K. C. Kuo, J. Snyder, and H. Hansen, *Cancer 41*:1871 (1978).
50. E. J. Wilkinson, L. L. Hause, E. A. Sasse, R. A. Pattillo, J. R. Milbrath, and J. D. Lewis, *Am. J. Clin. Pathol. 73*:669 (1980).
51. J. F. Chatal, F. Chupin, G. Ricolleau, J. L. Tellier, A. le Mevel, P. Fumoleau, O. Godin, and B. P. le Mevel, *Eur. J. Cancer 17*:233 (1980).
52. R. Vrba, E. Alpert, and K. J. Isselbacher, *Proc. Nat. Acad. Sci. U.S.A. 72*: 4602 (1975).
53. S. E. Chism, L. W. Noel, J. V. Wells, P. Crewther, S. Hunt, J. J. Marchalonis, and H. H. Fudenberg, *Cancer Res. 37*:3100 (1977).
54. G. Pusztaszeri and J. P. Mach, *Immunochemistry 10*:197 (1973).
55. P. B. Dent, S. Carrel, and J. P. Mach, *J. Nat. Cancer Inst. 64*:309 (1980).
56. G. T. Rogers, G. A. Rawlins, P. A. Keep, E. H. Cooper, and K. D. Bagshawe, *Br. J. Cancer 44*:371 (1981).
57. H. Koprowski, Z. Steplewski, K. Mitchell, M. Herlyn, D. Herlyn, and P. Fuhrer, *Somatic Cell Genet. 5*:957 (1979).
58. V. Miggiano, C. Stahli, P. Haring, J. Schmidt, M. LeDain, B. Glatthaar, and T. Staehelin, in *Proceedings of the Twenty-Eighth Colloquium* (H. Peeters, ed), Pergamon, Oxford, 1979, p. 501.
59. R. S. Accolla, S. Carrel, and J. P. Mach, *Proc. Nat. Acad. Sci., U.S.A. 77*:563 (1980).
60. K. F. Mitchell, *Cancer Immunol. Immunother. 10*:1 (1980).
61. H. Z. Kupcik, V. R. Zurawski, Jr., J. G. R. Hurrell, N. Zamcheck, and P. H. Black, *Cancer Res. 41*:3306 (1981).
62. G. T. Rogers, G. A. Rawlins, and K. D. Bagshawe, *Br. J. Cancer 43*:1 (1981).
63. S. von Kleist and P. Burtin, in *Immunodiagnosis of Cancer* (R. B. Herberman and K. R. McIntire, eds.), Marcel Dekker, New York, 1979, p. 322.
64. M. Sehested, F. R. Hirsch, and K. Hou-Jensen, *Eur. J. Cancer Clin. Oncol. 17*: 1125 (1981).
65. F. H. DeLand, E. E. Kim, R. L. Corgan, S. Casper, F. J. Primus, E. Spremulli, N. Estes, and D. M. Goldenberg, *J. Nucl. Med. 20*:1243 (1979).
66. D. M. Goldenberg, E. E. Kim, F. H. DeLand, S. Bennett, F. J. Primus, *Cancer Res. 40*:2984 (1980).
67. L. Foulds, *Cancer Res. 14*:327 (1954).
68. I. R. Hart and I. J. Fidler, *Biochim. Biophys. Acta 651*:37 (1981).

69. R. S. Kerbel, *Nature 280*:358 (1979).
70. F. R. Miller and G. H. Heppner, *J. Nat. Cancer Inst. 63*:1457 (1979).
71. M. V. Pimm and R. W. Baldwin, *Int. J. Cancer 20*:37 (1977).
72. G. Poste, J. Doll, and I. J. Fidler, *Proc. Nat. Acad. Sci. U.S.A. 78*:6226 (1981).
73. R. T. Prehn, *J. Nat. Cancer Inst. 45*:1039 (1970).
74. J. P. Mach, S. Carrel, M. Forni, J. Ritschard, A. Donath, and P. Alberto, *N. Engl. J. Med. 303*:5 (1981).
75. D. M. Goldenberg, F. H. DeLand, E. E. Kim, and F. J. Primus, *Transplant Proc. 12*:188 (1980).
76. D. M. Goldenberg, E. E. Kim, F. H. DeLand, E. Spremulli, M. O. Nelson, J. P. Gockerman, F. J. Primus, R. L. Corgan, and E. Alpert, *Cancer 45*: 2500 (1980).
77. E. E. Kim, F. H. DeLand, M. O. Nelson, S. Bennett, G. Simmons, E. Alpert, and D. M. Goldenberg, *Cancer Res. 40*:3008 (1980).
78. S. E. Order, J. L. Klein, and P. K. Leichner, *Oncology 38*:154 (1981).
79. D. M. Goldenberg, E. E. Kim, F. H. DeLand, J. R. van Nagell, Jr., and N. Javadpour, *Science 208*:1284 (1980).
80. D. M. Goldenberg, E. E. Kim, and F. H. DeLand, *Proc. Nat. Acad. Sci. U.S.A. 78*:7754 (1981).
81. F. J. Primus and D. M. Goldenberg, *Cancer Res. 40*:2979 (1980).
82. G. Köhler and C. Milstein, *Nature 256*:494 (1975).
83. G. Köhler and C. Milstein, *Eur. J. Immunol. 6*:511 (1976).
84. T. Wilbanks, J. A. Peterson, S. Miller, L. Kaufman, D. Ortendahl, and R. L. Ceriani, *Cancer 48*:1768 (1981).
85. L. L. Houston, R. C. Nowinski, and I. D. Bernstein, *J. Immunol. 125*:837 (1980).
86. D. A. Scheinberg, M. Strand, and O. Gansow, *Science 215*:1511 (1982).
87. B. Ballou, G. Levine, T. R. Hakala, and D. Solter, *Science 206*:844 (1979).
88. J. P. Mach, F. Buchegger, M. Forni, J. Ritschard, L. Berche, J. D. Lumbroso, M. Schreyer, C. Giradet, R. S. Accolla, and S. Carrel, *Immunol. Today*:239 (1981).
89. V. Moshakis, R. A. J. McIlhinney, D. Raghavan, and A. M. Neville, *Br. J. Cancer 44*:91 (1981).
90. H. M. Warenius, G. Galfré, N. M. Bleehen, and C. Milstein, *Eur. J. Cancer Clin. Oncol. 17*:1009 (1981).

6 MONOCLONAL ANTIBODIES TO HUMAN LUNG TUMOR ANTIGENS

Frank Cuttitta, Steven T. Rosen,* Joseph Fedorko, Teresa Gregorio, Sylvia Stephenson, James Mulshine, Desmond N. Carney, Silvia Fargion, Paul G. Abrams,† Terry W. Moody,†† Adi F. Gazdar, and John D. Minna / National Cancer Institute and the National Naval Medical Center, Bethesda, Maryland

INTRODUCTION

The Köhler-Milstein technique for making monoclonal antibodies offers a powerful tool for investigating tumor cell biology (1). Monoclonal antibodies to cell-surface antigens that distinguish malignant cells from nonmalignant tissue have potential diagnostic and therapeutic value. In addition, such discriminatory reagents would allow for the identification of key events in the oncogenic process at

---

Present affiliations:
*Northwestern University Department of Medicine, Chicago, Illinois.
†National Cancer Institute-Frederick Cancer Research Facility, Frederick, Maryland.
†† George Washington University School of Medicine and Health Sciences, Washington, D.C.

the molecular level. Several laboratories have developed monoclonal antibodies with selectivity for breast cancer (2), lymphomas (3), neuroblastoma (4), leukemias (5,6), gliomas (7), colon cancer (8-10), and malignant melanoma (11-14). Miller and Levy (15-17) have successfully utilized anti-idiotypic monoclonal antibody for the treatment of B-cell lymphoma. Recently, our laboratory and others have reported the use of somatic cell hybridization for the production of monoclonal antibodies to human lung cancer (18-21).

By the end of 1982, over 100,000 new cases of primary lung carcinoma were reported in the United States alone. These pulmonary malignancies characteristically present as one of four major histological types (adenocarcinoma, large cell carcinoma, squamous carcinoma, and small cell carcinoma). These histological types have different etiologies, treatment, biology, and natural histories (22-24). For example, small cell lung cancer (SCLC) in over 95% of cases is beyond the bounds of surgical resection at the time of presentation and the primary treatment is combination chemotherapy with or without radiotherapy (22). In contrast, nonsmall cell lung cancers (NSCLC) are resistant to available chemotherapy and are usually treated with surgery or radiotherapy (22). Though morphological differences at the light-microscopic level usually distinguish "classic" SCLC from NSCLC tumors, atypical "variant" forms of neoplasm occur in about 6% of SCLC at presentation, causing confusion in the histological typing of the tumor (25). For this reason, many biochemical and cytogenetic markers are now being developed to better define pulmonary neoplasms (23,26). The use of tumor type-specific monoclonal antibodies would help eliminate many of the difficulties associated with the histological typing of lung cancer. These reagents could also play a major role in the early diagnosis, staging, and rational selection of therapy for primary lung carcinomas.

Our laboratory has used a two-front approach in developing monoclonal antibodies with selectivity for human lung cancer. The first involved immunizing with "undefined antigens" expressed on whole cell preparations of lung cancer cell lines, followed by extensive screening to isolate those hybridomas having "tumorselective" properties. Toward this end, we have incorporated nonlung cancer lines (autologous to the immunizing tumor line when available) into our initial screening strategy to eliminate those antibodies directed against commonly expressed human antigens. In our second method, we have developed monoclonal antibodies to "defined" tumor cell markers such as the neuropeptide bombesin and the cytoplasmic enzyme neuron-specific enolase. In this manner, we were able to derive monoclonal reagents recognizing entities with defined structure, biochemical function and tumor-associated properties. This chapter discusses the production, characterization, and use of monoclonal antibodies that demonstrate specificity for several types of human lung cancer.

MONOCLONAL ANTIBODIES TO HUMAN LUNG CANCER

In the following section, we will present a brief overview of our experimental design and the screening strategy employed in the derivation of lung cancer-selective monoclonal antibodies. The technical information outlined below will encompass the utilization of both "defined" and "undefined" antigens as initial immunogens for the production of such tumor-selective reagents. For more detailed accounts of the hybridoma technology cited, see Cuttitta et al. (18) and Minna et al. (19).

In developing monoclonal antibodies to primary lung carcinoma, our laboratory's initial endeavor was founded on the availability of well-characterized human lung cancer lines. We had previously established the technical means for the routine in vitro cultivation of pulmonary neoplasms, particularly SCLC (27-30). These tissue culture lines had been verified to be of the specified tumor type by the following criteria: (a) morphological examination at the light- and electron-microscopic level, (b) chromosomal and isoenzyme characterization, (c) nude mouse heterotransplant studies, and (d) expression of appropriate tumor cell markers (27-34). Prompted by the accessibility of such tumor cell lines, we began to investigate their use as immunogens for monoclonal antibody development. A series of immunization trials were accomplished by challenging BALB/c mice or Sprague-Dawley, and Fisher rats with one or more lung cancer lines, SCLC (NCI-H69, NCI-H187, or NCI-H64), large cell variant of SCLC (NCI-N231/417), adenocarcinoma (NCI-H125), and large cell carcinoma (NCI-H157). In generating somatic cell hybridomas, we have used the polyethylene glycol procedure of Galfré et al. (35). Resulting splenocytes were fused to one of three mouse myeloma cell lines (P3-x63, P3-NS1-1-Ag4-1, x63-Ag8.653) (1,35,36). The fusion products of each spleen were dispensed into eight 96-well microtiter plates and selectively grown in a modification of the formula of Kennett et al. (37). Following a 2-week incubation period, individual culture supernatants were assessed for lung cancer binding activity by immunoradioautography. This procedure is diagrammatically represented in Figure 1. We have devised this type of solid-phase assay to accommodate the rapid processing of hybridoma culture plates. In a routine screening exercise, hybrid culture fluids were tested against three 96-well target cell plates comprised of the initial immunogen lung carcinoma line, another similar tumor line, and a nonlung cancer cell line. In several instances, autologous B-lymphoblastoid or skin fibroblast lines were concomitantly generated with their mate lung carcinoma counterparts and were incorporated into our primary screening strategy to eliminate monoclonal antibodies directed against histocompatibility antigens. As an example of this approach, Figure 2 illustrates the autoradiographic results produced in the screening of potential anti-SCLC monoclonal antibodies. Multiple binding patterns are clearly discernable on the three target

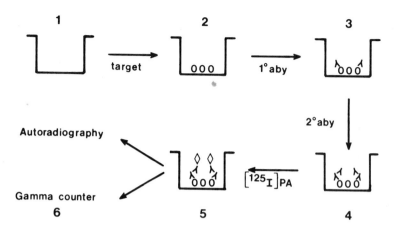

Figure 1 Schematic diagram of the routine radioimmunoassay used in assessing hybridoma products. The assay is summarized in six sequential steps that illustrate the cross section of one well of a 96-well polyvinyl chloride microtiter plate (Dynatech). Step 2 involves the solid phasing of an appropriate target material (whole cell preparation or soluble protein). In step 3, the resulting supernatants of cultured hybridoma cells are transferred to their respective target plates. This is accomplished under sterile conditions, in one operation, using a 96-well microreplication device (19). Adhering monoclonal antibodies are then detected by the addition of a secondary antibody (polyvalent rabbit anti-mouse or anti-rat, respectively) (step 4), followed by the introduction of [^{125}I] protein A (step 5). The deposition of radioactive label is measured directly in a gamma counter or indirectly by autoradiography (step 6).

cell plates, represented by (A) SCLC line NCI-H69 (immunogen), (B) SCLC line NCI-H128, and (C), B-lymphoblastoid line NCI-H128BL (autologous mate to NCI-H128). The circled wells delineate those hybridomas expressing selective binding for SCLC. Once tumor recognition had been established, hybrids were stabilized by repeated "minicloning" (38) and subsequently single cell cloned by "limiting dilution" (19). The technology thus far presented is a summation of the experimental design we have adopted in generating monoclonal antibodies to "undefined" antigens expressed on pulmonary neoplasms.

As an alternative method in developing monoclonal antibodies with selectivity for human lung cancer, we have examined the use of pre-established tumor cell markers as initial immunogens. Small cell lung cancer tumors and cell lines have properties of amine precursor uptake and decarboxylation (APUD) cells (23,39), as exemplified by the presence of high levels of L-dopa decarboxylase (27,40) and neuron-specific enolase (41,42). These APUD-like pulmonary malignancies classically express endocrine function and have been shown to secrete many

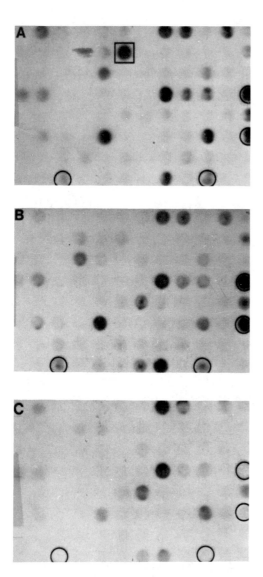

Figure 2 Example of the immunoautoradiographic results produced during the primary screening of hybridoma culture supernatants for anti-SCLC activity. The target plates consisted of solid-phase whole cell preparations and are represented as (A) SCLC line NCI-H69 (immunizing line), (B) SCLC line NCI-H128, and (C) autologous B-lymphoblastoid line NCI-H128BL. The assay was performed according to the protocol illustrated in Figure 1. Deposition of radioactive tracer was evaluated by overnight autoradiography on Kodak XR-5 (XAR-5) film using a DuPont lightning-plus intensifying screen. The circled wells delineate those hybrids that produced anti-SCLC antibody and which were thus chosen for further study. The boxed well in (A) exhibits a unique binding pattern for the immunogen SCLC line (NCI-H69) and possibly represents HLA recognition.

Table 1 Numerical Summation of the Screening Results Generated During the Preliminary Testing of Monoclonal Antibodies to "Undefined" and "Defined" Antigens Expressed on Human Lung Cancer Cells

	Undefined antigens		Defined antigen
	SCLC[a]	NSCLC[b]	Bombesin[c]
Fusions	15	1	2
Total number of wells seeded	10,213 (100)[d]	672 (100)	1536 (100)
Wells with hybrid growth	4,680 (45.8)	169 (25.2)	903 (58.8)
Wells showing selective antigen binding[e]	188 (1.9)	38 (5.7)	12 (0.8)
Wells with selective antigen binding following stabilization[f]	81 (0.8)	5 (0.7)	6 (0.4)

[a]Summary of mouse-mouse and rat-mouse fusions directed against whole cell preparations of SCLC lines NCI-H69, NCI-H187, or NCI-H64.

[b]Summary of mouse-mouse fusion directed against whole cell preparation of NSCLC line NCI-H157 (large cell carcinoma).

[c]Summary of mouse-mouse fusion directed against lys-3-bombesin analog.

[d]The number in parentheses is the percentage of total wells tested.

[e]Positive autoradiographic signal for the immunizing agent (SCLC, NSCLC, or bombesin, respectively) and negative on nonlung cancer cell lines (B-lymphoblastoid or fibroblastoid lines) or biologically unrelated neuropeptide (substance P).

[f]Maintained selective antigen binding following the minicloning and single cell cloning process.

polypeptide hormones (43). Such endocrine-like behavior clinically manifests as paraneoplastic syndrome in 25% of SCLC patients (44). Recently, we have demonstrated that the neuropeptide bombesin is produced by many, if not all, SCLC lines thus far tested and is not detectable in NSCLC lines (32). Based on these observations, three SCLC biochemical markers were proposed as likely candidates for monoclonal antibody development: L-dopa decarboxylase, neuron-specific enolase, and bombesin. We began our preliminary trials with bombesin (BN), since this antigen was well defined structurally (known amino acid sequence), had an assigned biochemical function, and was commercially available as a synthetic preparation. Heterologous antisera to BN had previously been produced in rabbits using the lys-3 derivative of the neuropeptide coupled to bovine serum albumin (BSA) by the carbodiimide reaction (45). Thus, we utilized the lys-3-BN-BSA conjugate to hyperimmunize BALB/c mice as a precondition step for the generation of monoclonal antibodies. Lymphoid spleen cells were fused to the nonsecreting mouse myeloma line x63-Ag8.653. Resulting hybridoma culture supernatants were evaluated for the presence of anti-bombesin antibody by a solid-phase radioimmunoassay (Fig. 1). Individual culture fluids were screened on three target plates, consisting of bombesin, substance P (structurally related neuropeptide), and BSA (indifferent protein) and assessed autoradiographically. Hybridomas expressing selective bombesin binding activity (negative for substance P and BSA) were stabilized by previously described protocols and subjected to further characterization. We have also begun a collaborative effort to produce monoclonal antibodies to neuron-specific enolase with Dr. Paul Marangos of the National Institutes of Health, but these studies are in their rudimentary stage of development and will not be expounded upon at this time.

The numerical evaluation of our attempts to derive monoclonal antibodies with selective-recognition for human lung cancer is presented in Table 1. In 18 separate fusions, involving mouse-mouse or rat-mouse hybrids, 12,426 wells were tested using appropriate screening strategies, and only 238 wells (1.9%) showed selective binding for human lung cancer or tumor cell marker, respectively. The technical difficulties in generating anti-human lung cancer antibodies become even more evident when one considers that of the 238 hybrids initially showing selective binding, less than 39% (92 wells) maintain their antibody production following stabilization procedures. Thus the overall efficiency in deriving stable hybridomas with anti-human lung cancer activity is 0.7%. Interestingly, this low derivation efficiency was a consistent finding and did not significantly vary with respect to the immunogen used (i.e., whole cell preparations of SCLC or NSCLC or soluble protein, BN).

CHARACTERIZATION OF MONOCLONAL ANTIBODIES SELECTIVE FOR HUMAN LUNG CANCER

The stabilized hybridomas that fulfilled our initial screening restrictions were extensively examined as to their binding specificity. Toward this end, hybrids directed against a given tumor cell type were assessed for their recognition of similar lung cancer cell lines to ensure maintenance of selective binding. The binding titration curve of a rat anti-SCLC monoclonal antibody (604A9) is represented in Figure 3 and exemplifies the antibody's binding pattern on three autologous pairs of cell lines. Antibody 604A9 was initially derived against SCLC lines NCI-H187/NCI-H60 and was shown to maintain its tumor selectivity when tested against other SCLC lines (NCI-H390, NCI-H209, and NCI-H128). In addition, this antibody gave insignificant binding reactions when tested on autologous nonlung cancer cell lines (skin fibroblast line NCI-H390SK3 and B-lymphoblastoid lines NCI-

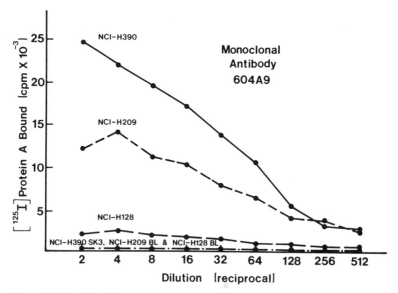

Figure 3   Titration binding curve of a rat anti-SCLC monoclonal antibody (604A9) on three autologous pairs of cell lines. Twofold serial dilutions of 604A9 culture supernatant were assayed on respective target cell plates according to previously described protocols (see Fig. 1). The antibody demonstrated significant binding for the three SCLC lines NCI-H390, NCI-H209, and NCI-H128. However, in contrast, the autologous NSCLC target cell lines (skin fibroblast NCI-H390SK3 and B-lymphoblastoid lines NCI-H209BL and NCI-H128BL) failed to show antibody binding. Points represent quadruplicate determinations.

H209BL and NCI-H128BL). These observations clearly demonstrate that antibody 604A9 recognizes an antigen universally expressed on SCLC lines but not detectable (within the limits of our assay system) on autologous nonlung cancer lines.

Our second approach in evaluating the integrity of anti-SCLC antibodies was to confirm that these reagents did not recognize an antigenic product of in vitro cultivation or an antigen commonly expressed on normal lung tissue. Of critical importance was the demonstration that such antibodies would react with small cell tumor samples taken directly from patients without intervening culture and would not bind to normal lung specimens. Table 2 illustrates the radioimmunoassay (RIA) assessment of mouse antibody 534F8 and rat antibody 604A9 binding reactions on necropsy samples of tumor-bearing and normal organs taken from SCLC and nontumorous patients. These reagents clearly discriminate tissue specimens having SCLC involvement from those samples that lack the tumor. In addi-

Table 2 Binding of Monoclonal Antibodies 534F8 and 604A9 to Necropsy Specimens of SCLC Tumors and Various Normal Tissues

Target tissue	RIA analysis	
	534F8[a]	604A9[b]
Small cell lung cancer cell lines	+[c]	+
B-lymphoblastoid cell lines	−[d]	−
Small cell lung cancer, liver metastasis, patient 1	+	+
Uninvolved liver from patient 1	−	−
Small cell lung cancer, lung metastasis, patient 2	+	+
Uninvolved lung from patient 2	−	−
Normal tissue from necropsy specimens (nonpulmonary malignant disorders)		
Lung	−	−
Liver	−	−
Adrenal	−	−
Brain	−	−
Colon	−	−
Kidney[e]	+	−
Gallbladder	−	−
Muscle, skeletal	−	−
Muscle, cardiac	−	−
Spleen	−	−

[a]Mouse IgM kappa monoclonal antibody derived against SCLC line NCI-H69.
[b]Rat IgM kappa monoclonal antibody derived against SCLC line NCI-H187.
[c]+, RIA binding ratio (BR) >5, where BR = (cpm test − cpm background) ÷ cpm background.
[d]−, RIA binding ratio <2.
[e]534F8 consistently gave a positive reaction for normal kidney. Examination by immunohistochemistry verified this binding to be localized at the renal proximal tubules.

tion, 534F8 and 604A9 did not react with a variety of organ specimens harvested from donors without malignant disease. There is, however, an apparent exception when examining the binding characteristic of 534F8 for renal tissue. With the use of immunohistochemical staining techniques, we have verified this finding and have demonstrated selective deposition of 534F8 at the proximal tubules of the kidney.

Table 3 Binding of Antibody 2A11 to Solid-Phase Peptides as Determined by Indirect Radioimmunoassay

Peptide	RIA analysis[a]
Bombesin (BN)[b]	+[c]
Synthetic analogs of BN	
Tyr-4-BN	+
Lys-3-BN	+
Na Gly-5-BN	+
BN-OH	−[d]
Tyr-12-BN	−
Peptides biochemically similar to BN	
Alytesin	+
Litorin	+
Ranatensin	+
Neuropeptides biochemically unrelated to BN	
Bradykinin	−
Beta-endorphin	−
Somatostatin	−
Calcitonin	−
Physalaemin	−
Eledosin	−
Substance P	−
Neurotensin	−

[a] Antibody binding determined by indirect RIA using rabbit anti-mouse IgG and [^{125}I] protein A.
[b] Bombesin (pGlu-Gln-Arg-Leu-Gly-Asn-Gln-Trp-Ala-Val-Gly-His-Leu-Met-NH$_2$).
[c] +, RIA binding ratio > 10.
[d] −, RIA binding ratio < 1.

In characterizing anti-bombesin monoclonal antibodies we have examined their binding reaction by RIA on the following solid-phase materials: (a) synthetic analogs of bombesin, (b) biochemically similar peptides, and (c) unrelated neuropeptides. Table 3 is an example of the data generated when mouse antibody 2A11 was tested for its binding specificity. These results strongly support the exquisite recognition antibody 2A11 has for bombesin and related neuropeptides. The lack of binding observed for BN-OH and Tyr-12-BN analogs was shown to be induced by the alteration in the antigenic determinant of 2A11. We have demon-

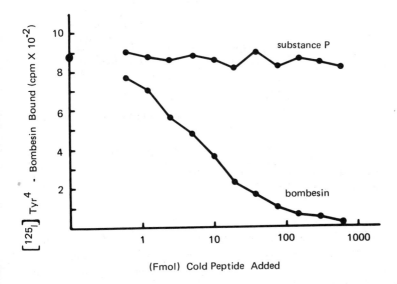

(Fmol) Cold Peptide Added

Figure 4 Illustration of the quantitative inhibition assay for bombesin (BN), using solid-phase anti body 2A11. Anti-bombesin monoclonal antibody 2A11 was attached to the bottom of a 96-well polyvinyl chloride microtiter plate with minimal loss in antigenic recognition. When [^{125}I] Tyr-4-BN was concomitantly introduced with increasing concentrations of cold BN, a linear inhibition in isotope deposition resulted. The circled point on the ordinate represents 100% binding of [^{125}I] Tyr-4-BN (binding in the absence of cold BN). A 50% inhibition in the curve was produced by 6-8 fmol of cold BN. The effective range of BN detection by this assay was 2-90 fmol. To validate the specificity of the assay, substance P (neuropeptide structurally similar to BN) was tested over the appropriate range of 1-1000 fmol without significantly inhibiting the binding of ^{125}I-labeled BN analog. Points represent triplicate determinations.

strated by a quantitative inhibition assay that 2A11 bonds to the C-terminal region of bombesin (amino acids 7-14). Thus structural alterations in this region of the molecule will induce abrogation of 2A11 binding. Interestingly, this region of the neuropeptide is also responsible for biological activity (46). Utilizing solid-phase antibody 2A11 and ^{125}I-labeled Tyr-4-BN, we have developed a quantitative inhibition assay that can detect as little as 2 fmol (2 $\times$ 10^{-15} mol) of BN tissue extracts (Fig. 4). To validate the specificity of our detection system, we have used substance P at a concentration of 1000 fmol without significantly inhibiting the binding of [^{125}I] Tyr-4-BN. Thus far only SCLC lines have detectable

Table 4 Major Antigenic Determinants Expressed on Human Lung Cancer

Antigenic group	Prototype antibody[a]	Biochemical characteristic of antigen
SCLC-1	534F8	Glycolipid (LNFPIII)[b]
SCLC-2	604A9	Glycolipid
SCLC-3	2HH7	Protein (p120)
AC-1	503D8	Protein (p86 and p130)
AC-2	505C12	?
LC-1	3D4	Protein (p30)

[a]Antibody used to first characterize the respective antigen.
[b]LNFPIII (lacto-N-fucopentaose III).

levels of BN (range, 5-300 fmol/mg protein extracted), whereas other lung cancer cell lines (adenocarcinoma, large cell carcinoma, squamous cell carcinoma, bronchioloalveolar, and mesothelioma) have been confirmed as negative producers of this neuropeptide (BN $<$ 2 fmol/mg protein extracted).

MAJOR CLASSES OF LUNG CANCER ANTIGENS DETECTED BY MONOCLONAL ANTIBODIES

In preparing monoclonal antibodies to human lung cancer, we have so far found six major antigenic specificities (Table 4). These distinct antigenic specificities are determined by preferential binding or lack of binding to various lung cancer cell lines, competitive inhibition of binding of a labeled monoclonal antibody by another antibody, and biochemical characterization of the antigenic determinant. The antigens have the prefix of the histological type of the immunizing lung cancer line. SCLC-1 is the glycolipid lacto-N-fucopentaose III (LNFPIII) (as characterized by Drs. Laura Huang and Victor Ginsburg of the National Institutes of Health). This glycolipid is immunodominant on SCLC lines and we have commonly found hybridoma antibodies against it. Interestingly, these antibodies have all been of the IgM kappa isotype. The LNFPIII antigen is also found on NSCLC (18,47), colon cancer (48), breast cancer (18), and neuroblastoma (18); and interestingly, it has been shown to be the stage-specific embryonic antigen (SSEA-1) found on early mouse embryos (49). SCLC-2 antigen is apparently another glycolipid that is only rarely found on NSCLC and not yet seen on neuroblastoma cells. SCLC-3 antigen is a protein of 120,000 daltons found on large cell derivatives of SCLC, at lower levels of SCLC NSCLC, and melanoma cells. AC-1 antigen is a protein of 86,000 and 130,000 daltons in a secreted form found on NSCLC and rarely on SCLC. AC-2 is found on NSCLC, melanoma, and some fibroblasts. LC-1 is a protein of 30,000 daltons found on NSCLC, rarely on SCLC, and is expressed on melanoma cells. From two-dimensional gel analysis of membrane proteins, there are 12 distinct proteins found on SCLC not found on NSCLC and 14 unique proteins found on NSCLC but not expressed on SCLC (50). This initial group of six antibodies is only a beginning toward a complete monoclonal antibody-based immunological map of the surface of lung cancer cells. We have done the most detailed work in completing this map using SCLC. By using direct binding analysis, we have detected at least 15 different antigenic determinants on SCLC; 12 of these are not expressed on normal lung, liver, fibroblasts, or melanoma cells. It is possible, however, that several of these antigenic determinants are present on the same molecule. Interestingly, a large number of these determinants appear to be glycolipids.

At present, despite our large sample size, we have no one antibody that only reacts with SCLC and not with any NSCLC or vice versa. These shared lung cancer-associated antigens may represent more evidence in favor of a common stem cell origin for the different lung cancer types. However, by using a panel of antibodies prepared either against SCLC or the NSCLC type and testing individual tumors with multiple antibodies, we predict it should be possible to type tumors with these reagents. Likewise, we want to have at least one antibody that would react with every lung cancer of a given histological type. The antibodies selected by our screening strategy detect determinants common to most lung cancers of that type. Thus the use of several of these antibodies allows us to get a positive reaction with nearly all lung tumors tested.

IMMUNOHISTOCHEMICAL DETECTION OF HUMAN LUNG CANCER

Immunohistochemistry plays a fundamental role in the complete characterization of tumor-selective monoclonal antibodies. Many of the developmental and technical considerations of this methodology have been covered in recent review articles (51,52). We have utilized the avidin-biotin complex technique (53,54) for our routine assessment of hybridoma products. Nickel chloride was incorporated into the immune reaction to enhance the color deposition at the site of antibody-antigen complexing (55). In addition, methyl green was used as a counterstain to increase contrast and highlight immunological staining. This approach allows us to determine the potential usefulness of anti-tumor reagents as diagnostic tools for examining pathological specimens. In addition, if anti-tumor antibodies are to be utilized in therapy, any binding reactions to normal (nonmalignant) tissue structures must be identified. Such reactions can be best observed by immunohistochemical techniques. We have routinely screened potentially useful tumor-selective reagents against a panel of normal tissue taken from several organs (heart, liver, spleen, lung, kidney, brain, bowel, etc.) for assessment of antibody binding to subpopulations of cells. Figure 5 (a) represents a typical example used in assessing the binding recognition of SCLC foci in liver metastases by antibody 534F8. Focal SCLC involvement is clearly demonstrated with antibody 534F8, while "normal" hepatocytes are not stained by the antibody. Interestingly, some metastatic SCLC nodules were not detected by immunological staining, illustrating the hetero-

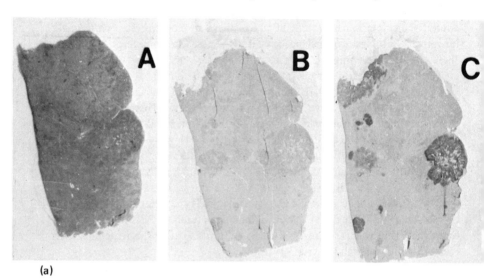

(a)

Figure 5 Immunohistochemical analysis of anti-tumor monoclonal antibodies on form lin-fixed paraffin-embedded tissue specimens using the avidin-biotin complex techniqu (a) Composite picture representing the immunoperoxidase staining of a necropsy sect: of liver involved with metastatic SCLC: hematoxylin-eosin stain (A), immunoperoxid reaction without (B) and with (C) mouse anti-SCLC monoclonal antibody 534F8. Sev focal infiltrates of SCLC are clearly visible as dense nodules in the tissue mass, exempl ing selective immune staining by antibody 534F8. However, the more diffuse infiltrat of SCLC lack immune deposition of stain and illustrate the existence of tumor antige heterogeneity within the same tissue section. (b) Normal kidney section stained with antibody 534F8. The lacto-N-fucopentaose III (LNFPIII) antigen was shown to be co partmentalized in the proximal tubules of normal renal tissue. Note that the glomerul and surrounding arterioles are devoid of any staining. (c) Immunohistochemical staini of a tumor from a nude mouse induced by the SCLC line NCI-H378 with a rat anti-SC monoclonal antibody (604A9). Uniform staining of the tumor mass can be observed, lustrating the conservation of the tumor antigen for 604A9 by most of the malignant cells. (d) Hematoxylin-eosin stain of a nude mouse tumor of adenocarcinoma of the l (NCI-H23). (e) Serial section of this tumor nodule stained by a mouse anti-large cell a body (3D4), exemplifying the cross-reactivity of this antibody for other histological types of lung tumors. Heterogeneity of tumor antigen expression is shown by the vari tion in immune stain deposition on the tumor cells.

Plate 2

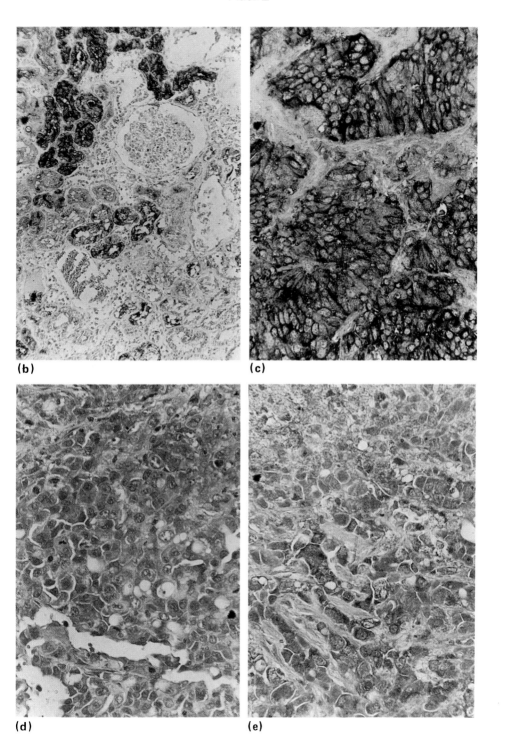

(b)

(c)

(d)

(e)

geneity of tumor antigen expression found within a given patient. Though antibody 534F8 has been shown to react with the majority of SCLC tumors, its potential use as a therapeutic tool is limited based on its reactivity with the proximal tubules of normal kidney [Fig. 5(b)(Plate2, facing page 174); Table 2]. With the use of immunohistochemical techniques we have shown that the 534F8 antigen (LNFPIII) is not homogeneously expressed in renal tissue but, rather, confined to a specific substructure of the kidney. When screening 534F8 against our panel of normal tissue, the antibody demonstrated marked deposition at the renal proximal tubules [Fig. 5(b),(Plate 2)]. The glomerulus and surrounding arterioles were devoid of immunologically induced stain. What role LNFPIII plays in normal proximal tubular function or early in embryonic development, where it is also found (49), is unknown. The exploration of tumor antigen compartmentalization in normal tissue and the evaluation of the heterogeneity of tumor antigen expression within individual tumors is best explored with immunohistochemical technology.

Because some monoclonal antibody-detected antigens may be inactivated by fixation procedures, we have used nude mouse heterotransplants of appropriate lung cancer cell lines as an antigen-positive tissue specimen source for the immunochemical screening of monoclonal antibodies. Figure 5(c) (Plate 2) represents a nude mouse tumor of SCLC line NCI-H378 as stained by a rat anti-SCLC monoclonal antibody (604A9). Interestingly, with this antibody we obtained a uniform deposition of immune staining on the tumor mass, with only an occasional SCLC cell being devoid of stain. Thus, in this instance, the tumor antigen for 604A9 was conserved by the vast majority of malignant cells. This antibody, in contrast to 534F8, does not stain any normal kidney structures.

We have also utilized nude mouse tumors to study the cross-reactivity of specific anti-lung cancer antibodies on different histological types of pulmonary neoplasms. The cross-reacting property of a mouse anti-large cell antibody (3D4) on a nude mouse tumor of adenocarcinoma of the lung (NCI-H23) is illustrated in Figure 5(d) and (e). The hematoxylin-eosin section [Fig. 5(d)(Plate 2)] was used to verify the histological type of lung cancer examined. The cross-reactivity profile of antibody 3D4 for the respective adenocarcinoma tumor is demonstrated in Figure 5(e)(Plate 2). The heterogeneity of tumor antigen expression is again exemplified in this picture, as seen by the variation in immune stain deposition on the tumor cells. In conclusion, we feel immunohistochemistry offers a potent mechanism for evaluating anti-tumor monoclonal antibodies and can be used to assess the potential usefulness of such reagents in a clinical setting. We have also shown that the immunochemical technique can play an important role in identifying subsets of normal cells within a tissue mass that express monoclonal antibody-defined antigens.

MONOCLONAL ANTIBODIES TO HUMAN LUNG CANCER: POTENTIAL DIAGNOSTIC AND THERAPEUTIC USE

We have reviewed our experimental design, screening strategy, and characterization restrictions employed in the derivation of lung cancer-selective monoclonal antibodies. Utilizing this technology, we have developed anti-tumor reagents that demonstrate preferential binding for human lung cancer cell lines and delineate pulmonary neoplastic expression in necropsy specimens. These reagents failed to react with a variety of autologous non-lung cancer cell lines and normal tissues. Furthermore, we have discussed the practical application of tumor-selective antibodies in the histological typing of human lung cancer. Such an immunological identification scheme would offer clinicians a rational means for selecting appropriate therapies in the treatment of lung carcinomas.

As with any other therapeutic agent, the anti-tumor monoclonal antibodies will have to undergo a series of clinical trials to determine toxicity and efficacy of the reagent. These antibodies can also be used for evaluating the clinical status of patients: Imaging studies using isotope-labeled antibodies (56-59) can assess the extent of tumor involvement and measure the effectiveness of therapy; detection of circulating antigen can be used as a diagnostic indicator or be correlated to the response to therapy (60). Of potential therapeutic value in the treatment of lung cancer are those monoclonal antibodies that have direct cytotoxic or growth-inhibiting effects on pulmonary malignancies. This type of approach to tumor therapy has recently been demonstrated for the treatment of B-cell lymphoma using anti-idiotype monoclonal antibodies (15-17). Ancillary reagents used for increasing the killing potency of monoclonal antibodies include conjugating drugs, toxins, radionuclides, or polymorphonuclear leukocytes and the use of antibody specificity to target therapy (56,61,62). In addition, antibodies can convey tumor cell specificity to liposomes containing cytotoxic agents (63). All of these clinical applications await the isolation and characterization of antibodies with sufficient tumor selectivity and the design of appropriate clinical trials.

A more novel approach to lung cancer therapy could be produced by monoclonal antibodies that block the stimulating effects of "autocrine" mediators. It has been proposed by Sporn and Todaro (64) that malignant cells may produce hormone-like peptides that help propagate the tumor mass. This autostimulating effect has been coined "autocrine secretion" and is the underlying basis of the sarcoma growth factor, which was first isolated from the conditioned medium of cultures of mouse 3T3 cells transformed by Moloney sarcoma virus (65). Similar growth factors have been isolated from the conditioned medium of cultures of a variety of human tumor cell lines (66). As we have previously discussed, SCLC tumors and cell lines have been shown to exhibit multiple hormone secretion (43, 67,68). In addition, a neuroendocrine-like function has also been assigned to this histological type of lung cancer by the demonstration that SCLC cells contain bombesin (32,69,70). Recently, Carney and Oie (71) from our laboratory have shown that bombesin has a growth-stimulating effect on SCLC propagation in vitro, thereby implicating this neuropeptide in an "autocrine" mode of action. We feel that monoclonal antibodies that block mediator-receptor interaction (i.e., anti-mediator or anti-receptor antibodies) should effectively suppress tumor cell growth. Indeed, there is experimental precedence that supports this line of thinking. Warren and co-workers (72) have produced a rat monoclonal antibody to human nerve growth factor that cross-reacts with mouse nerve growth factor and mitigates the mediator's biological activity on mouse neurites. Trowbridge and Frederick (73) have developed a monoclonal antibody to the transferrin receptor that blocks transferring binding and abrogate human tumor cell proliferation. Our anti-bombesin antibody (2A11) has been shown to block bombesin-receptor interaction (Dr. T. Moody, George Washington University, unpublished observation) and thus has potential SCLC suppressive properties. A confirmatory study for evaluating the effect of antibody 2A11 on SCLC growth is now underway in our laboratory (Drs. Carney and Fargion), with preliminary data showing promising results.

Although the impact of Kohler and Milstein's initial observations have not yet been fully exploited by tumor cell biologists, their technological achievement has made a major contribution in the diagnosis and therapeutic approach to human malignancies. We feel the potential usefulness of monoclonal antibodies in a therapeutic sense could be maximized by adjuvant application, that is to say, concomitant introduction of anti-tumor reagents as a mixed cocktail, combining cytotoxic antibodies with those antibodies that suppress tumor cell propagation, to invoke a synergistic response to the total malignant process. The concept of using adjuvant antibody therapy promises interesting possibilities for the future treatment of human neoplasms.

CONCLUSION

In this chapter we have presented a brief overview of the fundamental technology utilized in the derivation of lung cancer-selective monoclonal antibodies. We have outlined the potential usefulness of such reagents as diagnostic and therapeutic tools against human pulmonary malignancies. In addition, we have introduced an innovative approach for suppressing tumor cell growth by using monoclonal antibodies that nullify the biological effect of specific "autocrine factors." It is evident that tumor cell biologists and clinicians have only begun to appreciate the seemingly unlimited potential of Köhler and Milstein's original findings. We feel that a true renaissance in the study of human malignancies can be achieved with the use of appropriate monoclonal antibodies and that these molecular probes will ultimately lead to a better understanding of the cellular processes governing tumor growth, genetics, and metastasis.

REFERENCES

1. G. Köhler and C. Milstein, *Nature 256*:495 (1975).
2. J. Schlom, D. Wunderlich, and Y. A. Teramoto, *Proc. Nat. Acad. Sci. U.S.A. 77*:6841 (1980).
3. L. M. Nadler, P. Stashenko, R. Hardy, and S. F. Schlossman, *J. Immunol. 125*:570 (1980).
4. R. H. Kennett and F. Gilbert, *Science 203*:1120 (1979).
5. R. Levy, J. Dilley, R. I. Fox, and R. Warnke, *Proc. Nat. Acad. Sci. U.S.A. 76*:6552 (1979).
6. J. Rite, J. M. Pesando, J. Notis-McConarty, H. Lazarus, and S. F. Schlossman, *Nature 283*:583 (1980).
7. J. F. Schregg, A. C. Diserens, S. Carrel, R. S. Accola, and N. de Tribolet, *Cancer Res. 41*:1290 (1981).
8. M. Herlyn, Z. Steplewski, D. Herlyn, and H. Koprowski, *Proc. Nat. Acad. Sci. U.S.A. 76*:1438 (1980).
9. H. Koprowski, Z. Steplewski, K. Mitchell, M. Herlyn, D. Herlyn, and P. Fuhrer, *Somatic Cell Genet. 5*:957 (1979).
10. J. L. Magnani, M. Brochkaus, D. F. Smith, U. Ginsburg, M. Blasczyk, K. F. Mitchell, Z. Steplewski, and H. Koprowski, *Science 212*:55 (1981).
11. H. Koprowski, Z. Steplewski, D. Herlyn, and M. Herlyn, *Proc. Nat. Acad. Sci. U.S.A. 75*:3405 (1978).
12. K. Imai, A. Ng, and S. Ferrone, *J. Nat. Cancer Inst. 66*:489 (1981).
13. M. Y. Yeh, I. Hellstrom, J. P. Brown, G. A. Warner, J. A. Hansen, and R. E. Hellstrom, *Proc. Nat. Acad. Sci. U.S.A. 79*:2927 (1979).
14. W. G. Dippold, K. O. Lloyd, L. T. C. Li, H. Ikeda, H. F. Oettgen, and L. J. Old, *Proc. Nat. Acad. Sci. U.S.A. 77*:6114 (1980).
15. R. A. Miller, D. G. Maloney, J. McKillop, and R. Levy, *Blood 58*:78 (1981).
16. R. A. Miller and R. Levy, *Lancet 2*:226 (1981).
17. R. A. Miller, D. G. Maloney, R. Warnke, and R. Levy, *N. Engl. J. Med. 306*: 517 (1982).
18. F. Cuttitta, S. Rosen, A. F. Gazdar, and J. D. Minna, *Proc. Nat. Acad. Sci. U.S.A. 78*:4591 (1981).
19. J. D. Minna, F. Cuttitta, S. Rosen, P. A. Bunn, D. N. Carney, A. F. Gazdar, and S. Krasnow, *In Vitro 17*:1058 (1981).
20. T. Mazauric, K. F. Mitchell, G. J. Letchworth, H. Koprowski, and Z. Steplewski, *Cancer Res. 42*:150 (1982).
21. B. G. Brenner, S. Jothy, J. Shuster, and A. Fuks, *Cancer Res. 42*:3187 (1982).
22. J. D. Minna, G. A. Higgins, and E. J. Glatstein, in *Principles and Practice of Oncology* (V. T. DeVita et al., eds.), Lippincott, Philadelphia, 1981, p. 396.

23. A. F. Gazdar, D. N. Carney, J. G. Guccion, and S. B. Baylin, in *Small Cell Lung Cancer* (F. A. Greco et al., eds.), Grune and Stratton, New York, 1981, p. 145.

24. M. J. Matthews and P. R. Gordon, in *Lung Cancer—Clinical Diagnosis and Treatment* (M. J. Strauss, ed.), Grune and Stratton, New York, 1977, p. 49.

25. M. J. Matthews and A. F. Gazdar, in *Lung Cancer—Advances in Research and Treatment* (R. B. Livingston, ed.), Martinus Nijhoff, The Hague, 1981, p. 283.

26. A. F. Gazdar, D. N. Carney, J. G. Guccion, J. Whang-Peng, M. H. Zweig, T W. Moody, P. J. Marangos, and J. D. Minna, submitted for publication.

27. A. F. Gazdar, D. N. Carney, E. K. Russell, H. L. Sims, S. B. Baylin, P. A. Bunn, J. G. Guccion, and J. D. Minna, *Cancer Res. 40*:3502 (1980).

28. D. N. Carney, A. F. Gazdar, and J. D. Minna, *Cancer Res. 40*:1820 (1980).

29. E. Simms, A. F. Gazdar, P. G. Abrams, and J. D. Minna, *Cancer Res. 40*: 4356 (1980).

30. D. N. Carney, P. A. Bunn, A. F. Gazdar, J. A. Pagan, and J. D. Minna, *Proc. Nat. Acad. Sci. U.S.A. 78*:3185 (1981).

31. A. F. Gazdar, M. H. Zweig, D. N. Carney, A. C. Van Steirtegh, S. B. Baylin, and J. D. Minna, *Cancer Res. 41*:2773 (1981).

32. T. W. Moody, C. B. Pert, A. F. Gazdar, D. N. Carney, and J. D. Minna, *Science 214*:1246 (1981).

33. P. A. Radice and W. C. Dermody, *Proc. Am. Assoc. Cancer Res. 21*:41 (1980).

34. J. Whang-Peng, C. S. Kao-Shan, E. C. Les, P. A. Bunn, D. N. Carney, A. F. Gazdar, and J. D. Minna, *Science 215*:181 (1982).

35. G. Galfré, S. C. Howe, C. Milstein, G. W. Butcher, and J. D. Howard, *Nature 266*:550 (1977).

36. J. F. Kearney, A. Radbruch, and B. Liesegang, *J. Immunol. 123*:1548 (1979).

37. R. H. Kennett, K. A. Denis, A. S. Tung, and N. R. Klinman, *Curr. Top. Microbiol. Immunol. 81*:77 (1978).

38. R. C. Nowinski, M. E. Lostrom, M. R. Tam, M. R. Stone, and W. N. Brunette, *Virology 93*:111 (1979).

39. A. G. Pearse, *J. Histochem. Cytochem. 17*:303 (1969).

40. S. B. Baylin, M. D. Abeloff, G. Goodwin, D. N. Carney, and A. F. Gazdar, *Cancer Res. 40*:1990 (1980).

41. D. Schmechel, P. J. Marangos, and M. Brightman, *Nature 276*:834 (1978).

42. F. J. Tapia, J. M. Polak, A. J. Barbosa, S. R. Bloom, P. J. Marangos, C. Dermody, and A. G. Pearse, *Lancet 1*:808 (1981).

43. G. D. Sorenson, O. S. Pettengill, T. Brinck-Johnsen, C. C. Cate, and L. H. Maurer, *Cancer 47*:1289 (1981).

44. R. T. Egan, L. H. Maurer, R. J. Forcier, and M. Tolloh, *Cancer 33*:527 (1974).

45. T. W. Moody and C. B. Pert, *Biochem. Biophys. Res. Commun. 90*:7 (1979).

46. T. W. Moody, C. B. Pert, J. Rivier, and M. R. Brown, *Proc. Nat. Acad. Sci. U.S.A. 75*:5372 (1978).

47. H. -J. Yang and S. Hakomori, *J. Biol. Chem. 246*:1192 (1971).

48. M. Brockhaus, J. L. Magnani, M. Herlyn, M. Blaszczyk, Z. Steplewski, H. Koprowski, and V. Ginsburg, *Arch. Biochem. Biophys. 217*:000 (1982).

49. H. C. Gooi, T. Feizi, A. Kapadia, B. B. Knowles, D. Solter, and M. J. Evans, *Nature 292*:156 (1981).

50. S. B. Baylin, A. F. Gazdar, J. D. Minna, S. D. Bernal, and J. H. Shaper, *Proc. Nat. Acad. Sci. U.S.A. 79*:4650 (1982).

51. C. R. Taylor, *Arch. Pathol. Lab. Med. 102*:113 (1978).

52. A. G. Fan and P. K. Nakane, *J. Immunol. Methods 47*:129 (1981).

53. S. M. Hsu, L. Raine, and H. Fanger, *Am. J. Clin. Pathol. 75*:734 (1981).

54. S. M. Hsu, L. Raine, and H. Fanger, *J. Histochem. Cytochem. 29*:577 (1981).

55. S. M. Hsu and E. Soban, *J. Hisotchem. Cytochem. 30*:000 (1982).

56. D. A. Scheinberg, M. Strand, and O. A. Gansow, *Science 215*:1511 (1982).

57. D. A. Scheinberg and M. Strand, *Cancer Res. 42*:44 (1982).

58. B. Ballou, G. Levine, T. R. Hakala, and S. Solter, *Science 206*:844 (1979).

59. P. A. Farrands, A. C. Perkins, M. V. Pimm, J. D. Hardy, M. J. Embleton, R. W. Baldwin, and J. D. Hardcastle, *Lancet 2*:397 (1982).

60. H. Koprowski, M. Herlyn, Z. Steplewski, and H. F. Sears, *Science 212*:53 (1981).

61. S. Olsnes, *Nature 290*:84 (1981).

62. M. Belles-Isles and M. Page, *Int. J. Immunopharmacol. 3*:97 (1981).

63. L. D. Leserman, P. Machy, and J. Barbet, *Nature 293*:226 (1981).

64. M. B. Sporn and G. J. Todaro, *N. Engl. J. Med. 303*:878 (1980).

65. J. E. DeLarco and G. J. Todaro, *Proc. Nat. Acad. Sci. U.S.A. 75*:4001 (1978).

66. G. J. Todaro, C. Fryling, and J. E. DeLarco, *Proc. Nat. Acad. Sci. U.S.A. 77*:5258 (1980).

67. M. Hattori, H. Imura, S. Matsukura, Y. Yoshimoto, K. Sekita, T. Tomomatsu, M. Kyogoku, and T. Kameya, *Cancer 43*:2429 (1979).

68. Y. Hirata, S. Matsukura, H. Imura, T. Yakura, S. Ihjima, C. Nagase, and M. Itoh, *Cancer 38*:2572 (1976).

69. S. M. Wood, J. R. Wood, M. A. Ghatei, Y. C. Lee, D. O'Shaughnessy, and S. R. Bloom, *J. Clin. Endocrinol. Metab. 53*:1310 (1982).

70. M. D. Erisman, R. A. Linnoila, O. Hernandez, R. P. DiAugustine, and L. H. Lazarus, *Proc. Nat. Acad. Sci. U.S.A. 79*:2379 (1982).

71. H. K. Oie and D. N. Carney, in *The Endocrine Lung in Health and Disease* (K. L. Becker and A. F. Gazdar, eds.), Saunders, Philadelphia (in press).

72. S. L. Warren, M. Fanger, and K. E. Neet, *Science 210*:910 (1980).

73. I. S. Trowbridge and L. Frederick, *Proc. Nat. Acad. Sci. U.S.A. 79*:1175 (1982).

7 MONOCLONAL ANTIBODIES TO OSTEOGENIC SARCOMA ANTIGENS

Michael Jim Embleton / Cancer Research Campaign Laboratories, University of Nottingham, Nottingham, England

INTRODUCTION

The detection of antigens associated with human tumors has in the past been imprecise and often fraught with problems of an artifactual nature. This is largely because, apart from studies in which cancer patients have been tested for delayed cutaneous hypersensitivity to tumor extracts, the majority of investigations have employed in vitro methods to assess the reactivity of sera or lymphocytes against tumor cells or subcellular fractions. Assays for cell-mediated cytotoxicity are no longer considered to be appropriate for identifying tumor-associated antigens, because the most efficient mediators of cytotoxicity in most assays are natural killer cells, which are present in both healthy donors and cancer patients to approxi-

Table 1 Detection of Serum Antibodies Against Cell Lines from Two Osteogenic Sarcoma Patients by Indirect Radiolabeled Protein A Assay

Serum donors	Target cell donor M. U.		Target cell donor P. R.	
	Tumor (791T)	Fibroblasts	Tumor (788T)	Fibroblasts
Tumor donor	7/16	6/10	0/14	0/14
Other osteogenic sarcoma patients	4/8	4/8	–	–
Other cancer patients	2/16	–	–	–
Normal control donors	6/41	6/26	0/11	1/19
Multiparous pregnant donors	0/21	0/21	0/15	0/15

mately equal degrees. Other assays for cell-mediated immunity exist, but they
have not achieved the popularity at one time attained by cytotoxicity tests.

Serology of human tumors is also beset with problems, but despite this there
is evidence indicating that patients with some tumors, including osteogenic sarcoma, are able to mount an immune reaction against their tumor.

There have been a few reports of cell-mediated immunity to osteogenic sarcomas, detected either by cytotoxicity (1,2) or by lymphocyte blastogenesis
assays (3,4), but most of the evidence has been obtained by serological methods.
The earliest report was in 1968 from Morton and Malmgren (5), who demonstrated
antibody reactions by observing cytoplasmic immunofluorescence of fixed cells
obtained from imprints of sarcoma tissues. Four osteogenic sarcoma patients
were reactive against their own tumor and reactivity was also seen in sera from
members of their families (85%) or close associates (91%). Normal donor sera
were positive in 29% of the cases. Later studies, mainly employing cultured osteogenic sarcoma cells, have amply confirmed and extended these observations by
means of immunofluorescence, complement fixation, and complement-dependent
cytotoxicity assays (6-14). On the basis of such work, one group tentatively identified three classes of antigen associated with osteogenic sarcomas, which they
designated S1, S2, and S3 (15-18). These antigens were not, however, specific
for osteogenic sarcoma.

An overall appraisal of these and later investigations (19-22) reveals several
important problems. In many studies it was difficult or impossible to detect antibody activity against fresh osteogenic sarcoma cells, the cells becoming positive

only after culture. Moreover, the expression of antigens tended to fluctuate over a period of time. Even more crucial, in some studies it has been clearly shown that sera from osteogenic sarcoma patients react equally well against cultured fibroblasts and that sera from normal subjects are as reactive as those from sarcoma patients (15,19,20). Data obtained by the author also show this trend (Table 1). Sera from the autochthonous host or allogeneic osteogenic sarcoma patients were reactive against both tumor cells and fibroblasts derived from one patient (M. U.) in a radiolabeled protein A binding assay. Control sera were also positive with both tumor cells and fibroblasts, although the proportion of positives was less than that seen with sarcoma patients. With a second patient (P. R.), however, neither autochthonous nor control sera reacted with cultured target cells.

At one time, cross-reactivity observed between patient and allogeneic tumors and the frequent finding of reactivity by regular associates of the patients were considered to constitute evidence for a viral etiology. However, cross-reactivity with normal sera and normal cells would dismiss this possibility. Various factors have been identified as causing nonspecific reactivity of sera with osteogenic sarcomas. Bloom (13) has shown that mycoplasma infection of target cells increases their tendency to react with human sera, and that cross-reactivity may often be due to the expression of blood group antigens by cultured tumor cells (14). Rosenberg and colleagues claim that cross-reactions such as those observed between osteogenic sarcomas, fibroblasts, and normal sera are due to the expression of fetal antigens in cultured cells (19,20). They were able to show that absorption of normal sera with fetal tissue removed cytolytic activity for both osteogenic sarcoma cells and fibroblasts, and that similar absorption of sarcoma patients' sera removed activity against fibroblasts while antibody lysing tumor cells was retained (21). The suggestion was that osteogenic sarcoma patients had antibodies to tumor-associated antigens in addition to antibodies to fetal antigens, detection of the former being prevented by the cross-reactivity of the latter. However, as shown in Table 1, multiparous donors did not react with osteogenic sarcoma lines 791T and 788T and, furthermore, attempts to absorb antibody with fetal tissue failed (A. S. Eiras and M. J. Embleton, unpublished data). Another suggested cause of cross-reactivity is the presence of antibodies to culture medium components, especially fetal calf serum, which may become incorporated into cell membranes. Thus Irie and Morton (22) identified fetal calf serum as the origin of a new membrane antigen acquired by cultured cells and suggested that human sera often contain antibodies to this component. Yet a further possibility is that immune complexes in sera might bind nonspecifically to cultured cells, and several authors have shown that osteogenic sarcoma patients tend to have high levels of circulating immune complexes (23-26).

In view of the aforementioned problems, the use of the patients' sera for detection of antigens associated with osteogenic sarcoma cannot be considered a practical proposition. Xenogeneic antisera are also unsuitable because it is impossible to be sure that all nonrelevant antibodies are removed by absorption. In this light, monoclonal antibodies produced by somatic cell hybrids offer an attractive alternative, and it is for this reason that monoclonal antibodies were prepared against osteogenic sarcoma cell line 791T (27,28).

CHARACTERIZATION OF MONOCLONAL ANTIBODIES TO OSTEOGENIC SARCOMAS

Characterization and Specificity

BALB/c mice were immunized against the osteogenic sarcoma cell line 791T by two intraperitoneal injections of 10^7 cells 1 week apart. One week later the mice were given 2×10^6 cells by intracardiac injection and after a further period of 5 days one mouse was sacrificed and its spleen cells were fused with cells of the BALB/c myeloma P3-NS1-Ag-4 (abbreviated to P3NS1) by the method of Galfré et al. (29). The supernatants of the resulting hybridoma cultures were screened for antibody binding to 791T cells using an indirect radioiodinated protein A assay (27). Two supernatants showed preferential binding to 791T cells, but were negative with a small panel of normal fibroblasts or unrelated tumor lines. These two 791T-positive hybridomas were cloned in soft agar and monoclonal antibodies produced by them were tested, using the radioiodinated protein A assay, on a range of target cells, including cultured osteogenic sarcoma cells, other cultured tumor cells, cultured fibroblasts, and some freshly prepared normal cells (Table 2). The most strongly reactive of these antibodies was designated α791T/36, and the other (with a low titer and binding fewer counts per minute of [^{125}I] protein per 10^5 791T cells) was designated α791T/48(27,28). Antibody α791T/36 bound to 7 of 13 osteogenic sarcoma lines, the strongest reactions occurring with 791T and 788T. Compared with this, α791T/48 bound to only 3 of the 13 lines. Neither antibody reacted with fibroblasts derived from the tumor donor (791SK from skin, or 860 and 870 from cultures of tumor-derived cells) or with fibroblasts from donors of cross-reactive osteogenic sarcomas (e.g., 788SK and 805SK). Reactions with lymphocytes and erythrocytes from a range of donors were also negative. Immunoperoxidase staining of frozen sections also revealed no reactivity of α791T/36 with human liver, lymphoid, brain, or breast tissue. It thus appeared that both monoclonal antibodies recognized antigens expressed on tumors rather than on normal cells, although it cannot be discounted that more exhaustive testing might reveal reactivity against some normal components.

Cross-tests on cells cultured from other tumor types indicated that neither antibody was specific for osteogenic sarcomas. Antibody α791T/36 was strongly positive for prostate carcinoma EB33 and HeLa cells, and more weakly reactive with colon carcinoma lines HT29, Loach, and LS174T, and lung carcinoma A549.

Antibody α791T/48 cross-reacted with none of these lines, but reacted with breast carcinoma SKBr3 and a fibroblastic fetal bone marrow line, 74BM. The only cell lines against which both hybridomas were reactive were osteogenic sarcomas 791T and 788T. This strongly suggests that the two monoclonal antibodies recognized separate epitopes, which both happen to be shared by 791T and 788T, but are otherwise randomly distributed among other tumor cell lines and possibly some fetal cells.

Absorption studies confirmed the cross-reactivity of α791T/36 determined in the direct tests. In the absorption tests, aliquots of supernatant diluted 1:10 were incubated with various cell lines, at 10^8 cells per milliliter, before being tested for antibody activity against 791T target cells or the cell line used for absorption. The results (Table 3) indicated that absorption with any of the cross-reactive cell lines could remove antibody reactive with both 791T and the absorbing cells, but absorption with non-cross-reactive cells (Mel-2a, Mel-57, and PA-1) had little effect. The positive cross-reactions were therefore due to a shared epitope rather than nonspecific antibody uptake.

Purification of both antibodies was achieved by affinity chromatography on protein A linked to Sepharose 4B. Ascites lines prepared by passaging the cloned hybridomas in BALB/c mice produced antibody concentrations in ascites fluid 50-100 times that in culture supernatants. The subclasses of the two preparations were determined by radioisotopic assays in which purified antibody was adsorbed to vinyl microtiter plates, followed by reaction with ^{125}I-labeled specific subclass antisera. By this means it was determined that both were IgG_{2b}, and also that both hybridoma supernatants contained the mouse kappa light chain characteristic of the P3NS1 myeloma.

Since IgG_{2b} is a complement-fixing subclass, it was of interest to determine whether the monoclonal antibodies could mediate complement-dependent cytotoxicity. This was established using a ^{51}Cr release assay employing rabbit complement (Fig. 1). Both antibodies were cytotoxic in the presence of complement, this reactivity being greater with α791T/36. Cytolysis of different target cells followed exactly the same specificity as previously established in [^{125}I] protein A binding assays.

Direct Binding to Target Cells

To directly detect the binding properties of α791T/36 and α791T/48, the monoclonal antibodies were labeled with ^{125}I, using the chloramine T procedure (30), giving preparations with a specific activity of about 10 μg/mg protein. The specificity of binding of these labeled products was tested on a selected range of target cells, as shown in Table 4. The sensitivity of direct binding by labeled antibody was much less than that of the indirect protein A binding assay, but on the whole the previously established specificity was preserved. Antibody α791T/36

Table 2 Cells Reacting with Monoclonal Antibodies Against Osteogenic
Sarcoma Line 791T

Tissue type	Reactions with antibody α791T/36		Reactions with antibody α791T/48	
	Positive	Negative	Positive	Negative
Osteogenic sarcoma	791T[a]	781T	791T	845T
	788T[b]	803T	788T	805T
	845T	836T	781T	2 OS
	805T[c]	706T		T278
	2 OS	888T		393T
	T278	792T		803T
	393T			836T
				206T
				888T
				792T
Colon carcinoma	HT29	HCT8		HT29
	Loach	HRT18		HCT8
	LS174T			HRT18
				Loach
Breast carcinoma		734B	SKBr3	734B
		SKBr3		HS578T
		HS578T		MCF-7
		MCF-7		
Lung carcinoma	A549	A427		A549
		9812		A427
				9812
Prostate carcinoma	EB33			EB33
Cervix carcinoma	HeLa			HeLa
Bladder carcinoma		T24		T24
Ovarian carcinoma		PA-1		PA-1
Melanoma		MeWO		MeWO
		Mel-2a		Mel-2a
		Mel-57		Mel-57
		NK1-4		NK1-4
		RPMI 5966		RPMI 5966
		Mel-Swift		Mel-Swift
Lymphoblastoid cells		Raji		Raji
		K562		K562

Table 2 (Continued)

Skin fibroblasts	791SK[a]		791SK
	788SK[b]		788SK
	805SK[c]		803SK
	803SK		181SK
	836SK		
	181SK		
Lung fibroblasts	618Lu		618Lu
Tumor-derived	860[a]		860
fibroblasts	870[a]		870
Fetal bone marrow	181BM	74BM	
	74BM		
Freshly prepared	Erythro-		Erythro-
normal cells	cytes		cytes
	Leukocytes		Leukocytes
Frozen sections[d]	Liver		
	Spleen		
	Brain		
	Breast		

[a]These lines were derived from donor M. U.
[b]These lines were derived from donor P. R.
[c]These lines were derived from donor Q. L.
[d]Frozen sections were tested by immunoperoxidase staining.

bound strongly to 791T, 788T, and HeLa cells, although weakly reactive cell lines (A549, HT29) gave only background levels of binding, no higher than seen with cell lines known to be non-cross-reactive with 791T (Table 2). Binding of labeled α791T/48 was very weak compared with α791T/36, but nevertheless it bound more strongly to 791T and 788T than to other cell lines. It was, however, negative with breast carcinoma SKBr3, to which it was reactive in indirect protein A tests.

Using directly labeled antibodies, and knowing that the specificity of binding to the strongly reacting cell lines was unchanged by the radioiodination procedure, it was possible to make an estimate of the number of antibody binding sites on 791T target cells. Cells were incubated with increasing quantities of radiolabeled antibody until saturation was achieved. Saturation corresponded to binding of 2.2×10^6 IgG molecules per cell in the case of α791T/36, and 2×10^5 IgG molecules per cell in the case of α791T/48, using calculations devised by Fazekas de St. Groth (31). Osteogenic sarcoma 788T and HeLa cells bound 1.6×10^6 and 1.9×10^6 α791T/36 IgG molecules per cell, respectively, and more weakly

Table 3 Absorption of α791T/36 Monoclonal Antibody by Cultured Tumor Cells

Absorbing cells	Percentage of absorption[a] of antibody reacting with target cells					
	791T	788T	EB33	HeLa	A549	HT29
791T osteogenic sarcoma	97	91	94	90	96	76
788T osteogenic sarcoma	92	93				
EB33 prostate carcinoma	95		94			
HeLa cervix carcinoma	94			92		
A549 lung carcinoma	100				75	
HT29 colon carcinoma	70					70
Mel-2a melanoma[b]	24					
Mel-57 melanoma	15					
PA-1 ovarian carcinoma	11					

[a]Absorption was accomplished by incubating 10^8 cells per milliliter of hybridoma supernatant (diluted 1:10) for 1 hr at 37°C. Cells were removed by centrifugation and the absorbed supernatant was tested using a [^{125}I] protein A binding assay (27).
[b]Melanomas Mel-2a and Mel-57 and ovarian tumor PA-1 were not cross-reactive with α791T/36 (Table 2).

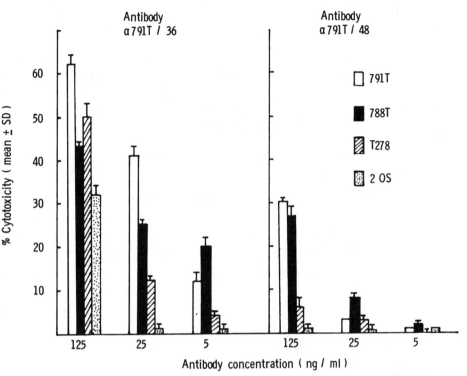

Figure 1 Complement-dependent cytotoxicity against human tumor cells by two monoclonal antibodies to osteogenic sarcoma line 791T. Aliquots of 10^4 ^{51}Cr-labeled cells were incubated with affinity-purified monoclonal antibody (100 μl per well) in round-bottom microtiter plates and 100 μl of rabbit serum were added as a source of complement. After 2 hr. of incubation at $37°$C the percentage release of ^{51}Cr was estimated by measuring the radioactivity of supernatant samples. Culture medium was used as a negative control and cells exposed to 1% sodium dodecyl sulfate provided a "maximum release" figure. The percent of cytotoxicity was calculated as

$$\frac{\%\,^{51}\text{Cr release in test} - \%\,^{51}\text{Cr release in controls}}{\text{maximum}\,\%\,^{51}\text{Cr release} - \%\,^{51}\text{Cr release in controls}} \times 100$$

Complement alone or antibody with heat-activated complement were not cytotoxic.

reactive osteogenic sarcomas (T278, 393T, and 2 OS) bound between 4.3×10^5 and 5.3×10^5. These cells did not produce detectable cross-reactions with α791T/48 in previous tests (Table 2) and the number of α791T/48 IgG molecules they bound was between 2×10^4 and 4×10^4 molecules of α791T/48 per cell. These low levels of binding probably represent nonspecific protein adsorption.

Table 4 Binding of Radioiodinated Monoclonal Antibodies to Tumor
Target Cells

		Mean percentage of labeled antibody bound	
Target cell	Tumor type	791T/36	791T/48
791T	Osteogenic sarcoma	7.85	0.78
788T	Osteogenic sarcoma	8.83	0.52
888T	Osteogenic sarcoma	0.89	NT[a]
HeLa	Cervix carcinoma	8.07	0.27
HCT8	Colon carcinoma	0.91	0.22
HRT18	Colon carcinoma	1.12	0.14
HT29	Colon carcinoma	0.75	0.24
A549	Lung carcinoma	1.11	0.32
A427	Lung carcinoma	0.70	0.25
T24	Bladder carcinoma	0.97	0.18
EB33	Prostate carcinoma	NT	0.36
PA-1	Ovarian carcinoma	0.32	NT
SKBr3	Breast carcinoma	0.47	0.38
RPMI 5966	Melanoma	1.50	0.22

[a]NT, not tested.

Binding Inhibition Assays

The differing target cell specificities of the two anti-791T monoclonal antibodies
indicate that they probably react with different epitopes. Confirmation of this
was obtained in experiments in which the binding of the radioiodinated antibody (50
μg protein per 10^5 cells) was inhibited by pretreating the target cells with unlabeled antibody (4 mg per 10^5 cells). In these experiments the effects of "cold"
α791T/36 and α791T/48 were compared with the effects of culture medium (or
P3NS1 culture supernatant) or unrelated monoclonal antibodies (Table 5).
Binding of ^{125}I-labeled α791T/36 to 791T, 788T, and HeLa target cells was inhibited by "cold" α791T/36, but not by α791T/48 or two monoclonal antibodies
raised against a melanoma and a colorectal carcinoma cell line. Conversely, binding of labeled α791T/48 was inhibited only by nonlabeled α791T/48 and was
not affected by prior incubation of 791T or 788T target cells with α791T/36
or unrelated antibodies. It is thus clear that the two antibodies react with

Table 5 Inhibition of Binding of Radioiodinated Monoclonal Antibodies to Cells Pretreated with Unlabeled Antibodies

Target cell	Blocking antibody	Mean percentage of inhibition of binding of	
		α791T/36	α791T/48
791T	SC3982[a]	< 7.8	NT[b]
	αHTR18/2/33b[c]	< 1.3	5.3
	a791T/36	80.0	< 5.3
	a791T/48	< 9.3	62.6
788T	SC3982	9.2	NT
	aHRT18/2/33b	6.1	5.0
	a791T/36	71.2	< 1.5
	a791T/48	< 9.5	67.0
HeLa	SC3982	10.5	
	aHRT18/2/33b	K 6.0	
	a791T/36	68.3	
	a791T/48	5.9	

[a]Anti-melanoma monoclonal antibody.

[b]Anti-colon carcinoma monoclonal antibody.

[c]Anti-colon carcinoma.

separate epitopes, although these studies do not discern whether these epitopes are present on separate molecules or represent different portions of the same molecule.

Blocking tests were extended to serum from the donor of osteogenic sarcoma 791T (M. U.) in order to determine whether the epitope recognized by α791T/36 was also recognized by the patient (Table 6). In these experiments, autochthonous and control sera with known positive or negative activity against 791T cells in [^{125}I] protein A binding tests were preincubated with 791T target cells before incubation of target cells with ^{125}I-labeled α791T/36 monoclonal antibody. None of the sera tested inhibited binding of [^{125}I] α791T/36. It was thus apparent that antibodies that were present in some of the sera were not directed against the component recognized by the monoclonal antibody.

TUMOR-LOCALIZING PROPERTIES

Uptake by Osteogenic Sarcoma Xenografts

Monoclonal antibody 791T/36 binds much more strongly to 791T cells than α791T/48 and a larger number of molecules are bound at saturation, so this

Table 6 Inhibition of Binding of Radiolabeled α791T/36 Monoclonal Antibody by Tumor Donor Serum

Blocking serum		^{125}I binding ratio[a] in indirect protein A assay	Percentage of inhibition of binding of ^{125}I-labeled α791T/36
Normal donor serun			
	1	1.15	0
	2	0.92	0
	3	1.52	7
	4	8.27 ($P < 0.001$)[a]	3
Tumor host serum			
	1	2.80 ($P < 0.05$)	8
	2	3.30 ($P < 0.001$)	2
	3	1.19	1
	4	1.00	10
	5	2.82 ($P < 0.05$)	9
	6	1.80	2
	7	1.40	−3

[a] Binding ratio = mean cpm bound by cells treated with serum ÷ mean cpm bound by cells treated with culture medium.
[b] Statistical significance assessed by Student's t test.

antibody was chosen as a reagent to explore in vivo localization to 791T tumors growing in immunodeprived mice. Mice of the CBA strain were subjected to thymectomy, treatment with cytosine arabinoside, and whole body gamma irradiation according to the method published by Steel et al. (32). These mice develop progressively growing tumors 2 or 3 weeks after subcutaneous injection of 10^6 791T cells. Cells obtained by dissociation of 791T xenografts were assayed for expression of the α791T/36 defined antigen by fluorescence-activated cell sorting using α791T/36 conjugated to fluorescein isothiocyanate (FITC). Gating conditions for neoplastic cells were established using cultured 791T in order to exclude erythrocytes, infiltrating host lymphoid cells, and stromal cells contained among cells from the xenografts. The FITC-labeled α791T/36 bound to all the tumor cells. Addition of a fourfold excess of unlabeled α791T/36 during the initial staining procedure reduced the mean fluorescence per cell to about 18% of control level (expected reduction 20%). It was thus clear that 791T cells continue to express the monoclonal antibody-defined antigen when growing as a xenograft.

Radiodination of α791T/36 antibody with ^{125}I or ^{131}I was accomplished using the iodogen procedure (33) and preparations of specific activities of 0.25-1.0 μCi/ mg protein were used. Labeled antibody was injected intraperitoneally into the immunodeprived mice with or without 791T tumors, and 24 hr later their serum

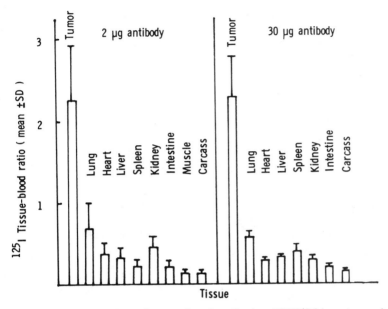

Figure 2 Localization of monoclonal antibody α791T/36 in osteogenic sarcoma 791T xenografts. Mice bearing 791T xenografts were injected intraperitoneally with ^{125}I-labeled α791T/36 at 2 doses (2 and 30 μg). Three days later blood, tumor, and various organs were removed and the percentage of radioactivity per gram of tissue was measured. The tissue/blood ratio was calculated as the mean percentage of radioactivity per gram of tissue divided by the percentage of radioactivity per gram of blood.

was removed and chromatographed on Sephacryl 300, in comparison with a mixture of labeled α791T/36 and normal mouse serum. In all three cases the elution profile was similar, radioactivity being associated with a peak corresponding to mouse immunoglobulin. Furthermore, radioactivity could be precipitated with rabbit anti-mouse immunoglobulin from serum of mice inoculated with radioiodinated α791T/36 and antibody in these sera was able to bind directly to 791T target cells. The antibody was therefore not grossly aggregated or degraded following injection into mice.

For organ distribution studies, the labeled antibody was similarly injected intraperitoneally into 791T tumor-bearing mice and 1-6 days later mice were sacrificed. They were exsanguinated and their tumor, visceral organs, muscle, and bone tissue were removed for estimation of radioactivity in a gamma counter. The activity was expressed as the percentage of injected radioactivity per gram of tissue, divided by the percentage of radioactivity per gram of blood. Tumors were examined 12-30 days after injection of cells (tumor mass 45-201 mg) and in all

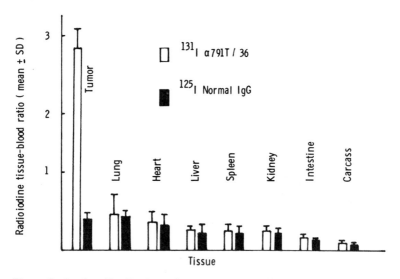

Figure 3 In vivo distribution of radiolabeled normal immunoglobulin compared with monoclonal antibody in 791T xenografted mice. Mice bearing 791T xeno-grafts were injected with ^{131}I-labeled α791T/36 and ^{125}I-labeled normal mouse IgG simultaneously. Three days later tissue/blood ratios for tumor and various organs were calculated as in Figure 2.

cases the tumor/blood ratios of radioactivity were significantly greater than ratios obtained with any of the normal tissues or the residual carcass. Figure 2 shows the organ distribution at 3 days after administration of ^{125}I-labeled 791T/36 at doses of 2 or 30 μg protein. The organ exhibiting the highest localization apart from the tumor was lung, and at both antibody doses the activity in the lung was much lower than in the tumor on a weight basis. Repeated tests with antibody at doses between 2 and 50 μg per mouse confirmed these findings. In some experiments mice were simultaneously inoculated with ^{131}I-labeled 791T/36 and ^{125}I-labeled normal mouse IgG$_{2b}$./ In this case, the tissue/blood ratios of normal immunoglobulin were low for the tumor and all normal tissues examined (Fig. 3), while the ratios for ^{131}I-labeled α791/36 were at a similar low level for normal tissues but high for 791T. Localization within 791T tissue was therefore not due to physical characteristics of the tissue which might result nonspecifically in pre-ferential accumulation of labeled immunoglobulin.

Further specificity checks were carried out with tumors, the reactivities of which were known in α791T/36 binding tests (Table 2). Osteogenic sarcoma lines 788T and 2 OS, colon carcinoma line HCT8, and bladder carcinoma line T24 were also grown as xenografts, and the mice were inoculated with ^{125}I-labeled α791T/36. Three days later their tumors and other organs were removed and the tissue/blood ratios of activity calculated. Osteogenic sarcomas 788T and

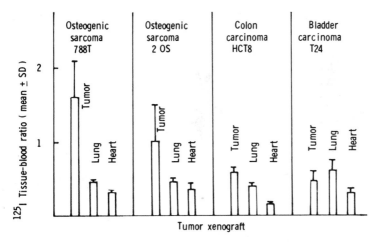

Figure 4 Localization of α791T/36 monoclonal antibody in tumors other than osteogenic sarcoma 791T. Mice bearing tumor xenografts were injected with ^{125}I-labeled α791T/36. Three days later tissue/blood ratios were calculated (as in Figure 2) for tumor and various organs, of which only lung and heart are shown. Liver, kidney, spleen, intestine, muscle, and residual carcass ratios were no higher than that shown for heart in each case. Antibody localization occurred in osteogenic sarcomas 788T and 2 OS, but not in colon carcinoma HCT8 or bladder carcinoma T24.

2 OS exhibited higher ratios than normal tissues (Fig. 4), but the non-cross-reactive lines HCT8 and T24 had ratios equivalent to those in normal tissues. In view of the fact that preferential tumor localization occurred only with tumors that react antigenically with the antibody, it was concluded that this was a true antibody phenomenon rather than due to nonspecific uptake by some tumors.

External Imaging of Xenografts

Mice bearing 791T tumor xenografts were given 20μCi of ^{131}I-labeled α791T/36 intraperitoneally and 48 hr later they were anesthetized with thiopentone. Gamma scintigraphy was carried out using a parallel hole collimator (400 KeV maximum), in which case mice were placed to facilitate an anterior view, or a pinhole collimator, in which case a posterior view was chosen. Distribution of radioactivity within the blood was assessed by intravenous injection of [99m Tc] pertechnetate (20 μCi) and images of ^{131}I and ^{99m}Tc were acquired. Views were stored and processed by computer in a 64 × 64 or 128 × 128 cell matrix. Image enhancement by computerized subtraction of ^{99m}Tc counts from ^{131}I counts clearly delineated subcutaneous 791T growths as areas of increased radioactivity (Fig. 5). Localization using the gamma camera was expressed as the ratio of counts within the region of interest around the tumor, divided by a region of

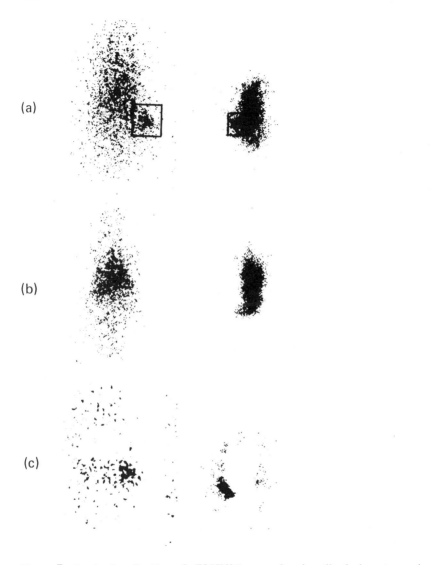

Figure 5   In vivo localization of α791T/36 monoclonal antibody in osteogenic sarcoma 791T xenografts demonstrated by external gamma scintigraphy. Mice bearing 791T xenografts were injected intraperitoneally with ^{131}I-labeled α791T/36 and three days later they were scanned on a gamma camera. Intravenous injection of [^{99m}Tc] pertechnate was also performed in order to acquire an image due to the blood pool. (a) Image acquired with [^{131}I]α791T/36. (b) Image acquired with [^{99m}Tc] pertechnate. (c) Computerized subtraction (a −b) showing enhanced image of tumor. The delineated area is the "region of interest" referred to in the text. The images here were obtained with two separate mice.

equivalent area on the contralateral side of the mouse. Typically this ratio was around 2:1 using $[^{131}I]\alpha$791T/36 only, and after subtraction of ^{99m}Tc it ranged up to 10:1. At this level of localization, achieved in larger tumors, between 11 and 13% of injected ^{131}I became localized within the tumor.

TARGETING OF THERAPEUTIC AGENTS

Therapeutic Drugs and Toxins

Knowing that tumor-directed monoclonal antibodies are able to localize in tumors, one of their most interesting potential applications is therapy, either directly by infusion of the purified antibody (34–36) or by using the antibody to direct a cytotoxic agent to the site (37–41). Of the two options, the latter seems at the present time to be more attractive. Passive serotherapy appears to be effective mainly with lymphoid tumors, while other tumors may be resistant to monoclonal antibody in vivo, although they may be susceptible to antibody-mediated cytotoxicity in vitro (42). Osteogenic sarcoma 791T, for example, is not suppressed in vivo by treatment of the immunodeprived murine host with α791T/36 monoclonal antibody.

Several cytotoxic agents have been conjugated to monoclonal antibodies for use as "immunotoxins," these including ricin A chain (37–40), ricin "blocked" by binding to lactose (41), diphtheria toxin A chain (38–40), and adriamycin (43). Using the 791T osteogenic sarcoma as a model, we are currently investigating conjugates prepared with these and a number of other conventional cytotoxic drugs. Most of the conjugates have been prepared using N-succinimidyl-3-(2-pyridyldithio) proprionate (SPDP) as a coupling agent, although adriamycin has been conjugated to a monoclonal antibody directed against a spontaneous rat tumor by a dextran bridge (43). Experience so far indicates that many agents tend to be inactivated by SPDP, as exemplified in Figure 6, which depicts the relative effects of adriamycin and an SPDP-coupled adriamycin–α791T/36 conjugate on survival of 791T cells in vitro. The cells were cultivated in the presence of the drug or conjugate for 24 hr, followed by labeling of the cells with $[^{75}Se]$ selenomethionine. A radiolabeled amino acid was used with this agent because in preliminary tests high rates of DNA repair led to confusion over the LD_{50} when labeled DNA precursors were used. Uptake of labeled amino acids, however, was correlated extremely well with numbers of surviving cells observed visually. The results (Fig. 6) show that the adriamycin was completely inactivated by direct coupling to the antibody, although in other experiments using dextran as a linking agent it produced therapeutic effects against a rat tumor (43). The ability of the antibody to bind to 791T target cells was hardly affected by the coupling procedure, as indicated by indirect $[^{125}I]$ protein A assays and competition with FITC-labeled α791T/36 in assays using a fluorescence-activated

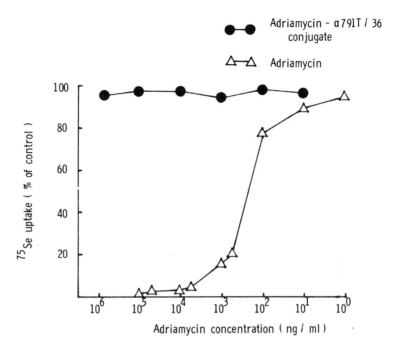

Figure 6   Effect of adriamycin and adriamycin-α791T/36 conjugate on survival of 791T cells in vitro. Adriamycin or adriamycin–α791T/36 conjugate (expressed as in nanograms of adriamycin per millimeter) were added to 791T target cells growing in microtiter plates and the cells were cultured for 24 hr at 37°C. The cells were then labeled with [^{75}Se] selenomethionine for 12 hr to assess the relative numbers of surviving cells. Survival is expressed as mean ^{75}Se uptake in treated wells calculated as a percentage of that in medium controls. Labeled DNA precursors gave misleading results owing to high rates of DNA repair, but ^{75}Se uptake was well correlated with visual scoring of stained preparations.

cell sorter. This has been a common feature of all conjugates, the α791T/36 antibody retaining between 80 and 100% of its normal activity.

The best SPDP conjugate so far tested with this antibody was prepared with ricin A chain, however, this agent had reduced activity against 791T cells in conjugate form compared with ricin alone when added to growing cultures (Fig. 7), although again antibody titers were only slightly impaired. A similar decrease in toxicity of conjugate compared with parent drug was observed in the case of a conjugate of α791T/36 and Vindesine (Fig. 8).

When target cells were preincubated with Vindesine-antibody conjugate, however, there was evidence of selective cytotoxic activity against 791T

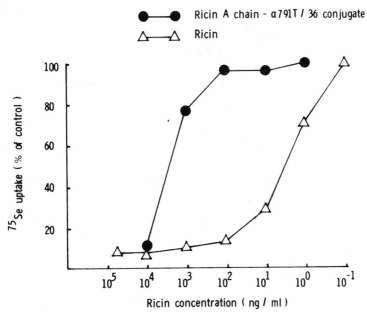

Figure 7 Effect of ricin or ricin A chain–conjugate on survival of 791T cells in vitro. Ricin or ricin-α791T/36 conjugate were added to 791T cells growing in microtiter plates and the cells were cultured for 24 hr and labeled with [75 Se] selenomethionine for 12 hr. Survival of 791T cells is expressed as in Figure 6. No ricin A chain was available for comparison.

compared with an antigenically non-cross-reactive melanoma line, Mel-57 (Fig. 9). 791T and Mel-57 target cells were preincubated with the drug or conjugate and washed before plating in microtiter plates. Vindesine alone was toxic to both cell lines, showing no selective activity. The conjugate, on the other hand. was toxic for 791T cells at concentrations that were not significantly active against Mel-57. Similar selective activity on the part of the conjugate was observed with four other cell lines that react with the antibody, but not with four nonreactive lines. This indicates the potential feasibility of selective tumor targeting, although at the present stage of development this is not sufficient to be the basis for an effective therapeutic response. There is obviously a need for the development of alternative coupling methods in order to achieve levels of cytotoxicity with the conjugate equivalent to those obtained with the free drug or toxin, and these studies are in progress.

Immunomodulators

In view of the reported therapeutic effects of interferon (IFN) on osteogenic sarcomas (44) and cytostatic effects observed in vitro (45), it was of interest

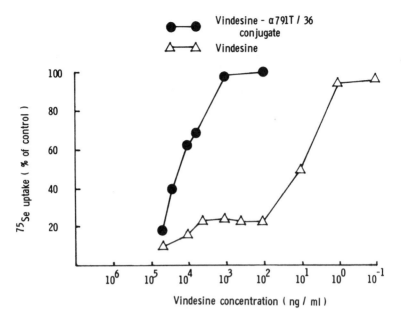

Figure 8 Effect of Vindesine and Vindesine-α791T/36 conjugate on survival of 791T cells in vitro. Vindesine or Vindesine-α791T/36 conjugate were added to 791T cells growing in microtiter plates and the cells were cultured for 24 hr and labeled with [⁷⁵Se] selenomethionine for 12 hr. Survival of 791T cells is expressed as in Figure 6.

to determine the effects of human lymphoblastoid IFN on osteogenic sarcoma 791T. In vitro studies showed no effect of either IFN or IFN-α791T/36 conjugates on the growth of 791T cells using assays in which cells were cultivated in the presence of IFN for periods of between 1 and 6 days, followed by labeling with [^{125}I] iodeoxyuridine or [^{75}Se] selenomethionine. Interferon also had no effect on the growth of 791T xenografts in Nu/Nu mice.

Since 791T was not directly susceptible to cytostasis by IFN, a decision was made to explore the effect of IFN on cell-mediated cytotoxicity mediated by natural killer (NK) cells. In these experiments peripheral blood lymphocytes from healthy donors were cultured for 6 hr with ^{51}Cr-labeled target cells at effector/target cells ratios 12.5:1, 6.25:1, and 1.56:1. When the percentage of cytotoxicity is plotted against effector/target ratios, slopes of regression fitted through the origin and the plots are directly proportional to the frequency of cytotoxic cells in the effector population (46). The effect of IFN was assessed by incubating the lymphocytes for 1 hr at 37°C with IFN (200 units/ml) followed by three

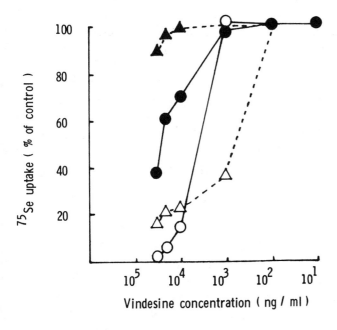

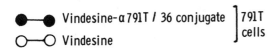

Figure 9 Effect of preincubation of target cells with Vindesine–α791T/36 conjugate. 791T or Mel-57 cells were incubated with Vindesine or Vindesine–α791T/36 conjugate for 15 min, then washed. Cells were plated at 5×10^3 per well in microtiter plates and cultured for 48 hrs, then labeled for 8 hr with [^{75}Se] selenomethionine. Survival of cells is expressed as in Figure 6.

washes, before addition to the target cells. Direct augmentation of NK cytotoxicity by IFN-α791T/36 conjugate (at 200 units/ml IFN) for two target cell lines is shown in Table 7. Erythroleukemia line K562 is a commonly used target in NK cell assays owing to its high sensitivity to NK cells: peripheral blood lymphocytes alone were cytotoxic for K562, and prior incubation with IFN or

Table 7 Augmentation of Natural Killer Cell Activity in Peripheral
Blood Lymphocytes by Interferon-Monoclonal Antibody Conjugate

Target cells	Effector cell treatment	Cytotoxicity (slope ± S.D.)	Augmentation (%)[a]
K562	Culture medium	8.23 ±0.20	–
	IFN	19.31 ±0.34	234.8 (P < 0.001)
	IFN–α791T/36 conjugate	11.55 ±0.22	140.4 (P < 0.001)
791T	Culture medium	2.15 ±0.29	–
	IFN	8.94 ±1.10	415.0 (P < 0.001)
	IFN–α791T/36 conjugate	6.78 ±0.16	315 (P < 0.001)

[a]Statistical significance assessed by Student's test

IFN-α791T/36 conjugate markedly enhanced this cytotoxicity. With ^{51} Cr-labeled 791T target cells lymphocytes alone had little cytotoxic effect, but this was augmented to a significant level by IFN or the conjugate.

This experiment indicated that IFN carried to the tumor site might have the property of locally activating NK cells against the tumor cells. This view is supported by a more exacting experiment in which 791T target cells preincubated with the IFN-α791T/36 conjugate were cultured with normal lymphocytes and ^{51} Cr-labeled K562 cells (Table 8). When the 791T cells had been preincubated with IFN mixed with α791T/36, they did not augment NK cytotoxicity against labeled K562 cells, but when 791T cells coated with the SPDP-prepared conjugate were tested, they produced augmentation of cytotoxicity equivalent to that observed when lymphocytes were exposed directly to IFN (Table 7). When T24 bladder carcinoma cells, nonreactive with α791T/36, were pretreated with the conjugate, they induced no augmentation of cytotoxicity for K562 in mixed culture (Table 8). Thus NK cell cytotoxicity against third-party target cells was augmented in these assays by IFN bound to 791T cells by the attached antibody. It could therefore be predicted that the IFN–monoclonal antibody conjugate, localizing in the tumor, might bind to some tumor cells and locally recruit cytotoxic cells against themselves and surrounding tumor cells.

The role of NK cells in tumor rejection is not firmly established and it is likely that cellular effector mechanisms involve a complex interplay of cells, but this does not compromise the possible beneficial effects of a targeted immunomodulator, because these agents may have a stimulating action on diverse effector cells. Because of the species specificity of human IFN, it has not been possible to test the conjugate in vivo against xenografts, where responding cells would be murine in

Table 8 Augmentation of Natural Killer Cell Activity Against ^{51}Cr-Labeled K562 by 791T Cells Coated with Interferon-Monoclonal Antibody Conjugate

Tumor cell pretreatment	Treated cells	Cytotoxicity (slope ± S.D.)	Augmentation (%)
Culture medium	791T	6.68 ±0.39	—
IFN and α791T/36 mixture	791T	7.46 ±0.57	111.7 (NS)[a]
IFN-α791T/36 conjugate	791T	14.36 ±2.04	214.9 (P < 0.01)[b]
Culture medium	T24	8.23 ±2.0	—
IFN and α791T/36 mixture	T24	7.81 ±0.19	94.9 (NS)
IFN-α791T/36	T24	8.69 ±0.33	105.6 (NS)

[a] NS, not significant
[b] Statistical significance assessed by Student's t test.

origin; however, the basic approach would be applicable to virtually any immuno-modulatory agent.

CONCLUSIONS AND FUTURE DEVELOPMENTS

The introduction of the hybridoma technique for producing monoclonal antibodies against tumors was heralded by many to provide an answer to whether or not human tumor-associated antigens really exist. This question has been answered to only a limited extent, however, in that the majority of anti-tumor monoclonal antibodies have been produced from immunized xenogeneic, usually murine, spleen cell donors. Some authors have raised human monoclonal antibodies to tumors by creating human-mouse hybridomas (47-49), in which case the fused lymphocytes were derived from cancer patients. Under these conditions antibodies produced by the hybrids can be regarded as products of a host immune response toward the tumor. Immunized mice, however, are capable of recognizing a wider range of antigens on the immunizing cells. Hybridomas producing unwanted antibodies (e.g., against normal adult cells) can be discarded after screening, but there is no guarantee that apparently tumor-associated antibodies are directed toward components that are recognized as an antigen by the host. Indeed, with osteogenic sarcoma 791T there was evidence to the contrary (Table 6). In other words, antigens detected by xenogeneic monoclonal antibodies tell us nothing about the possibility of host resistance to cancer; rather, they sidestep the issue of host immunity and offer an alternative approach toward the application of immunology to human cancer.

Human monoclonal antibodies have a theoretical advantage over xenogeneic monoclonal antibodies in that they might be better tolerated when administered to patients, but in studies where murine monoclonal antibodies have been infused into patients, they have induced no obvious ill effects (35, 36), so this may not be a real advantage. On the other hand, since production of murine monoclonal antibodies does not rely on a pre-existing host immune response to the tumor, it probably stands a better chance of success in the first instance. For biochemical studies the suitability of xenogeneic monoclonal antibodies depends upon the question being asked. Only human antibodies are likely to identify antigens involved in tumor immunity, but the biochemical study of antigens recognized by xenogeneic antibodies should nevertheless provide useful information on tumor cell membrane functions. Such antibodies can also be used to classify neoplasms, as in the case of leukemias (50). This could lead to a more precise judgment of prognosis and better choice of therapeutic modalities. For use in diagnostic tests and targeting, xenogeneic monoclonal antibodies will probably prove to be perfectly acceptable, provided that tumor specificity is sufficient.

The question of tumor specificity is a difficult one. While some reports claim that certain monoclonal antibodies are specific for a particular tumor type (51, 52), there are also reports indicating that hitherto putatively specific monoclonal antibodies have been found to react with other tumors or certain normal cells (53–55). It is likely that the majority of monoclonal antibodies will follow this pattern, as do the antibodies discussed in this chapter (27). However, they still have potential practical value so long as the antigen detected is expressed preferentially on maligant compared with normal tissue. Limitations posed by weak cross-reactivity with some normal cells will depend upon the importance of those cells relative to clinical benefits to be achieved with a monoclonal antibody.

Caution should be used when interpreting results obtained with monoclonal antibodies to cultured cell lines. Cultured tumor cells may not be antigenically typical of the tumor cell population from which they were derived, and it is well established that new artifactual antigens can occur as a result of culture (21, 22, 56). The cultured osteogenic sarcoma line 791T and the antibodies raised against it constitute a model system, and efforts to produce new anti-tumor monoclonal antibodies in the author's laboratory are now conducted with fresh, surgically removed tumor specimens. Indeed, in a recent report exactly this approach has been taken with tissue from a biopsy of osteogenic sarcoma (57). Five murine monoclonal antibodies raised against this tissue were tested by immunofluorescence on cryostat sections of various tumor and normal cells, and three of the antibodies appeared to be specific for osteosarcoma and chondrosarcoma, although it is to be noted that they bound weakly to some chondrocytes in apparently normal tissues.

Despite reservations about the use of cultured cells as immunogens, however, model systems lay the foundations upon which future clinical applications are based. For example, radiolabeled xenogeneic (polyclonal) anti-carcinoembryonic antigen antibodies are already being used clinically to determine tumor burden and tumor site by gamma scintigraphy (58), and the hope is that monoclonal antibodies may lead to significant improvements in this field (59). Experimental model systems are necessary to develop optimal ways in which to carry out such procedures.

It is too soon to predict the therapeutic success of anti-tumor agents targeted to tumors by linking to monoclonal antibodies, but the possible methods of coupling and the number of agents available are extensive enough to allow adequate scope for development. As pointed out above, this can be considered something of a side step for tumor immunology in comparison with latter-day attempts to boost the host's own response, but hopefully it may lead to more success.

ACKNOWLEDGMENTS

The author wishes to acknowledge the support of the Cancer Research Campaign, London, and helpful discussions with his colleagues Professor R. W. Baldwin and Drs. F. Dawood, G. R. Flannery, M. V. Pimm, M. R. Price, and R. A. Robins. Grateful thanks also to Mrs. M. Trevers and Mrs. B. Janes, who typed the manuscript. Certain drug–antibody conjugates were prepared by arrangement with Dr. G. F. Rowland and Professor A. Pihl. Lymphoblastoid interferon was provided by Burroughs Wellcome Ltd. Cell lines were provided by Drs. V. S. Byers, C. Sorg, P. Burtin, J. DeVries, and M. Moore, Professor M. A. Epstein, and the U.S. Naval Biomedical Center, Oakland, Calif. by arrangement with Dr. W. A. Nelson-Rees.

REFERENCES

1. J. G. Sinkovics, J. R. Cabiness, and C. C. Shullenberger, *Cancer 30*:1428 (1972).
2. A. M. Cohen, A. S. Ketcham, and D. L. Morton, *J. Nat. Cancer Inst. 50*:585 (1973).
3. F. Vanky, E. Klein, J. Stjernsward, and V. Nilsonne, *Int. J. Cancer 14*:277 (1974).
4. F. Vanky, J. Stjernsward, G. Klein, and V. Nilsonne, *J. Nat. Cancer Inst. 47*:95 (1971).
5. D. L. Morton and R. A. Malmgren, *Science 162*:1279 (1968).
6. M. Moore and L. A. Hughes, *Br. J. Cancer Suppl. 1*:175 (1973).
7. M. Moore, P. J. Witherow, C. H. G. Price, and S. A. Clough, *Int. J. Cancer 12*:428 (1973).
8. W. C. Wood and D. L. Morton, *Science 170*:1318 (1970).
9. D. L. Morton, F. R. Eilber, W. L. Joseph, W. C. Wood, E. Trahan, and A. S. Ketcham, *Ann. Surg. 172*:740 (1970).
10. F. R. Eilber and D. L. Morton, *J. Nat. Cancer Res. Inst. 44*:651 (1970).

11. W. C. Wood and D. L. Morton, *N. Engl. J. Med. 284*:569 (1981).
12. E. T. Bloom, *Cancer Res. 32*:960 (1972).
13. E. T. Bloom, *Proc. Soc. Exp. Biol. Med. 143*:244 (1973).
14. E. Bloom, J. L. Fahey, I. A. Peterson, G. Geering, M. Bernhard, and G. Trempe, *Int. J. Cancer 12*:21 (1973).
15. G. Giraldo, E. Beth, Y. Hirshaut, T. Aoki, L. J. Old, E. A. Boyse, and H. C. Chopra, *J. Exp. Med. 133*:454 (1971).
16. B. Mukherji and Y. Hirshaut, *Science 181*:440 (1973).
17. Y. Hirshaut, D. T. Pei, R. S. Marcove, B. Mukherji, A. R. Spielvogel, and E. Essner, *N. Engl. J. Med. 291*:1103 (1974).
18. J. Sethi and Y. Hirshaut, *J. Nat. Cancer Inst. 57*:489 (1976).
19. S. A. Rosenberg, *J. Nat. Cancer Inst. 58*:1233 (1977).
20. W. P. Thorpe, G. A. Parker, and S. A. Rosenberg, *J. Immunol. 119*:818 (1977).
21. W. P Thorpe and S. A. Rosenberg, *J. Nat. Cancer Inst. 62*:1143 (1979).
22. R. F. Irie and D. L. Morton, *J. Nat. Cancer Inst. 52*:1051 (1974).
23. A. N. Theofilopoulos, B. S. Andrews, M. M. Urist, D. L. Morton, and F. J. Dixon, *J. Immunol. 119*:657 (1977).
24. K. Y. Tsang, I. Singh, and W. S. Blakemore, *J. Nat. Cancer Inst. 62*:743 (1979).
25. R. W. Baldwin, C. Wright, and V. S. Byers, in *Compendium of Assays for Immunodiagnosis of Human Cancer* (R. B. Herberman, ed.) Elsevier/North-Holland, New York, 1979, p. 123.
26. A. S. Eiras, R. A. Robins, R. W. Baldwin, and V. S. Byers, *Int. J. Cancer 25*:735 (1980).
27. M. J. Embleton, B. Gunn, V. S. Byers, and R. W. Baldwin, *Br. J. Cancer 43*:582 (1981).
28. M. J. Embleton, B. Gunn, V. S. Byers, and R. W. Baldwin, *Transplant. Proc. 13*:1966 (1981).
29. G. Galfré, S. C. Howe, C. Milstein, G. W. Butcher, and J. C. Howard, *Nature 266*:550 (1977).
30. P. J. McConahey and F. J. Dixon, *Int. Arch. Allergy 29*:185 (1966).
31. S. Fazekas de St. Groth, in *Immunological Methods* (I. Lefkovits and B. Perris eds.) Academic, New York, 1979, p. 1.
32. G. G. Steel, V. D. Courtney, and A. Y. Rostrom, *Br. J. Cancer 37*:224 (1978).
33. P. J. Fraker and J. C. Speck, *Biochem. Biophys. Res. Commun. 80*:849 (1978).
34. I. D. Bernstein, M. R. Tam, and R. C. Nowinski, *Science 207*:68 (1980).
35. L. M. Nadler, P. Stashenko, R. Hardy, W. D. Kaplan, L. N. Button, D. W. Kufe, K. H. Antman, and S. F. Schlossman, *Cancer Res. 40*:3147 (1980).
36. J. Ritz, J. M. Pesando, S. E. Sallan, L. A. Clavell, J. Notis-McConarty, P. Rosenthal, and S. F. Schlossman, *Blood 58*:141 (1981).
37. H. E. Blythman, P. Casellas, O. Gros, P. Gros, F. K. Jansen, F. Paolucci, B. Pau, and H. Vidal, *Nature 290*:145 (1981).
38. D. G. Gilliland, Z. Steplewski, R. J. Collier, K. F. Mitchell, T. H. Chang, and H. Koprowski, *Proc. Nat. Acad. Sci. U.S.A. 77*:4539 (1980).
39. K. A. Krolick, C. Villemez, P. Isakson, J. W. Uhr, and E. S. Vitetta, *Proc, Nat. Acad. Sci. U.S.A. 77*:5419 (1980).

40. J. S. Trowbridge and D. L. Domingo, *Nature* 294:171 (1981).
41. R. J. Youle and D. M. Neville, *Proc. Nat. Acad. Sci. U.S.A.* 77:5483 (1980).
42. D. M. Herlyn and H. Koprowski, *Int. J. Cancer* 27:769 (1981).
43. M. V. Pimm, J. A. Jones, M. R. Price, J. G. Middle, M. J. Embleton, and R. W. Baldwin, *Cancer Immunol. Immunother.* 12:125 (1982).
44. H. Strander, K. Cantrell, S. Ingamarsson, P. Å. Jakobsson, U. Nilsonne, and G. Söderberg, *Fogarty Int. Center Proc.* 28:337 (1977).
45. H. Strander and S. Einhorn, *Int. J. Cancer* 19:468 (1977).
46. C. G. Brooks and G. R. Flannery, *Immunology* 39:187 (1980).
47. J. Schlom, D. Wunderlich, and Y. A. Teramoto, *Proc. Nat. Acad. Sci. U.S.A.* 776:841 (1980).
48. K. Sikora and J. Phillips. *Br. J. Cancer* 43:105 (1981).
49. K. Sikora and R. Wright, *Br. J. Cancer* 43:696 (1981).
50. M. F. Greaves in *Tumour Markers: Impact and Prospects* (E. Baelsma and P. Rumke, eds.), Elsevier/North-Holland, Amsterdam, 1979, p. 201.
51. S. Carrel, R. S. Accolla, A. L. Carmagnola, and J. P. Mach, *Cancer Res.* 40:2523 (1980).
52. M. Herlyn, Z. Steplewski, D. Herlyn, and H. Koprowski, *Proc. Nat. Acad. Sci. U.S.A.* 76:1438 (1979).
53. J. P. Brown, P. W. Wright, C. E. Hart, R. G. Woodbury, K. E. Hellström, and I. Hellström, *J. Biol. Chem.* 255:4980 (1980).
54. K. Imai, P. G. Natali, N. E. Kay, B. S. Wilson, and S. Ferrone, *Cancer Immunol. Immunother.* 12:159 (1982).
55. R. Sutherland, D. Delia, C. Scheider, R. Newman, J. Kemshead, and M. Greaves, *Proc. Nat. Acad. Sci. U.S.A.* 78:4515 (1981).
56. S. H. Golub, E. A. J. Svedmyr, J. F. Hewetson, G. Klein, and S. Singh, *Int. J. Cancer* 10:157 (1972).
57. S. Hosoi, T. Nakamura, S. Higashi, T. Yamamuro, S. Toyama, K. Shinomiya, and H. Mikawa, *Cancer Res.* 42:654 (1982).
58. D. M. Goldenberg, E. E. Kim, F. H. Deland, S. Bennett, and F. J. Primus, *Cancer Res.* 40:2984 (1980).
59. J. P. Mach, F. Buchegger, M. Forni, J. Richard, C. Berche, J. D. Lambroso, M. Schreyer, C. Giradet, R. Accola, and S. Carrel, *Immunol. Today* 2:239 (1981).

8 MONOCLONAL ANTIBODIES TO HUMAN LEUKEMIA ANTIGENS

Laida Vodinelich and Melvyn F. Greaves /Imperial Cancer Research Fund, London, England

INTRODUCTION

Leukemias form a group of neoplastic diseases arising predominantly in the bone marrow or lymphoid tissue. They are monoclonal cancers, since all cells of a given leukemia result from the selective growth of a single, neoplastically transformed or clonogenic cell (1, 2). The latter and its progeny may share a common aberrant karyotype (3), and at present this provides the only unequivocal example of a "leukemia-specific" feature or "marker" that distinguishes between normal and leukemic cells. However, the quest for the elusive leukemia-specific

antigens continues with some recent claims for their identification using monoclonal antibodies (4-7).

Traditional morphological and cytochemical studies on hemopoietic cells have
established that similar or identical morphological and cytochemical features
exist in normal and malignant cells. In this sense, for each leukemic cell type
there is a comparative normal hemopoietic cell type. During the past decade a
variety of immunological, enzymatic, or biochemical markers have been discovered on malignant and normal hemopoietic cells. They include surface membrane proteins and glycolipids, cytoplasmic immunoglobulins and enzymes,
and nuclear enzymes (8-13). The majority of antigens were orginally characterized by extensively absorbed heteroantisera raised against either normal or
leukemic lymphoid and myeloid cells. These reagents reacted with normal
lymphoid or myeloid cells and it was thus clear that they did not detect any
leukemia-specific markers. The technology was, nevertheless, useful, because
it identified the cellular affiliations of the major leukemic cell population of
a given leukemia, and provided probes for the study of normal hemopoiesis.
Besides, the resolution power of morphological and histochemical analysis was
limited, particularly so in the region of early hemopoietic precursor cells that
appeared "poorly differentiated" with respect to their morphology and cytochemistry. Such immature cells appeared to have no distinct features that
could classify them into a particular hemopoietic lineage. Heteroantisera against
the hemopoietic antigens were a further advancement, because they detected
antigens present or discrete subpopulations of lymphoid and nonlymphoid cells.
They could separate a large, intrinsically heterogeneous group of diseases into
smaller, objectively defined entities, clinically and biologically different from
one another.

Technical difficulties in the production of heteroantisera to leukemia hemopoietic cell antigens limited their broad application to biological and clinical
investigations. These antisera were subjected to repetitive absorptions with
cells of other cellular origins in order to make them antigen specific and, as
a consequence, the resulting reagents were frequently of low titer. Only small
volumes were available, which prohibited free exchange of reagents and inde-
pendent verification of specificity data. Also, owing to the diversity of the
immune response of the immunized animals (usually outbred rabbits, goats, or
monkeys), it was difficult to produce antisera with identical or reproducible
specificity.

Such difficulties are now being overcome by the use of monoclonal antibodies
(14) that are of restricted and more easily definable specificity by virtue of their
homogeneity, high titer, and, theoretically, unlimited quantity. These are specific
features of monoclonal antibodies that permit standardized, reproducible assays
and affinity isolation of the antigens involved.

Monoclonal antibodies have already provided the means of dissecting further
the heterogeneity and cell lineage relationships of hemopoietic cells and a more

Table 1 Monoclonal Antibodies Used in the Analysis of Leukemia Cells

Antibody	Cellular/molecular specificity	References
HLA associated		
W6/32 ⎱ B.B 7.7 ⎰	Monomorphic HLA ABC (gp 45–58)	128 128
BB 5 ⎱ EC3 ⎰	Beta-2-microglobulin (p 12)	128 128
DA-2 ⎱ OKIa-1 ⎰	Monomorphic HLA-DR (gp 28, 33)	83
T-lineage associated		
OKT 1 ⎫ L17F12 (Leu-1) ⎪ T101 ⎬ Pan-T (+B-CLL) UCH-T2, UCH-T3 ⎭	Pan-T (+B-CLL)	67 106 129, 130 131
OKT 3 ⎫ UCH-T1 (T28) ⎪ Leu-4 ⎬ MBG6 ⎭	Pan-mature T	80, 81, 68 131 126
OKT 4, (Leu 3a)	Helper/inducer subset	68, 70, 71
OKT 6 ⎱ NA134 ⎰	Thymic/cortex subset	74 107
OKT 5 ⎱ OKT 8 (leu-2a) ⎰	Suppressor/cytotoxic subset	69, 72
OKT 11 ⎱ 9.6 ⎰	E rosette receptor	35, 36 37
WT-1 ⎱ 3A-1 ⎰	Pan-T	82, 141, 142 143
B-lineage associated		
FMC 1	Pan-B	132
BA-1	Pan-B	118
PI153/3	Pan-B/neural	133
FMC7	B Subset	134
Nonlymphoid, hemopoietic cell associated		
OKM1	Monocytes (granulocytes)	90
MIN1	Granulocytes	135
TG1	Granulocytes	136
LICR-LON-R10	Glycophorin A (erythroid cells)	108
I/6A	Band III (erythroid cells)	108
AN51	Platelets (glycoprotein I)	111
J15	Platelets (glycoprotein IIb/IIIa)	

Table 1 (continued)

Common ALL associated		
J5		6, 54, 55, 58
VIL-A1	gp 100	64
AL-1		140
BA-2	p 24	119, 139
Pan-hemopoietic cell associated		
HLe-1	p40	136
OKT 10		75
Ubiquitous, cell proliferation associated		
OKT 9	(transferrin receptor)	22, 75
B3/25		91, 92
T58	gp 90 dimer	
42/6		137
5E9		138

precise diagnosis of leukemia (15-19). Their application to the biology and understanding of cancer of the hemopoietic system is wide. For example, they have been useful in detecting precise differentiation sequences in the erythroid lineage (20), biochemical isolation and characterization of relevant antigens (19-22), differential diagnosis of leukemias and lymphomas (17-19), and the detection of minimal disease (23). The use of monoclonal antibodies as potential immunotherapeutic agents in leukemia is also now being explored.

MONOCLONAL ANTIBODIES AND IMMUNOLOGICAL METHODS USED IN THE ANALYSIS OF LEUKEMIA ANTIGENS

Monoclonal Antibodies

New monoclonal antibodies are frequently reported in this field and it is impossible to describe them all in detail within the scope of this review. We intend to review those monoclonal antibodies that have been relatively well characterized and which, by the nature of their specificity, have a potential for application in the analysis and treatment of leukemia (Table 1). Most of these antibodies have been evaluated in our laboratory.

Several monoclonal antibodies to all hemopoietic lineages have been obtained, but the greatest advancement has been made in the reagents for the lymphoid differentiation antigens, notably T-cell-associated antigens. Although some of these reagents do not react exclusively with hemopoietic cells—some also bind to other tissues (24)—they may be lineage restricted within the hemopoietic cells and thus remain diagnostically useful. It has also been shown that some monoclonal antibodies, originating from different laboratories and different immunization procedures, react with the same molecule. Because of that, monoclonal antibodies of different connotations may represent the same type of reagent, with the same specificity. In some cases, reagents that react with the same antigen are not identical, in the sense that they bind to two different epitopes of that molecule. In other cases, they may have the same specificity but are different immunoglobulin subclasses with associated properties that are useful in biological investigations. The true identity of these related monoclonal antibodies can be established by parallel comparison of their reactivity with cell lines, fresh leukemias, normal fetal and mature hemopoietic cells, other tissues, and, more definitively, by biochemical analysis of the molecules they identify.

Immunofluorescence and Flow Cytofluorometry

The immunofluorescence method is based on the binding of (rodent monoclonal) antibodies to single cells. A second antibody, a fluorochrome-labeled affinity-purified IgG F $(ab')_2$ fragment of anti-mouse immunoglobluin, is then usually attached to the specific monoclonal antibody. The test sample of cells can be analyzed with fluorescence microscopy and flow cytometry (fluorescence-activated cell sorter or FACS, Becton Dickinson, Mountain View, Calif.). The details of the FACS and similar electronic analyzers and sorters have been published (25, 26). The FACS detects scattered light and fluorescent signals of individual cells by two separate photodetectors. These signals are related to the size and fluorescent brightness of the cells, determined by the binding of the antibody, and are displayed on a two-dimensional scatter diagram in which each spot represents a single cell in the analysis. The position of this spot, with regard to the ordinate, represents the cell's size, and its position on the abscissa indicates the intensity of fluorescence of the cells. As an analytical instrument the FACS can determine the percentage of positive cells in a heterogeneous population of cells, in comparison with the same cells when stained with control reagents (27). Average staining of the cells can be obtained by the FACS data analysis, selected at the point at which 50% of the cells in the sample are positive. The FACS can analyze 2000–8000 cells per second. A particular advantage of flow cytofluorometry using the FACS is that it gives a virtually instantaneous indication of the marker-defined characteristics of cell populations, which are not recognizable by any other means. Simultaneous staining of cells with two separate monoclonal antibodies differing in their immunoglobulin class is also possible. If such isotypes are bound with "second-layer" antibodies that are specific for different immunoglobulin classes, and coupled to different fluorochromes, the presence of two surface antigens on the same cell can be determined. Many other useful applications of FACS analysis in the study of leukemia have been described (27–30). Since it is possible to determine the DNA content using DNA binding dyes such as propidium iodide or mithramycin (31, 32), experiments can be designed to relate the cell cycle stage or cellular chromosome content in aneuploidy with antigen expression that is determined by the monoclonal antibody binding to cell surface. Abnormal DNA profiles of leukemic cells are often a consequence

of aneuploidy and can be linked with expression of certain antigenic determinants present on the aneuploid fraction of the cells. It has been shown that
some antigens (HLA-DR,A-B-C, beta-2-microglobulin and the gp 100/CALL) increase very little in quantity as the cells enlarge and go through S, G_2, and M phases
of the cell cycle. Some antigens, on the other hand, are completely associated
with cell proliferation (22). These multiparameter analyses are useful in the
study of leukemia and have practical implications, since growth fraction,
aneuploidy, and cell phenotype are in some instances linked to prognosis.

In addition to a variety of analytical functions, the FACS can be programmed
to physically separate subpopulations of cells on the basis of their fluorescence
intensity or size or both. Positive and negative cells can be collected separately
and then analyzed in smear preparations by classic hematological methods. It
is particularly significant that the separation of cell populations by FACS can
be performed in sterile conditions, and that this enables the study of cell populations in functional assays, such as colony tests in vitro and suppressor and
helper function assays.

Other Immunological Markers Used in the Analysis of Leukemic Cells

Binding of sheep erythrocytes to T lymphocytes (E rosettes) has for a long
time been a useful marker for the enumeration of mature and immature T cells
(33). It is now possible to replace it with monoclonal antibodies OKT 11, OKT
11A (34,35), Leu-5 (36), or 9.6 (37), although there may be instances where E-
rosette tests could be useful in addition to the monoclonal antibody test. These
monoclonal antibodies have advantages over E rosettes in application to tissue
sections (e.g., in lymphoma) (38).

Mouse erythrocytes spontaneously rosette with a subset of cells in the B-cell
lineage and B-CLL. Surface membrane immunoglobulin (SmIg) is another mature
B-cell marker, determined by heteroantisera to human immunoglobulin. Antisera
to human kappa and lambda light chains are useful in establishing the monoclonal nature of SmIg-positive B cells, which is associated with malignancy.
Monoclonal antibodies specific for heavy- or light-chain isotypes are now also
being developed.

Terminal deoxynucleotidyl transferase (TdT) is an important marker of
immature lymphocytes of both B and T lineage, and heteroantiserum to TdT
(39) is now used in preference to the enzymatic determination of TdT. In this
way TdT-positive cells can be identified in mixed cell populations, and a combination of cell-surface antigen fluorescence and intracellular fluorescence of
TdT greatly improves the methodology for cell type identification (37, 40, 41).

DIFFERENTIAL IMMUNODIAGNOSIS OF LEUKEMIA

During the last few years it has become clear that some hematologically
defined classes of leukemia could be subdivided into biologically and clinically
meaningful subclasses on the basis of immunological criteria. Major advances

Table 2 Immunological Subclasses of ALL

Subclass	Common phenotype	Approximate frequency (%)
Pre-T (thymic)-ALL	E_R^+ HuTLA$^+$ SmIg$^-$ Ia$^-$ TdT$^+$ CALL$^\pm$	15
Pre-B^a-ALL		
CALL	E_R^- HuTLA$^-$*SmIg$^-$ Ia$^+$ TdT$^+$ CALL$^+$	68
Null-ALL	E_R^- HuTLA$^-$ SmIg$^-$ Ia$^+$ TdT$^+$ CALL$^-$	15
B-ALL	E_R^- HuTLA$^-$ SmIg$^+$ Ia$^+$ TdT$^-$ CALL$^-$	2

^{a} With rearranged Ig genes. *HuTLA = human T lymphocyte antigens.

have been made in the field of acute lymphoblastic leukemia (ALL) that can be subdivided into subgroups with distinctive surface marker and intracellular enzyme phenotypes. It has also been shown that these subclasses represent different clinical entities, since they are associated with specific clinical features at presentation and have different prognoses and age distributions. Three categories of ALL can be detected with these extensively absorbed rabbit antisera (42-44): (a) thymic ALL (T-ALL) which reacts with polyclonal antisera against human T cell and forms E rosettes; (b) pre-B ALL with rearranged Ig genes (44a) with or without μ gene expression (48). Those within this group expressing the gp100 ALL associated antigen are referred to as common ALL, those that do not as "null" ALL; (c) B-ALL, which expresses the exclusively B-cell marker, surface membrane immunoglobulin (SmIg), of monoclonal nature with respect to its immunoglobulin light chains; the subset probably represents a disseminated B (non-Hodgkin) lymphoma rather than a true ALL. By far the largest subgroup in this classification is CALL, and the most rare is B-ALL. The CALL subclass has a striking age distribution that peaks at 2-6 years of age; other ALL subclasses do not have such frequency peaks, although T-ALL predominates in children and null-ALL is more often found in adults. These subclasses of ALL are prognostically different, the rank order of good prognosis being as follows: CALL > null-ALL > T-ALL > B-ALL. The prognostic differences are related to other clinical features, particularly the total white blood cell count. High white blood cell counts are correlated with poor prognosis. T-ALL is often associated with a mediastinal mass, and B-ALL with intestinal lymphadenopathy. T-ALL and B-ALL also show a strong bias toward males. These clinical features of ALL subclasses may be related to different etiologies of ALL diseases, although this has not yet been determined (45). The same subgroups of ALL are not defined by monoclonal antibodies.

CALL/Monoclonal J5

The CALL antigen (42-47) is expressed on common ALL (DR^+ TdT$^+$) cells, included in the pre-B subset of ALL (48). It is also expressed on a proportion of

Table 3 Reactivity of Monoclonal Antibody Against the gp 100/CALL Antigen
with Cells of Acute and Chronic Leukemias

Leukemia	J5 binding +	J5 binding −
Non-T, non-B ALL	772	149
B-ALL	2	23
T-ALL (thymic)	20	106
T lymphoma (thymic)	8	9
Mature B-cell leukemias[a]	3[b]	88
Mature T-cell leukemias[c]	0	52
AML	14	559
Erythroleukemia	0	27
CGL chronic phase	0	35
CGL blast crisis (TdT$^+$)	51	6
CGL blast crisis (TdT$^-$)	0	123
AUL (TdT$^+$)	15	3
AUL (TdT$^-$)	0	9

[a]Chronic lymphocytic leukemia, prolymphocytic leukemia, non-Hodgkin's lymphoma,
hairy cell leukemia, myeloma/plasma cell leukemia.

[b]Three cases belong to B-NHL.

[c]Sézary/mycosis fungoides, chronic lymphocytic leukemia, prolymphocytic leukemia,
NHL, T-lymphosarcoma cell leukemia.

T-ALL and on some cell lines derived from T-ALL or T-non-Hodgkins lymphoma
(NHL) (17, 49). Rare Epstein-Barr virus-negative (EBV$^-$) B lymphoma or
Burkitt lymphoma lines may also be positive, although EBV-transformed normal
B-cell lines are negative (49). The antigen has also been detected in cases diag-
nosed as acute undifferentiated leukemia (AUL) and in approximately one-third
of Philadelphia (Ph^1) chromosome-positive chronic granulocytic leukemias
(CGL) in blast crisis (50) (Table 3). The composite phenotype of CALL$^+$ DR$^+$
TdT$^+$ is exclusive, by definition, to CALL cells, irrespective of clinical diagnosis.
However, the intensity of staining varies within the leukemic clone of an indi-
vidual patient and the number of presumed leukemic cells stained can vary
(Fig. 1). The phenotype given reflects the predominant clone of leukemic
cells and need not necessarily apply for all leukemic cells of the same patient.
In the CALL subgroup a variable number of leukemic lymphoblasts may be
CALL antigen negative, TdT/HLA-DR positive, indicating a positive overlap
with "null" ALL pre-B subset.

Although some authors have failed to observe reactivity of their anti-CALL
reagents with normal bone marrow, there is convincing evidence, particularly
with pediatric or regenerating marrows, that normal cells exist that express

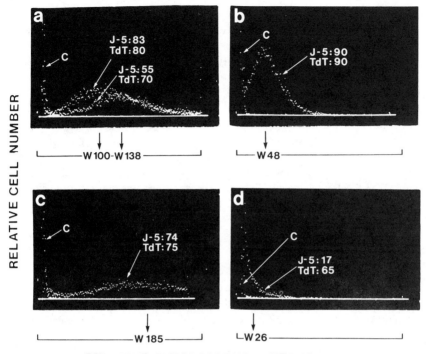

RELATIVE CELL NUMBER

RELATIVE FLUORESCENCE INTENSITY

Figure 1 Variability of staining with a monoclonal antibody (J5) within CALL (abscissa, fluorescence intensity; ordinate, number of cells; W denotes the channel window that represents the mean, or geometric, fluorescence intensity of 50% of positively stained cells). Within a population of CALL$^+$ cells of an individual patient, the antigen level can vary several fold. The mean fluorescence intensity can vary considerably from patient to patient (a–c). Variability in the *percentage* of J5$^+$ cells in CALL can be attributed to two causes: (1) When the percentage of blasts and TdT$^+$ cells is less than 90%, a distinct subpopulation of J5$^+$ cells is demonstrable by FACS analysis (a) a patient with 70% blasts). This subpopulation is invariably TdT$^+$ and usually approximates to the morphologically demonstrable lymphoblast population. (2) In some CALL, the population of J5$^+$ cells assessed by FACS is substantially less than the TdT$^+$ or lymphoblast population. It appears by FACS analysis of such cases (d) that a distinct subpopulation of J5$^+$ leukemic cells is not present but, rather, the distribution of CALL antigen is shifted to the left and only a proportion of cells are above the arbitrary threshold for positivity. Whether some leukemic cells in these cases are completely J5 negative cannot be resolved by the methods used here. These analyses emphasize that the distinction between the CALL and null-ALL subclasses of ALL (i.e., at the 10% J5$^+$ level) is itself quite arbitrary.

the CALL antigen. This appears to be present on bone marrow "lymphoid" cells that have nuclear terminal transferase (53). The structure identified by anti-CALL has been isolated from leukemic cells and characterized as a single glycosylated polypeptide of 95,000–100,000 daltons, with a pI of about 5.2, and is a nonintegral membrane protein (47, 54). A glycoprotein of 100,000 daltons has also been isolated from normal bone marrow using rabbit anti-CALL (54).

A monoclonal antibody (J5) has been reported (6) that appears to be against the same gp100 molecule as that previously identified with rabbit antisera. This reagent was considered to be different from rabbit anti-CALL, however, since it appeared to be unreactive with normal bone marrow and did not react with some T-ALL cell lines tested. Earlier work from the same laboratory has been interpreted to suggest that a "family" of gp100-like molecules exists (55); J5 was considered to have a restricted reactivity within this family and to be possibly leukemia specific, and the reagent has been used for immunotherapy of CALL patients (56).

The data in our laboratory suggest that monoclonal antibody J5 is indistinguishable in its binding selectivity to previously described absorbed rabbit antisera (56a). Both reagents identify a 95,000–100,000 dalton glycosylated polypeptide (54, 57), possibly via different determinants. The rabbit and mouse antibody-defined determinants clearly coredistribute in "capping" experiments. A glycoprotein of about 100,000 daltons can be precipitated from normal or regenerating marrow with J5 (54) and in common with earlier studies with rabbit antisera (47). Monoclonal antibody J5 reacts predominantly with the terminal transferase-positive cells in normal or nonleukemic marrow. In most cases the "normal" J5-positive cells in bone marrow are small cells with a relatively low density of the "CALL-associated" antigen. However, in some nonleukemic marrows, and particularly those that are regenerating with a "lymphocytosis," the J5-positive cells are difficult to distinguish unequivocally from leukemic blasts on the basis of these criteria, since ALL blasts are themselves very variable with respect to these characteristics. As with previously monitoring studies with rabbit anti-CALL (57), it is unlikely that J5 could accurately predict the onset of relapse in bone marrow. When studied with a panel of monoclonal antibodies, the majority of TdT$^+$ cells in nonleukemic bone marrows have the same composite antigenic phenotype as common acute lymphoblastic leukemia cells (23).

Some positive reactions are also seen with some but not all fetal thymuses. The antigenic determinants recognized by J5 and absorbed rabbit anti-CALL, therefore, seem to be associated with the same glycoprotein and are not leukemia specific.

Recent studies indicate that J5 may also react with some nonhemopoietic cells, including the proximal renal tubule, mammary epithelium, marrow-stromal endothelial cells, and fibroblasts (58). In common with many other monoclonal antibody defined antigens, the gp100 CALL-associated antigen appears to have a broad expression on a variety of tissues, but is highly restricted in the hemopoietic system. Antibody J5 (or xenogenic antibody) does not react detectably with mature lymphocytes, erythrocytes, or myeloid cells, or with myeloid or erythroid precursors (C. Sieff and M. F. Greaves, unpublished observations). The majority of normal thymocytes and marrow "pre-B" cells are also unreactive. Reactivity with TdT-positive cells in marrow and some fetal thymocytes suggests that in normal hemopoietic differentiation, expression of this glycoprotein is associated preferentially with relatively immature lymphocytes and lymphocyte precursors belonging to both T- and B-cell lineages. This interpretation is strongly supported by studies on leukemic cells.

The most plausible interpretation of the currently available data, therefore, is that within the hemopoietic system the gp100/CALL antigen is normally expressed quite selectively on immature or precursor cells in the T and B lineages and can be considered operationally as a differentiation antigen of these cells (59, 60).

Monoclonal antibody J5 has for 3 years been included in a routine immunodiagnostic survey of leukemias in the United Kingdom (61, 62). More than 2000 hemopoietic malignancies have been tested. Antibody J5 shows concordant reactivity with rabbit anti-CALL and reveals a remarkable selectivity in expression of the "gp100/CALL" antigen. As anticipated from earlier studies, J5 reacts with leukemic blasts from a high proportion (84%) of patients with non-T, non-B ALL and is also reactive with a proportion of thymic ALL, thymic lymphomas, TdT-positive "AUL," and TdT-positive CGL in blast crisis. In agreement with the report of Bernard et al. (63), we find a higher frequency of J5 positivity in thymic lymphomas than in thymic ALL. In contrast, no mature T-cell leukemia has so far reacted with J5. A few (5 of 115) relatively mature (i.e., cell-surface Ig[+]). B-cell leukemias were positive, albeit with a very low density. Reactivity with some follicular lymphomas can be demonstrated by immunoperoxidase staining of tissue sections (63a). Plasma cell myelomas or leukemias were J5 negative.

Of 573 leukemias diagnosed initially as acute myeloid leukemia (AML), only 14 were J5 positive (56a). These comprised 10 AML at presentation and 4 AML in relapse. Review of these cases showed that only one was unequivocal AML and was treated as such. Three cases were mixed lymphoid-myeloid leukemias but were treated as AML, and 10 were rediagnosed as ALL.

Monoclonal antibodies against the gp100/CALL-associated antigen (6, 64), therefore, provide, in combination with TdT, an excellent probe for the differential diagnosis of lymphoid precursor cell leukemia. These leukemias may present as typical ALL or, alternatively, as AUL, non-Hodgkin's childhood lymphoma (NHL), or Ph[1]-positive leukemia (50). At a single cell level, a CALL[+]/TdT[+]

phenotype does not reliably distinguish a leukemic cell from normal, *except* when the cell(s) is extramedullary, for example, in the cerebrospinal fluid or testis (65).

Although J5 reacts with some nonhemopoietic tissues (58), it is still valuable in the differential diagnosis of leukemias. For example, J5 in combination with TdT, tested in parallel with a series of monoclonal antibodies reactive with cells of neuroectodermal origin successfully discriminates between ALL cells and infiltrating tumors of neural crest derivation, for example, neuroblastoma in children (24; J. Kemshead and M. Greaves, unpublished observations).

T-ALL and Mature T-Cell Malignancies

Recent studies with monoclonal antibodies have documented the antigenic heterogeneity of human T-cell leukemias and emphasized the close relationship between leukemic phenotypes and corresponding characteristics of normal T cells in different functional subsets, or at various stages of T-cell differentation (Fig. 2). Thus T-acute lymphoblastic leukemias and T-NHL in childhood possess immature or thymic phenotypes, in contrast to T-cutaneous lymphomas and chronic or prolymphocytic leukemias, which exhibit "helper/inducer" or suppressor/cytotoxic" phenotypes (15, 63, 66).

The composite phenotypes of cells from 172 untreated patients were classified according to a presumptive sequence of T-lymphocyte differentiation (Fig. 2; Table 4). The cells were tested with the OKT series of monoclonal antibodies (67–75) and other markers. The groupings designated are similar to those of Reinherz et al. (15), with some modifications based on the analyses described elsewhere (16, 17, 66). Six categories of T-cell phenotype are designated (Table 4), four of thymic type and two of mature T cells. The results are tabulated in Table 5 according to clinical subgroup and reactivity with particular markers. These data confirm previous observations that T-ALL cells exclusively possess thymic or very "early" thymic phenotypes. T-NHL of children (convoluted lymphoblastic lymphoma or Sternberg's sarcoma with a mediastinal mass) also has an exclusive thymic phenotype, although, irrespective of the origin of the sample tested (node biopsy, peritoneal exudate, blood, or marrow), it more frequently (then T-ALL) expresses the composite, cortical thymocyte phenotype.

Five clinical groups with exclusively mature T-cell phenotypes were identified. All 48 of these patients were adults, 21–74 years of age, who exhibited distinct clinical and hematological features (16, 17). Sezary syndrome and mycosis fungoides had, with one exception, exclusive "helper/inducer" phenotypes as other groups have reported in smaller series (63, 66, 76). One case of leukemic mycosis fungoides presented as unequivocal "suppressor/cytotoxic" (OKT 4$^-$/ OKT 8$^+$) phenotype. Chronic lymphocytic leukemia possesses either "helper/ inducer" or "suppressor/cytotoxic" phenotypes. Only one PLL had a suppressor phenotype, seven having "helper/inducer" phenotypes and two having unexpected mixed OKT 4$^+$/OKT 8$^+$ (OKT 3$^+$, TdT $^-$) phenotypes. A new and particularly

Table 4 Putative Normal Differentiation Sequence Used to "Map" T-Cell Leukemias

Phenotype		Markers[a]											
		OKT series								"T"	Others		
		1	3	4	6	8	9	10	11		E_R	TdT
T Precursors													
Early/prethymic	1	+w	−	−	−	−		+	−	+	−	+
	2	+w	−	−	−	−	+/−	+	+	+	+	+
	3[b]	+w	−	+/−	+/−	+/−		+	+	+	+	+
Cortical thymic	4	+w	+/−	+	+	+	−	+	+	+	+	+
Mature T													
"Inducer/helper" T	5	+	+	+	−	−	−[c]	−[c]	+	+	+	−
"Suppressor" T	6	+	+	−	−	+	−[c]	−[c]	+	+	+	−

[a] −, < 5% cell staining (or rosetting); +, > 25% cell staining (or rosetting); +w, weak staining on all cells; +/−, variable expression: "T," rabbit or horse anti-T; E_R, sheep erythrocyte rosettes; WT1, antibody positive.

[b] Leukemic cells in this category have incomplete expression of OKT 4, OKT 6, and OKT 8-defined antigens that are coordinately expressed on most cortical thymocytes, that is, leukemias may be OKT 4+ OKT 6− OKT 8−; OKT 4+ OKT 6+ OKT 8−, OKT 4− OKT 6+ OKT 8−, OKT 4− OKT 6− OKT 8+, or OKT 4− OKT 6+ OKT 8+. With rare exceptions, these are all TdT+ OKT 3−. Note also that in many cases less than 100% (i.e., 10-90%) of leukemic cells may express any one of these antigens designated as positive and these positive cells may be weakly stained compared with normal thymic cortex.

[c] May be expressed on active mature cells.

Table 5 Phenotypic Heterogeneity of T-Cell Leukemias

	Diagnostic subgroup[a]						
	ALL	T-NHL(c)	Cutaneous[b] lymphoma	CLL	PLL	LBL NHL	LCL
T Precursors							
Early/pre-T 1.	11	0	0	0	0	0	0
Early/pre-T 2.	17	1	0	0	0	0	0
Early/pre-T 3.	73	5	0	0	0	0	0
Cortical thymocyte	6	11	0	0	0	0	0
Mature T							
"Helper/inducer"	0	0	17	5	7	3	3
"Suppressor/cytotoxic"	0	0	1	6	1	2	0
Uncertain	0	0	0	0	2[c]	0	1[d]
Total	107	17	18	11	10	5	4

[a]ALL, acute lymphoblastic leukemia; NHL(c), non-Hodgkin's lymphoma in children; CLL, chronic lymphocytic leukemia; LBL, lymphoblastic lymphoma (in adults); LCL, lymphosarcoma cell leukemia, or adult T cell leukemia (associated with human T cell leukemia retrovirus).
[b]Sézary syndrome or mycosis fungoides (with leukemic cells in the blood).
[c]Both cases reactive simultaneously with OKT 4 and OKT 8.
[d]Mature T cells (OKT 3[+] TdT[-]), but unreactive with OKT 4 or OKT 8.

INTRATHYMIC MATURATION

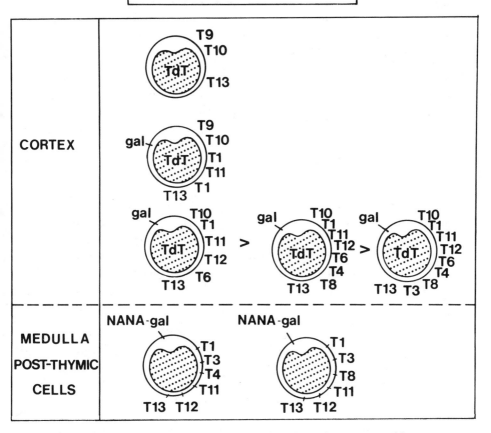

Figure 2 Intrathymic maturation. Numbers (T1, 3, etc.) represent arbitrary coding for T-cell surface protein antigens. TdT, terminal deoxynucleotidyl transferase; Gal, terminal β-D-galactosyl-1 (1, 3) N-acetyl-D galactosamine (recognized by peanut lectin, *Arachis hypogeae*); NANA-gal, terminal neuraminic acid-gal (not recognized by peanut lectin). Note: Thymic medulla cell types have a very similar antigen phenotype to nature, circulating T-cell subsets. T13 = antigen (p40) recognized by antibodies WT1 and 3As.

interesting subgroup, termed T-lymphosarcoma cell leukemia, has recently been identified (77). In the United Kingdom this relatively rare leukemia is so far exclusively found in first-generation immigrants from the Caribbean area (77) and is associated with the presence of antibody against the p24 antigen of a unique RNA virus found in Japanese adult T-cell leukemia and rare T-cell leukemias in the United States (78, 79). Four of these cases have been "typed" with monoclonal antibodies; three showed an unequivocal "helper/inducer" phenotype, and one had a presumptive mature T-cell phenotype ($OKT3^+/TdT^-$) but was OKT 4$^-$/ OKT 8$^-$. It is interesting that three cases of mature ("helper/inducer") leukemia were reactive with monoclonal antibodies against monomorphic determinants of HLA-DR (and with human alloantisera to DR).

One additional lymphocytic leukemia was considered to be chronic lymphocytic leukemia. The majority of cells in this patient reacted with OKT 11A (34) and produced (weak) sheep erythrocyte rosettes. The cells were unreactive with OKT 1 (67), OKT 3 (83, 80, 81), OKT 4 (68, 70, 71), OKT 6 (74), and OKT 8 (69, 74) and a pan-T monoclonal WT1 (82). A biopsy specimen obtained from a thymoma also portrayed an intriguing phenotype: $T3^+ T4^- T8^- T9^+ T11^+ TdT^-$, that is, an activated mature T cell without functional subset markers.

Although none of these monoclonal antibodies are T-ALL specific, the combination of TdT with monoclonals specific for T antigens operationally identifies thymic leukemia in extrathymic sites (e.g., marrow) (40). At present OKT 11 and WT1-like antibodies are the most suitable reagents for this purpose.

These phenotypes are considered to reflect the developmental position of apparent maturation arrest in the majority of leukemic cells in individual patients. OKIa-1 (HLA-DR) (83), OKT 10 (75), and OKT 9 (75) binding reflects the activation or proliferation status of the leukemia; however, it is likely that this feature is itself linked in part to the differentiation stage. The phenotypes are, however, imperfect replicas of the normal counterpart and several abnormal or asynchronous phenotypes are detected, for example, increased HLA expression, loss of T11A/E-rosette expression or TdT (66). Nevertheless, the phenotypes show a striking lineage fidelity (84); no expression of cell-surface antigens normally associated with other hemopoietic lineages is usually observed.

These composite phenotypes also suggest candidate "target" cells for T-cell leukemia. Thus T-ALL and T-NHL with thymic phenotypes occurring in our patients probably originate in early T-lineage stem cells with a variable level of maturation arrest imposed, whereas the mature T leukemias in adults most likely originate in immunocompetent lymphocytes belonging to either of two major subsets. The etiology of these two major subtypes of T-lineage malignancy is likely to be distinct and, as mentioned above, an RNA virus is implicated in one subset of mature T leukemias that has striking geographical associations.

A further important feature of these T-cell phenotypes and associated maturation arrest patterns is their capacity to be modulated in vitro. We succeeded in modulating the OKT-defined phenotype in nine lines to date (85), as well as in two fresh T-ALL. The pattern of modulation appears to mimic normal T-cell differentiation, and it is particularly interesting that cells with simultaneous expression of OKT 4- and OKT 8-defined determinants become restricted to OKT 8 positivity through the selective loss of the OKT 4 binding determinant.

Several of the induced alterations in membrane antigen expression have been confirmed biochemically, for example, increase in the OKT 1/p67 molecule, decrease in the OKT 9/gp90 molecule, and decrease in lectin binding glycoproteins.

We interpret these data to indicate that despite their aneuploid and highly malignant nature (having outlived their donors by several years!), some T-ALL cells at least are still capable of relatively normal differentiation if a presumed regulatory defect is bypassed with "abnormal" inducers. Those inducible lines may provide an ideal model system for investigating the molecular biology of T-cell differentiation. The possible binary option of OKT 4^+ or OKT $5/8^+$ phenotypes for the cortical thymocyte leukemia equivalent may in particular provide an especially useful system to analyze the basis of the genetic decision-making process in differentiation.

The antigenic changes observed with T-cell lines all parallel those observed in normal maturation and are accompanied by a decrease or slowing in cell cycling. These observations provide further support for the view that maturation arrest in leukemia may be a reversible regulatory defect that "uncouples" maturation and proliferation (86).

Some of the monoclonal antibody-defined T-cell-associated determinants studied can also be induced by activating normal T cells that are normally antigen negative. More than 90% of circulating T cells are OKT 9^-/OKT 10^- but become positive when activated by lectins or calcium ionophore plus TPA (16, 87). The observations of leukemia cell lines and normal T cells suggested a possible relationship of OKT 9 binding to proliferation status. This possibility has been investigated in detail (16).

Reinherz et al. (15) used OKT 9 as an early thymocyte marker. We confirmed that this monoclonal antibody does indeed react preferentially with T-ALL (88), but it does not identify a T-cell-specific differentiation antigen. Serological and biochemical analyses have clearly shown that OKT 9 defines a structure associated with proliferation on a wide spectrum of normal and malignant cell types. Expression of the OKT 9-defined determinant is correlated with the cycling cell fraction in T-ALL (16), as well as with the dividing cells in fetal thymus, fetal liver, and normal adult bone marrow. Leukemic cell lines (e.g., HL-60, HPB-ALL) (89) induced to mature lose OKT 9 binding capacity concomitantly with the appearance of other maturation-associated determinants, for example, OKM1 (90), and either exit from the cell cycle (HL-60) or slow down the proliferation rate (T-ALL). The density of the OKT 9 antigen varies only minimally throughout the cell cycle (data not shown) and our current view is that this membrane antigen is not, strictly speaking, a cell cycle/proliferation antigen but, rather, a determinant on a structure whose expression is regulated by active growth and/or metabolism.

The OKT 9 antigen has been isolated from T-ALL, neuroblastoma, pancreatic carcinoma, and melanoma. Its biochemical characteristics are essentially identical to those described by Omary et al. (91, 92) using monoclonal antibody B3/25 and are similar to those of the transferrin receptor (93). Definitive evidence that OKT 9 indeed detects the transferrin receptor comes from an observation that it can coprecipitate iodinated transferrin bound to its membrane receptors, although it does not bind to transferrin itself or inhibit the binding of transferrin to its receptor (16). Monoclonal B3/25, described by Omary et al. (91), also appears to be directed against the transferrin receptor (92).

The availability of monoclonal antibodies against transferrin receptors provides the opportunity for further study of this important iron delivery system. Due to mammalian species barriers and receptor mutants would be difficult to obtain for an "obligatory" antigenic structure, it has not so far been possible to use transferrin binding to human-mouse somatic cell hybrids to chromosomally map the genes controlling this receptor. OKT 9 antibody, however, does not bind to mouse transferrin receptors and it has therefore been possible to "map" the transferrin receptor via the OKT 9 binding determinant. The latter appears to segregate in human–mouse hybrids with chromosome 3, which we therefore presume carries either structural or regulatory genes for assembling the transferrin receptor (94).

Blast Crisis of Chronic Granulocytic Leukemia

Chronic granulocytic leukemia (CGL) almost inevitably progresses to a highly malignant acute leukemia or blast crisis that is associated with additional chromosomal changes and which is variously referred to as accelerated phase, acute transformation, or blast cell crisis (95). The characteristics of blast cells usually resemble myeloblasts seen in AML (96); however, in a number of cases they may have morphological and/or cytochemical features of lymphoblasts (96, 97). In rare cases the blast cells may be predominantly myelomonocytic, erythroid (98), or megarkaryoblastic (99). Mixtures of these various cell types are also common.

We have tested 275 cases of blast crisis of Philadelphia chromosome- (Ph[1]) positive CGL in adults for expression of lymphoid or "ALL" markers, for example, TdT, CALL antigen, intracellular μ chains, and T- and B-cell markers (100). Retrospectively, some of the acute leukemias (lymphoid, myeloid, or mixed) we have similarly analyzed have turned out to be Ph[1] positive. More recently we have used a panel of monoclonal antibodies (Table 1) (62), including anti-glycophorin and anti-platelet monoclonal reagents to screen for putative erythroid and platelet precursor involvement. Approximately one-third of cases have a dominant, immature lymphoid phenotype corresponding to those documented in common ALL and "null"-ALL of children and adults (101). The former includes a proportion (above one-sixth) that have "pre-B" phenotypes as defined by the presence of cytoplasmic μ immunoglobulin heavy chains (102) (Table 6). In most cases (103), there is a correlation between morphology, cytochemistry, immunology, and enzymology (TdT) in the designation of blast

Table 6 Cellular Phenotypes in Blast Crisis of Ph^1-Positive CGL: Summary 1975–1980

Phenotype	Number of patients
CGL	87
CGL blast crisis	275
Dominant "lymphoid" ("L" type)	88 (32%)
CALL	76 (μ^+, 16%; μ^- 84%)
Null-ALL	12
T-ALL	0
B-ALL	0
Dominant nonlymphoid ("myeloid" or "M" type)	174 (63%)
Rare variants	
Erythroid	4
Monocytic	2
Megakaryoblastic	4
Mixed codominant "L" + "M"	13 (5%)

crises as predominantly lymphoid or myeloid. Most blast crises are, however, to some extent mixed or heterogeneous, and the different cell preparations and assays used (e.g., enzymatic versus immunofluorescent detection of TdT) may distort the real contributions of the different cell types.

The majority of the nonlymphoid blast crises were defined by negative immunological criteria (although the majority have myeloblastic morphology and cytochemistry); most, however, are reactive with rabbit anti-myeloid sera (104), but not with the currently available monoclonal anti-granulocyte/mono-cyte reagents that react preferentially with relatively mature myeloid cells (i.e., in chronic phase CGL). Approximately 20% of these nonlymphoid cases (29 of 174), in contrast to all lymphoblastic blast crises, have been HLA-DR ("Ia" antigen) negative. This may be of some relevance, since pluripotential stem cells themselves (105), in contrast to the lineage-committed progenitor cells (14, 105), are thought to be HLA-DR negative.

Acute Undifferentiated Leukemia

A small proportion (5–15%) of acute leukemias in adults and children have been difficult to classify by available morphological and cytochemical methods. The strategy for dealing with such leukemias varies; they may be termed "stem cell," "undifferentiated" (i.e., AUL), or "nonlymphoid." Their treatment varies and may be selected on the basis of the age bias of lymphoid versus myeloid leukemias, that is, young "AUL" treated as ALL and older patients treated as "AML."

In a group of 22 "AUL" patients, 19 were shown to be of a definite lymphoid or myeloid phenotype and 12 had a common ALL phenotype (105a). Of these 12, 2 had a Ph^1 chromosome and 1 of these subsequently reverted to chronic granulocytic leukemia. A total of 3 patients had a null-ALL phenotype (CALL $^-$, TdT $^+$, DR $^+$). One of the common ALL and one null-ALL had a significant proportion of cells with cytoplasmic μ chain, that is, pre-B cells. Two patients had an unequivocal B-cell phenotype with light-chain-type-restricted cell-surface immunoglobulin. One patient was negative with OKT 1, 3, 4, 6, 8, and 11—as well as Leu-1 (106) and NA134 (107)—but strongly positive with WT1. Two further cases reacted with anti-myeloid sera and three others had no distinctive markers.

These data therefore indicate that "AUL" is heterogeneous and in most cases can be identified as "lymphoid" or, more rarely, "myeloid." Finally, the re-identification of a substantial proportion of AUL as ALL was in part supported by the subsequent clinical course observed in these patients.

Erythroleukemia

Monoclonal antibody LICR-LON-R10 does not react with lymphoid or myeloid cells, but does stain various numbers of nucleated cells in bone marrow; these cells are morphologically identifiable as erythroid (108, 109). It has been reported that erythroid progenitor populations in marrow and blood, that is, BFU-E and CFU-E, were more than 90% glycophorin A negative as assessed by FACS analysis and sorting (14). Glycophorin A expression therefore is correlated reasonably well in normal tissue with the post-CFU-E stage of erythroid lineage maturation. Leukemias originating in multipotential stem cells or erythroid progenitors and in maturation arrest in these "compartments" would not be expected to be glycophorin A positive, unless some asynchrony of gene expression occurred.

Erythroleukemias, in contrast to most cases diagnosed as AML, were HLA-DR negative, but had a very variable proportion of glycophorin-positive cells. In several cases, the majority of erythroblasts were negative for glycophorin. Of 721 nonerythroid leukemias studied for glycophorin expression, only 17 had a significant proportion of glycophorin-positive blast cells (109a). Of these 17, 5 were, however, diagnosed as AML with a marked erythroid component and 3 were considered to be erythroid blast crises of CML. Of the remaining "nonerythroid" leukemias, four were "myeloid" blast crises of CML, one considered to be a possible megakaryoblastic crisis of CML (but was anti-platelet monoclonal negative), two were AML, and one was AMML. One case was diagnosed as acute megakaryoblastic leukemia, but had two cell populations: one reactive with both platelet glycoprotein I monoclonal AN51 (111) and with platelet peroxidase. Only two cases diagnosed and treated initially as ALL were found to be glycophorin positive. Both patients were less than 6 months old and had an equivocal diagnosis of ALL. The blast cells expressed no lymphoid or ALL markers.

A variety of leukemic cell lines were investigated and only K562 was glycophorin positive. These data therefore confirm the results of Andersson et al. (110), although the number of glycophorin A-positive leukemias is considerably less than indicated in the small series studied in Finland. The reason for this discrepancy is unknown. One possibility concerns the differences in the antibodies used to detect glycophorin A. Andersson and colleagues used a rabbit antiserum absorbed with mutant glycophorin A-negative erythrocytes (109, 110). One possibility is that this reagent detects more antigenic determinants than the monoclonal antibody. In addition, we have considered the possibility that the latter reagent could be directed against a carbohydrate determinant and, thereby, only react with erythroid cells (since glycosylation increases during cell maturation). However, we consider these explanations unlikely. In a comparative study with rabbit anti-glycophorin A (kindly provided by Dr. L. Andersson), we found similar intensities of erythroid staining, as evaluated by the FACS and similarly failed to separate BFU-E in the glycophorin A-positive fraction using either murine monoclonal or rabbit antibodies. Additionally, monoclonal anti-glycophorin LICR-LON-R10 appears to recognize a protein region of the glycophorin molecule.

We interpret our data to indicate that the highly selective glycophorin A expression seen in normal hemopoiesis is maintained in leukemia. Glycophorin-positive leukemias can present as overt erythroleukemias (M6, AML) or mixed leukemias, that is early erythroblasts with megakaryoblasts or myeloblasts. The latter leukemia indicates a clonal origin from bi- or multipotential stem cells, as does the finding of glycophorin-positive blast crises of CML. Only very rarely do cases diagnosed as AML or ALL express glycophorin. We suggest that these are genuine immature erythroid cells, and not myeloblasts or lymphoblasts aberrantly expressing glycophorin A.

Megakaryoblastic Leukemia

Megakaryoblastic leukemia, a malignant transformation of platelet precursors, is probably relatively rare. However, some authors claim that a considerable proportion of Ph[1] chromosome-positive CGL in blast crisis may have a dominant subclone in maturation arrest at the small megakaryoblast level of differentiation (as detected by platelet peroxidase staining by electron microscopy) (99). One implication of that finding was that blast crises, which are regarded as CALL-like, might be megakaryoblastic. We found that five out of eight "possible" Ph[1]-negative megakaryoblastic leukemias had between 20 to 68% of cells weakly positive with monoclonal AN51, which is specific for glycoprotein I of human platelets and megakaryocytes (111). Only one other acute leukemia investigated (out of 60 tested to date) had a major AN51$^+$ population, and this was the "AUL" patient who had a dual anti-glycophorin/anti-platelet-positive population. Four cases of CGL blast crisis (out of 16 tested so far) did, however, have a minor (5–16%) AN51$^+$ population, including one case that was considered to be erythroblastic (with glycophorin-positive cells). AN51 may, however, like anti-glycophorin monoclonal LICR-LON-R10, be an inadequate probe for detecting very early platelet precursors if, as is quite possible, it binds to a determinant whose expression is correlated with maturation in the platelet lineage. The involvement of both erythroid and platelet precursors in acute leukemias could therefore be underestimated.

ARE THERE LEUKEMIA-SPECIFIC MONOCLONAL ANTIBODIES?

Several recent reports on monoclonal antibodies claim specificity for subgroups of leukemia, as they were found to react with leukemic cell lines and cells from leukemia patients, but not with normal hemopoietic tissues (Table 7).

Ab89 (5) was produced by immunizing mice with tumor cells from a patient with diffuse poorly differentiated lymphocytic lymphoma (D-PDLL). This monoclonal antibody reacted with the same patient's tumor cells, but not with other hemopoietic cells. Other tumor or normal cells and mitogen-stimulated cells did not appear to bind Ab89, and the antibody did not react with HLA-AB antigens or surface immunoglobulin (5). This antibody also reacted with B-cell tumors from other individuals—D-PDLL and two B-CLL. The antigen detected by this monoclonal antibody appears restricted to a subset of mature neoplastic B-lymphoid cells. The authors, however, stressed that owing to the detection limits of their screening methods (immunofluorescence and quantitative absorption), the possibility exists that Ab89 may also react with a small population of normal cells or that it reacts with an antigen present on other cells in low amounts.

Antibody 38.13 (7) was shown to react specifically with cells derived from Burkitt tumors, including EBV$^+$ and EBV$^-$ Burkitt lymphomas. Normal B-cell lines and normal lymphoid cells were not reactive. The antibody was also unreactive with B-CLL, acute lymphoid and myeloid leukemias, and B-cell lymphomas.

Antibody CALL-2 (4) reportedly reacts with some cultured T-ALL cell lines and human T-ALL leukemias. Normal cells and other acute or chronic leukemia cells were unreactive with CALL-2. However, the binding of this antibody was assessed solely by means of complement-mediated cytotoxicity.

Antibodies of this type could be important with respect to the diagnosis and treatment of leukemia and lymphoma. However, their specificity needs further

Table 7 Putative Leukemia Specific Monoclonal Antibodies

Monoclonal antibody	Reactive with	Reference
CALL 2	T-ALL lines	4
	T-ALL fresh leukemia cells	4
Ab89	Subgroup of B cell lymphomas	5
38.13	Burkitt tumors (EBV^+ and EBV^-)	141
Anti-idiotype specific	Individual B-NHL	112

investigation on a greater number of fresh leukemia cells and normal tissues, using the most sensitive detection methods available.

Monoclonal anti-idiotype antibodies represent a special case in this group of anti-leukemia reagents. Although the idiotype determinant does not represent a cancer-specific antigen in terms of malignant expression, it is, in this case, a surface determinant unique to the neoplastic cell, because it exists on the cell that has expanded as a neoplastic clone but not on other B cells of the same or of any other individual. Such an antibody has been produced by Miller et al. (112).

THE POTENTIAL ROLE OF MONOCLONAL ANTIBODIES IN THE THERAPY OF LEUKEMIA

The development of monoclonal antibodies to hemopoietic cell antigens has renewed attempts at serotherapy of leukemias and lymphomas. Heteroantisera raised against leukemia antigens proved to be inadequate for the same reasons that often made them unsuitable for diagnostic purposes (113, 114). In addition, they involved the administration of large quantities of foreign proteins and a risk of allergic reactions. Many of these problems are overcome by the use of purified monoclonal antibodies. Therapeutic potential of monoclonal antibodies to leukemia cell membrane antigens based on their ability to kill or physically remove (e.g., on affinity absorbents, magnetic beads) leukemia cells. Some monoclonal antibodies of this kind have also been used for the removal of allogeneically competent T cells of the donor prior to transplantation. It has been shown that such treatment decreases risks of graft-versus-host disease.

Several strategies are available for the treatment of leukemia with monoclonal antibodies. It is important to appreciate that these different strategies demand different qualitative features of the monoclonal antibody used. Although an antibody binding exclusively to cancer cells would be ideal for all purposes, this may not be obtainable; more significantly, it may not be required. Also, a substantial quantitative difference between tumor cells and normal tissue might be sufficient for practical therapeutic purposes. In the context of monoclonal "cleansing" of autologous marrow, the only specificity requirement is that the monoclonal antibody distinguish the clonogenic fraction of tumor cells from normal marrow stem cells. Miller and Levy (115) reported a transient clinical response in a patient with cutaneous lymphoma (Sezary syndrome) injected several times with a monoclonal anti-T-lymphocyte antibody. Miller et al. (116) also reported monoclonal therapy of an adult patient with drug-resistant T-cell leukemia. Two injections of 1 mg of monoclonal anti-T cell (L17F12/Leu-1) were given. Each produced a dramatic fall in blood lymphocytes that returned to pretreatment levels over the ensuing 24 hr. After the first injection, circulating free antigen in serum became detectable for the first time. A further 5-mg dose of monoclonal antibody was ineffective, presumably because it was "blocked" by free antigen. Antigenic "modulation" (i.e., loss of antigen) was also found transiently following each course of therapy. This patient also produced some anti-mouse immunoglobulins. Although this patient tolerated antibody therapy well, this case vividly illustrates some of the likely difficulties in the therapeutic use of monoclonal antibodies. Even if the "target" antigen is not normally present in serum, large amounts can appear following the initial incomplete but extensive ablative effects of monoclonal antibody; this can compromise subsequent injections, particularly if these are required within a few days. The very rapid return of leukemia cells is also a disturbing feature. Although these cells could be the "original" circulating leukemic cells returning to the circulation after being temporarily "held up" in the liver, it is more likely that they are new leukemia cells entering the circulation, derived from a clonogenic population that was relatively unaffected by the monoclonal antibody. It is possible that the removal of the circulating leukemic cells could have increased the proliferation of these precursor cells. This result is not altogether unexpected, since much earlier experience with "conventional" anti-lymphocyte antibodies in mice clearly demonstrated the ease of removing (via opsonization in the liver) the circulating lymphocyte populations, while leaving the more static or transient populations in lymph nodes and spleen intact.

A conclusion that can be made from this single patient report and the one by Nadler et al. (117) is that fairly large amounts of monoclonal antibody may have to be injected to destroy clonogenic cells and that this will be more likely to achieve success when the tumor burden has been decreased by chemotherapy. It follows also that it will be important to find out whether the clonogenic population in fact expresses the same "target" antigen as the bulk of the tumor cell population.

Ritz et al. (56) similarly treated four ALL patients with monoclonal J5 (several hundred milligrams per patient). A transient decrease in circulating blast cells was observed. The re-emerging blasts had "modulated" their gp100 "ALL" antigen, which reappeared after a short-term culture. This indicated that in vivo the antigen was being continually "capped off" by the antibody. Similar observations were made several years ago with animal leukemias and illustrate a potential difficulty with monoclonal immunotherapy.

Nadler et al. (117) attempted serotherapy of a patient with a drug-resistant, advanced lymphoma, using the monoclonal antibody Ab89 (5). This antibody was shown to be cytotoxic to lymphoma cells in vitro. Only a very transient decrease in tumor cell burden was achieved, and the ineffective response in vitro was almost certainly attributable to the large amount of cell free antigen in serum that effectively absorbed the large amounts of monoclonal antibody injected (> 150 mg).

Ritz and colleagues (118) have used monoclonal antibody J5 (anti-CALL) to remove residual ALL cells in vitro from autologous bone marrow prior to re-infusion into four patients primed with ablative chemotherapy and total body irradiation. All four patients had a successful marrow engraftment and two remained in complete remission more than 1 year after transplantation. These preliminary results are encouraging, but it is too early to judge their therapeutic efficacy. It has been suggested that cocktails of monoclonal antibodies might be more effective in autologous marrow "cleanup" than individual reagents (G. Janossy and J. Kersey, personal communication). For example, in CALL, J5-like antibodies could be supplemented by monoclonal antibodies such as BA-1 (118) and BA-2 (119), which together as a "cocktail" would cover any antigenic heterogeneity of the clonogenic leukemic cells.

The preparation of immunotoxins may also be useful for the immunotherapy of human leukemia, as demonstrated by recent animal studies. Monoclonal antibodies against the Thy-1.1 antigen conjugated with the A chain of ricin (120, 121), abrin, or gelonin (122) effectively and selectively kill transplantable Thy-1.1 antigen-positive mouse leukemias when the cells are treated in vitro. Similarly, rabbit and monoclonal antibodies specific for a B-cell lymphoma immunoglobulin idiotype were found to be effective lytic agents for these tumor cells when conjugated to ricin A chain (123). Thorpe and Ross (122) have found that monoclonal anti-human T-cell antibody NA134 conjugated with diphtheria toxin inhibits protein synthesis in vitro of the T leukemic cell line MOLT-4. Similarly, Raso et al. (124) report that the J5–ricin conjugate inhibited protein synthesis in the cell line Nalm-1.

It is important to note, however, that the efficacy of many of these conjugates was several orders of magnitude less than native toxin, and without exception results achieved with in vivo injection have so far been disappointing; only marginal effects on established leukemias have been obtained.

The use of monoclonal anti-T antibodies has additionally been explored for the purposes of elimination of graft-versus-host disease in HLA matched allogeneic bone marrow transplantation. Opsonization of the donor T cells with OKT 3 has been shown to reduce the incidence of graft-versus-host disease (125). The incubation of bone marrow with complement and a combination of anti-T monoclonal antibodies OKT 3/OKT 3/MBG6 (126) achieved a successful removal of over 99% of detectable T cells from the donor marrow (127).

The use of tissue or cell type-specific monoclonal antibodies (unconjugated or conjugated) to remove residual tumor cells from marrow prior to reinfusion will probably be the subject of a number of studies over the coming few years.

SUMMARY

Monoclonal antibodies raised against leukemic or normal hemopoietic cells have been extensively used for the characterization of cell-surface antigens. Panels of monoclonal antibodies can be used to define a composite phenotype of each leukemia/lymphoma subclass that corresponds approximately to particular stages of hemopoietic differentiation. Overall, leukemic cells appear to retain a conserved antigenic phenotype that reflects their (a) cellular/lineage origin, (b) level of maturation arrest, and (c) proliferative activity. Most leukemia-associated antigens identified with monoclonal antibodies are therefore normal gene products "appropriately" expressed. A few putatively leukemia/lymphoma-*specific* monoclonal antibodies have, however, been recently reported.

In combination with other markers (e.g., TdT assay, karyotype) and flow cytometry, monoclonal antibody typing of leukemias is of value for differential diagnosis of leukemias and possibly for monitoring residual or re-emerging disease. Even in the absence of leukemia specificity, monoclonal antibodies have a therapeutic potential that is currently being explored.

ACKNOWLEDGMENTS

We are grateful to those colleagues who made available the monoclonal antibodies mentioned in Table 1, and to those physicians and hematologists who referred leukemic samples. We are particularly grateful to Mrs. J. Needham for her excellent help in typing this manuscript.

REFERENCES

1. P. J. Fialkow, *Biochim. Biophys. Acta 458*:283 (1976).
2. P. C. Nowell, *Science 195*:23 (1976).
3. J. D. Rowley, *Semin. Hematol. 15*:301 (1978)
4. C. -T. Deng, P. Terasaki, J. Chia, and R. Billing, *Lancet 1*:01 (1982).

5. L. M. Nadler, P. Stashenko, R. Hardy, and S. F. Schlossman, *J. Immunol.* *125*: 570 (1980).
6. J. Ritz, J. M. Pesando, J. Notis-McConarty, H. Lazarus, and S. F. Schlossman, *Nature 283*:583 (1980)
7. J. Wiels, M. Fellows, and T. Tursz, *Proc. Nat. Acad. Sci. U.S.A. 78*:6485 (1981).
8. S. Thierfelder, H. Rodt, and E. Thiel (eds.), *Immunological Diagnosis of Leukemias and Lymphomas*, Springer-Verlag, New York, 1976.
9. M. F. Greaves, *Prog. Hamatol. 9*:255 (1975).
10. M. D. Cooper and M. Seligmann, in *B and T Cells in Immune Recognition* (F. Loor and G. Roelants, ed.), 1977, p. 377.
11. M. M. Roberts and M. F. Greaves, *Br. J. Hematol. 38*:439 (1978).
12. F. Bollum, *Blood, 54*:1203 (1979).
13. R. B. Ellis, N. T. Rapson, A. D. Patrick, and M. F. Greaves, *N. Engl. J. Med. 298*:476 (1978).
14. C. Milstein, G. Galfré, D. S. Secher, and T. Springer, *Cell Biol. Int. Rep. 3*:1 (1979).
15. E.L. Reinherz, P. C. Kung, G. Goldstein, R. H. Levey, and S. F. Schlossman, *Proc. Nat. Acad. Sci. U.S.A. 77*:1588 (1980).
16. M. F. Greaves, D. Delia, R. Sutherland, J. Rao, W. Verbi, J. Kemshead, G. Hariri, G. Goldstein, and P. Kung, *Int. J. Immunopharmacol. 3*:283 (1981).
17. M. F. Greaves, J. Rao, G. Hariri, W. Verbi, D. Catovsky, P. Kung, and G. Goldstein, *Leukemia Res. 5*:281–299 (1981).
18. W. Knapp, *Leukemia Markers*, Academic, New York, 1981.
19. M. F. Greaves, J. B. Robinson, D. Delia, J. Ritz, S. Schlossman, C. Sieff, G. Goldstein, P. Kung, F. Bollum, and P. Edwards, in *Modern Trends in Human Leukemia*, Vol. 4 (R. Neth, R. C. Gallo, T. Graf, K. Mannweiler, and K. Winkler, eds.), Springer-Verlag, Berlin, 1981, p. 296.
20. J. Robinson, C. Sieff, D. Delia, P. A. W. Edwards, and M. F. Greaves, *Nature 289*:68 (1981).
21. R. A. Newman, R. Sutherland, and M. F. Greaves, *J. Immunol. 126*:2024 (1981).
22. R. Sutherland, D. Delia, C. Schneider, R. Newman, J. Kemshead, and M. Greaves, *Proc. Nat. Acad. Sci. U.S.A. 78*:4515 (1981).
23. G. Janossy, F. J. Bollum, K. F. Bradstock, and J. Ashley, *Blood 56*:430 (1980).
24. J. T. Kemshead, J. Fritschy, U. Asser, D. R. Sutherland, and M. F. Greaves, *Hybridoma 1*:109 (1982).
25. L. A. Herzenberg and L. A. Herzenberg, in *Handbook of Experimental Immunology*, Vol. 2, (D. M. Weir, ed.), Blackwell, Oxford, 1977.
26. M. R. Melamed, P. F. Mullaney, and M. L. Mendelsohn (eds.), *Flow Cytometry and Sorting*, Wiley, New York, 1979.
27. G. Janossy, M. M. Roberts, D. Capellaro, M. F. Greaves, and G. E. Francis, in *Immunofluorescence and Related Staining Techniques* (W. Knapp, K. Holabar, and G. Wick, eds.), Elsevier/North-Holland, New York, 1978, p. 111.

28. G. Janossy, G. E. Francis, D. Capellaro, A. H. Goldstone, and M. F. Greaves, *Nature* 276:176 (1978).

29. D. Catovsky, S. Pittman, M. O'Brien, M. Cherchi, C. Costello, R. Foa, E. Pearce, A. V. Hoffbrand, G. Janossy, K. Ganehagura, and M. F. Greaves, *Am. J. Clin. Pathol.* 72:736 (1979).

30. M. F. Greaves, in *Advances in Comparative Leukemia Research 1979.* (D. S. Yohn, B. A. Lapin, and J. R. Blakeslee, eds.), Elsevier/North-Holland, New York, 1980, p. 235.

31. M. A. Boss, D. Delia, J. B. Robinson, and M. F. Greaves, *Blood* 56:910 (1980).

32. D. Delia, M. Greaves, R. Newman, R. Sutherland, J. Minowada, P. Kung, and G. Goldstein, *Int. J. Cancer* 29:23 (1982).

33. M. Jondal, G. Holm, and H. Wigzell, *J. Exp. Med.* 136:207 (1972).

34. W. Verbi, M. F. Greaves, C. Schneider, K. Koubek, G. Janossy, P. C. Kung, and G. Goldstein, *Eur. J. Immunol.* 12:81 (1982).

35. J. Van Wauwe, J. Goosens, W. Decock, P. Kung, and G. Goldstein, *Immunology* 44:865 (1981).

36. F. D. Howard, J. A. Ledbetter, J. Wong, C. P. Bieber, E. B. Stinson, and L. A. Herzenberg, *J. Immunol.* 126:2117 (1981)

37. M. Kamoun, P. J. Martin, J. A. Hansen, M. A. Brown, A. W. Siadak, and R. C. Nowinski, *J. Exp. Med.* 153:207 (1981).

38. G. Janossy, N. Tidman, E. S. Papageorgiou, P. C. Kung, and G. Goldstein, *J. Immunol.* 1261608 (1981).

39. F. Bollum, *Blood* 54:1203 (1979).

40. G. Janossy, J. A. Thomas, G. Pizzolo, S. M. Granger, J. McLaughlin, J. A. Habeshaw, A. G. Stansfeld, and J. Sloane, *Br. J. Cancer* 42:224 (1980).

41. K. F. Bradstock, G. Janossy, A. V. Hoffbrand, K. Ganeshaguru, P. Llewellin, H. G. Prentice, and F. J. Bollum, *Br. J. Haematol.* 47:121 (1981).

42. M. F. Greaves, G. Brown, N. Rapson, and T. A. Lister, *Clin. Immunol. Immunopathol.* 4:67 (1975).

43. M. F. Greaves and G. Janossy, in *In Vitro Methods in Cell Mediated Immunity*, 2nd ed. (B. Bloom and J. David, eds.) Academic, New York, 1976, p. 89.

44. L. Borella, L. Sen, and J. T. Casper, *J. Immunol.* 118:309 (1977).

44a. S. J. Korsmeyer, P. A. Hieter, J. V. Ravetch, D. G. Poplack, T. A. Waldmann, and P. Leder, *Proc. Natl. Acad. Sci. U.S.A.* 78:7096 (1981).

45. M. F. Greaves, *Cancer Res.* 41:4752 (1981).

46. M. F. Greaves, D. Delia, G. Janossy, N. Rapson, J. Chessells, M. Woods, and G. Prentice, *Leukemia Res.* 4:15 (1980).

47. R. A. Newman, R. Sutherland, and M. F. Greaves, *J. Immunol.* 126:2024 (1981).

48. M. F. Greaves, W. Verbi, L. Volger, M. Cooper, R. Ellis, K. Ganeshaguru, V. Hoffbrand, G. Janossy, and F. J. Bollum, *Leukemia Res.* 3:353 (1979).

49. J. Minowada, J. Janossy, M. F. Greaves, T. Tsubota, B. I. S. Srivastava, S. Morikawa, and E. Tatsumi, *J. Nat. Cancer Inst.* 60:1269 (1978).

50. G. Janossy, M. F. Greaves, B. Sutherland, J. Durrant, and C. Lewis, *Leukemia Res.* 1:289 (1977).

51. M. F. Greaves, D. Delia, G. Janossy, N. Rapson, J. Chessells, M. Woods, and G. Prentice, *Leukemia Res. 4*:15 (1980).
52. M. F. Greaves, G. Janossy, G. E. Francis, and J. Minowada, in *Differentiation of Normal and Neoplastic Hematopoietic Cells* (B. Clarkson, P. A. Marks, and J. Till, eds.) Cold Spring Harbor Laboratory, New York, 1978, p. 823.
53. G. Janossy, F. Bollum, K. Bradstock, N. Rapson, and M. F. Greaves, *J. Immunol. 123*:1525 (1979).
54. R. A. Newman, D. R. Sutherland, and M. F. Greaves, in *Modern Trends in Human Leukemia*, Vol. 4 (R. Neth, R. C. Gallo, T. Graf, K. Mannweiler, and K. Winkler, eds.), Springer-Verlag, Berlin, 1981, p. 326.
55. J. M. Pesando, J. Ritz, H. Levine, C. Terhorst, H. Lazarus, and S. F. Schlossman, *J. Immunol. 124*:2794 (1980).
56. J. Ritz, J. M. Pesando, S. E. Sallan, L. A. Clavell, J. Notis-McConarty, P. Rosenthal, and S. F. Schlossman, *Blood 58*:141 (1981).
56a. M. F. Greaves, G. Hariri, R. A. Newman, D. R. Sutherland, M. A. Ritter, and J. Ritz, *Blood 61*:628 (1983).
57. R. Sutherland, J. Smart, J. Niaudet, and M. F. Greaves, *Leukemia Res. 2*: 115 (1978).
58. R. S. R. S. Metzgar, M. J. Borowitz, N. H. Jones, and B. L. Dowell, *J. Exp. Med. 154*:1249 (1981).
59. M. F. Greaves, in *Human Lymphocyte Differentiation: Its Application to Cancer* (B. Serrou and C. Rosenfeld, eds.) Elsevier/North-Holland, Amsterdam, 1978, p. 253.
60. G. Janossy, in *Leukemia Markers* (W. Knapp, ed.), Academic, New York, 1981, p. 45.
61. M. F. Greaves, in *Leukemia Markers* (W. Knapp, ed.) Academic, New York, 1981, p. 463.
62. M. F. Greaves, J. B. Robinson, D. Delia, J. Ritz, S. Schlossman, C. Sieff, G. Goldstein, P. Kurg, F. Bollum, and P. Edwards, in *Modern Trends in Human Leukemia*, Vol. 4 (R. Neth, R. C. Gallo, T. Graf, K. Mannweiler, and K. Winkler, eds.), Springer-Verlag, Berlin, 1981, p. 296.
63. A. Bernard, L. Boumsell, E. L. Reinherz, L. M. Nadler, J. Ritz, H. Coppin, Y. Richard, F. Valensi, J. Dausset, G. Flandrin, J. Lemerie, and S. F. Schlossman, *Blood 57*:1105 (1981).
63a. J. A. Habeshaw, D. Bailey, A. G. Stansfeld, and M. F. Greaves, *Br. J. Cancer 47*:327 (1983).
64. K. Liszka, O. Majdic, P. Bettelheim, and W. Knapp, in *Leukemia Markers* (W. Knapp, ed.), Academic, New York, 1981, p. 61.
65. M. F. Greaves, A. Paxton, G. Janossy, C. Pain, S. Johnson, and T. A. Lister, *Leukemia Res. 4*:1 (1980).
66. M. F. Greaves, J. Rao, G. Hariri, W. Verbi, D. Catovsky, P. Kung, and G. Goldstein, *Leukemia Res. 5*281 (1981).
67. E. L. Reinherz, P. C. Kung, G. Goldstein, and S. F. Schlossman, *J. Immunol. 123*:1312 (1979).
68. P. C. Kung, G. Goldstein, E. L. Reinerz, and S. F. Schlossman, *Science 206*: 347 (1979).

69. E. L. Reinherz, P. C. Kung, G. Goldstein, and S. F. Schlossman, *J. Immunol.* *124*:1301 (1980).
70. E. L. Reinherz, P. C. Kung, Goldstein, and S. F. Schlossman, *Proc. Nat. Acad. Sci. U.S.A.* *76*:4061 (1979).
71. E. L. Reinherz, P. C. Kung, G. Goldstein, and S. F. Schlossman, *J. Immunol.* *123*:2894 (1979).
72. C. Terhorst, A. Van Agthoven, E. Reinherz, and S. F. Schlossman, *Science* *209*:520 (1980).
73. E. L. Reinherz and S. F. Schlossman, *Cell 19*:821 (1980).
74. E. L. Reinherz, P. C. Kung, G. Goldstein, R. H. Levey, and S. F. Schlossman, *Proc. Nat. Acad. Sci. U.S.A.* *77*:1588 (1980).
75. C. Terhorst, A. Van Agthoven, K. LeClair, P. Snow, E. Reinherz, and S. F. Schlossman, *Cell 23*:771 (1981).
76. E. Thiel, H. Rodt, D. Huhn, B. Netzel, H. Grosse-Wilde, K. Ganeshaguru, and S. Thierfelder, *Blood 56*:759 (1980).
77. D. Catovsky, M. F. Greaves, M. Rose, D. A. G. Galton, A. W. G. Goolden, D. R. McCluskey, J. M. White, I. Lampert, G. Bourikas, R. Ireland, A. I. Brownell, J. M. Bridges, W. A. Blattner, and R. C. Gallo, *Lancet 1*:639 (1982).
78. B. J. Poiesz, R. W. Ruscetti, M. S. Reitz, V. S. Kalyanaraman, and R. C. Gallo, *Nature 292*:268 (1981)
80. J. P. Van Wauwe, J. R. de Mey, and J. G. Goossens, *J. Immunol.* *124*:2708 (198
81. T. W. Chang, P. C. Kung, S. P. Gingras, and G. Goldstein, *Proc. Nat. Acad. Sci. U.S.A.* *78*:1805 (1981).
82. W. J. M. Tax, H. W. Willems, M. D. A. Kibbelaar, de Groot, J., P. J. A. Capel, R. M. W. de Waal, P. Reekers, and R. A. P. Koene, in *Protides of the Biological Fluids* (H. Peeters, ed.), Pergamon, Oxford, 1982.
83. E. L. Reinherz, L. Moretta, M. Roper, J. M. Breard, M. C. Mingari, M. D. Cooper and S. F. Schlossman, *J. Exp. Med.* *151*–969 (1980).
84. M. F. Greaves, *J. Cell. Physiol. Suppl. 1*:113 (1982).
85. D. Delia, M. F. Greaves, R. A. Newman, D. R. Sutherland, J. Minowada, P. Kung, and G. Goldstein, *Int. J. Cancer 29*:23 (1982).
86. M. F. Greaves, D. Delia, R. Newman, and L. Vodinelich, *Monoclonal Antibodies in Clinical Medicine* (A. McMichael and J. Fabre, eds.), Academic, London 129–165.
87. J. W. Larrick and P. Cresswell, *J. Supramol. Struct. 11*:579 (1979).
88. M. F. Greaves, D. Delia, R. Sutherland, J. Rao, W. Verbi, J. Kemshead, J. Robinson, G. Hariri, G. Goldstein, and P. Kung, *Int. J. Immunopharmacol. 3*:283 (1981).
89. M. A. Boss, D. Delia, J. B. Robinson, and M. F. Greaves, *Blood 56*:910 (1980).
90. J. Breard, E. L. Reinherz, P. C. Kung, G. Goldstein, and S. F. Schlossman, *J. Immunol.* *124*:1943 (1980).
91. M. B. Omary, I. S. Trowbridge, and J. Minowada, *Nature 286*:888 (1980).
92. I. S. Trowbridge and M. B. Omary, *Proc. Nat. Acad. Sci. U.S.A.* *78*:3039 (1981).
93. G. M. P. Galbraith, and W. P. Faulk, *Cell. Immunol. 49*:215 (1980).

94. P. N. Goodfellow, G. Banting, R. Sutherland, M. Greaves, E. Solomon, and S. Povey, *Somatic Cell Genet. 8*:1970.
95. J. C. Barton and M. E. Conrad, *Am. J. Hematol. 4*:291 (1978).
96. S. Rosenthal, G. P. Canellos, V. T. DeVita, and H. R. Gralnick, *Blood 49*:705 (1977).
97. L. C. Peterson, C. D. Bloomfield, and R. D. Brunning, *Am. J. Med. 63*:542 (1977).
98. S. Rosenthal, G. P. Canellos, J. Whang-Peng, and H. R. Gralnick, *Am. J. Med. 63*:542 (1977).
99. J. Breton-Gorius, F. Reyes, J. P. Vernant, M. Tulliez, and B. Dreyfus, *Br. J. Haematol. 39*:295 (1978).
100. M. F. Greaves, in *Chronic Granulocytic Leukemia* (M. T. Shaw, ed.), 1982, p. 15.
101. M. F. Greaves and G. Janossy, *Biochim. Biophys. Acta 516*:193 (1978).
102. L. B. Vogler, W. M. Crist, P. C. Vinson, A. Sarrif, M. C. Brattain, and M. A. Coleman, *Blood 54*:1164 (1979).
103. G. Janossy, R. F. Woodruff, A. Paxton, M. F. Greaves, D. Capellaro, B. Kirk, E. M. Innes, O. B. Eden, C. Lewis, D. Catovsky and A. V. Hoffbrand, *Blood 51*:861 (1978).
104. M. M. Roberts and M. F. Greaves, *Br. J. Haematol. 38*:439 (1978).
105. M. A. S. Moore, H. E. Broxmeyer, A. P. C. Sheridan, P. A. Meyers, N. Jacobsen, and R. J. Winchester, *Blood 55*:682 (1980).
105a. M. F. Greaves, R. Bell, J. Amess, and T. A. Lister, *Leukemia Res.* (in press).
106. E. G. Engleman, R. Warnke, R. I. Fox, J. Dilley, C. J. Benike, and R. Levey, *Proc. Nat. Acad. Sci. U.S.A. 78*:1791 (1981).
107. A. J. McMichael, J. R. Pilch, G. Galfre, D. Y. Mason, J. W. Fabre, and C. Milstein, *Eur. J. Immunol. 9*:205 (1979).
108. P. A. W. Edwards, *Biochem. Soc. Trans. 8*:334 (1980).
109. L. C. Andersson, C. G. Gahmberg, I. Teerenhovi, and P. Vuopio, *Int. J. Cancer 24*:717 (1979).
109a. M. F. Greaves, C. Sieff, and P. A. W. Edwards, *Blood 61*:645 (1983).
110. L. C. Andersson, M. Jokinen, and C. G. Gahmberg, *Nature 278*:364 (1979).
111. A. J. McMichael, N. A. Rust, J. R. Pilch, R. Sochynsky, J. Morton, D. Y. Mason, C.Ruan, G. Tobelem, and J. Caen, *Br. J. Haematol. 49*:501 (1981).
112. R. A. Miller, D. G. Maloney, R. Warnke, and R. Levey, *N. Engl. J. Med. 306*:517 (1982).
113. P. W. Wright and I. D. Bernstein, *Prog. Exp. Tumor Res. 25*:140 (1980).
114. G. A. Currie, *Int. J. Cancer 26*:141 (1978).
115. R. A. Miller and R. Levey, *Lancet 2*:226 (1981).
116. R. A. Miller, D. G. Maloney, J. McMaloney, J. McKillop, and R. Levey, *Blood 58*:78 (1981).
117. L. M. Nadler, P. Stashenko, R. Hardy, W. Kaplan, L. N. Button, D. W. Kufe, K. H. Antman, and S. F. Schlossman, *Cancer Res. 40*:3147 (1980).
118. J. Ritz, S. E. Sallan, R. C. Bast, J. M. Lipton, L. A. Clavell, M. Feeney, T. Hercend, D. G. Nathan, and S. F. Schlossman, *Lancet 2*:60 (1982).

119. J. H. Kersey, T. W. LeBien, C. S. Abramson, R. Newman, R. Sutherland, and M. Greaves, *J. Exp. Med. 153*:726 (1981).

120. R. J. Youle and D. M. Neville, *Proc. Nat. Acad. Sci. U.S.A. 77*:5483 (1980).

121. H. E. Blythman, P. Casellas, O. Gros, F. K. Jansen, F. Paolucci, B. Pau, and H. Vidal, *Nature 290*:145 (1981).

122. P. E. Thorpe and W. C. Ross, *Immunol. Rev. 62*:119 (1982).

123. E. S. Vitetta, K. A. Krolick, and J. W. Uhr, *Immunol. Rev. 62*:159 (1982).

124. V. Raso, J. Ritz, M. Basala, and S. F. Schlossman, *Cancer Res. 42*:457 (1982).

125. A. H. Filipovich, P. B. McGlave, N. K. Ramsey, G. Goldstein, P. F. Warkentin, and J. H. Kersey, *Lancet i:*8284 (1982).

126. J. M. Bastin, G. Granger, N. Tidman, G. Janossy, and A. J. McMichael, *Clin. Exp. Immunol. 46*:597 (1981).

127. S. Granger, G. Janossy, G. Francis, H. Blacklock, L. W. Poulter, and A. V. Hoffbrand, *Br. J. Haematol. 50*:367 (1982).

128. F. M. Brodsky, P. Parham, C. J. Crumpton, and W. F. Bodmer, *Immunol. Rev. 47*:3 (1979).

129. R. Taetle and I. Royston, *Blood 56*:943 (1980).

130. I. Royston, J. A. Majda, S. M. Baird, B. L. Meserve, and J. C. Griffiths, *J. Immunol. 125*:725 (1980).

131. P. C. L. Beverley and R. E. Callard, in *29th Annual Colloquim on Protides of the Biological Fluids* (H. Peeters, ed.) Pergamon, Oxford, 1981.

132. D. A. Brooks, I. Beckman, J. Bradley, P. J. McNamara, M. E. Zola and H. Zola, *J. Exp. Immunol. 39*:477 (1980).

133. M. F. Greaves, W. Verbi, J. Kemshead, and R. Kennett, *Blood 56*:1141 (1980).

134. D. Catovsky, M. Cherchi, D. Brooks, J. Bradley, and H. Zola, *Blood 88*:406 (1981).

135. J. T. Kemshead, D. Bicknell, and M. F. Greaves, *Pediatr. 15*:1282 (1981).

136. P. C. L. Beverley, D. Linch, and D. Delia, *Nature 287*:332 (1980).

137. I. S. Trowbridge and F. Lopez, *Proc. Natl. Acad. Sci. U.S.A. 79*:1175 (1982).

138. B. F. Haynes, M. Hemier, T. Cotner, D. L. Mann, G. S. Eisenbarth, J. L. Strominger, and A. S. Fauci, *J. Immunol. 127*:347 (1981).

139. R. A. Newman, D. R. Sutherland, T. W. LeBien, J. H. Kersey, and M. F. Greaves, *Biochim. Biophys. Acta 701*:318 (1982).

140. A-M. Lebacq-Verheyden, A-M. Ravoet, H. Hazin, D. R. Sutherland, N. Tidman, and M. F. Greaves, *Int. J. Cancer 32*:273 (1983).

141. J. Wiels, M. Fellous, and T. Tursz, *Proc. Natl. Acad. Sci. U.S.A. 78*:6485 (1981).

9 MONOCLONAL ANTIBODIES REACTIVE WITH HUMAN OVARIAN CARCINOMA

Robert C. Bast, Jr., and Robert C. Knapp /Dana-Farber Cancer Institute, Brigham and Women's Hospital, Harvard Medical School, Boston, Massachusetts

INTRODUCTION

Ovarian cancer continues to be a difficult disease to diagnose and to treat. Tumors localized to the ovary rarely produce distinctive symptoms; regular pelvic examinations often fail to detect tumor before it has metastasized; and cervical cytology is of little value in screening for occult ovarian cancer. Consequently, more than two-thirds of ovarian carcinomas have metastasized outside the pelvis by the time they are finally detected (1). At this stage of disease, patients can no longer be cured by surgical excision of the tumor or by pelvic irradiation. Total abdominal irradiation or intensive chemotherapy may cure a small number of patients in whom macroscopic tumor can be excised completely prior to the initiation of adjuvant therapy. In the remainder of patients with advanced disease, chemotherapy can produce regression of tumor nodules that remain following cytoreductive surgery, but tumor generally recurs within 2 years (1, 2). The prolonged disease-free interval observed in many patients does suggest that currently available therapy can reduce tumor burden to very low levels. Recurrence of metastatic ovarian carcinoma is observed most frequently in the abdominal cavity, where it can produce intestinal obstruction. Patients often die from starvation or from intercurrent infection rather than from organ failure due to invasive metastases.

Approximately 90% of the malignant ovarian tumors that develop in adults are thought to arise from modified peritoneal mesothelial cells which cover the surface of the ovary or line cysts that form immediately beneath the ovarian surface (2). Among the epithelial carcinomas, a number of types have been defined histologically. Serous, endometrioid, and mucinous tumors resemble the epithelial cells derived from the Müllerian duct that line the fetal fallopian tube, uterus, and endocervix, respectively. Serous tumors are observed most frequently and the "clear cell" carcinoma that contains abundant glycogen is one of the least common of the epithelial tumors. Carcinomas of the "clear cell" type can be particularly aggressive, but the overall histological grade appears to be more important than type in determining prognosis (1).

Epithelial ovarian carcinomas metastasize by several different routes. Exophytic tumors can shed cells that spread through the peritoneal cavity, forming serosal implants and blocking diaphragmatic lymphatics. Ovarian tumor cells can spread through lymphatic channels to the para-aortic, iliac, or inguinal nodes. Hematogenous metastases are rare, although they are seen with increasing frequency in patients whose survival has been prolonged by an initial response to chemotherapy (3). Given this pattern of spread, accurate staging of ovarian carcinoma requires laparotomy. Monitoring the response of intraperitoneal disease to chemotherapy necessitates "second look" procedures with additional laparotomies or laparoscopies. Understandably, a great deal of effort has been invested in finding markers that would detect occult disease or permit more convenient monitoring of response to treatment. Immunochemical techniques have been applied to the detection of tumor-associated antigens that would provide approximate markers.

POLYCLONAL HETEROANTISERA AGAINST HUMAN OVARIAN CARCINOMA

Over the last two decades a variety of polyclonal heteroantisera have been prepared against ovarian tumor-associated antigens (reviewed in Refs. 4-6). Ovarian carcinomas can exhibit histocompatibility, oncofetal or differentiation antigens that are shared with nonmalignant tissue in the adult fetus. HLA, Ia, carcinoembryonic antigen, alpha-fetoprotein, B-oncofetal antigen (BOFA), and human chorionic gonadotropin have been detected in epithelial or nonepithelial ovarian tumors. Several investigators have attempted to identify antigens that would be unique to ovarian malignancy. Heteroantisera have been raised against tumor tissue obtained at laparotomy, ovarian carcinoma cell lines, and antigen isolated from immune complexes in blood or ascites fluid. Particular attention has been given to antigens associated with the cytosol of disrupted cells. In some cases tissue homogenates have been extracted with perchloracetic acid to obtain mucoproteins. Heteroantisera have generally been raised in rabbits against whole cells, homogenates, supernatants clarified by ultracentrifugation, or partially purified mixtures of macromolecules. Antisera have then been absorbed exhaustively with ovary and other normal tissues. In many early reports the specificity of absorbed heteroantisera was characterized by immunodiffusion in gel. Recently investigators have used more sophisticated immunochemical techniques and have sometimes tested reactivity of antisera with tissue sections of ascites cells using indirect immunoflourescence. Most investigators have attempted to demonstrate that absorbed heteroantiserum will not react with extracts of normal ovary. Few reports have considered, however, that most ovarian tumors are thought to arise from the surface epithelium of normal ovary and that these cells would contribute only a small fraction of the material in tissue homogenates used for absorption or immunoprecipitation.

Useful information has been obtained in assaying reactivity of heteroantisera with antigen(s) in ovarian tumors from different patients. One antigen appeared restricted to the tumor of a single individual (7), another was shared by tumors from approximately 10% of ovarian cancer patients (8), and still others were more widely distributed (4, 9). Some antisera prepared against mucinous tumors appeared only to react with other mucinous tumors (10), whereas some antisera prepared against serous tumors reacted with ovarian carcinomas of both serous and mucinous histology (4, 9, 11).

Radioimmunoassays have been developed for two ovarian tumor-associated antigens: ovarian cystadenocarcinoma-associated antigen (OCAA) and ovarian carcinoma antigen (OCA). OCAA is a glycoprotein of high molecular weight that has been found in the cytoplasm of serous and mucinous cystadenocarcinomas, but not in the cytoplasm of benign ovarian tumors or the surface epithelium from normal ovary (4, 12, 13). Antigen levels are not frequently elevated early in the course of ovarian carcinoma and elevated levels of OCAA have been found in 30–33% of patients with advanced breast, colon, and cervical carcinoma. Consequently the assay has not proven useful in detecting occult primary tumors, but may hold greater promise for monitoring disease during treatment. OCAA levels were correlated with the course of clinical disease in 60% of 15 patients followed serially from 1 to 26 months. An elevation of OCAA preceded clinical evidence of disease progression by as much as 4 months.

OCA is another glycoprotein of high molecular weight that is associated with both serous and mucinous ovarian carcinomas (9, 14, 15). Levels of OCA have been elevated in 78% of patients with stage I ovarian carcinoma and in a similar fraction of patients with more advanced disease. Antigen levels of similar magnitude have, however, been detected in sera from 10% of normal individuals and from 10% of patients with benign ovarian disease (15). Considering the high rate of false positive reactions, OCA is not likely to provide a useful screening test for large populations. Recently, a 70,000-dalton moiety (NB/70K) has been isolated from preparations that contain OCA activity (16). Whether or not assays for the NB/70K will provide greater specificity remains to be resolved.

Detection of shed tumor antigen in the peripheral blood of patients with localized disease is consistent with what is known about the fate of antigen that is shed into the peritoneal cavity. Antigen shed from an exophytic lesion would traverse the peritoneum, enter lymphatic channels in the diaphragm, and pass through mediastinal lymphatics into the peripheral venous circulation. Antigen shed into a cystic lesion could establish a concentration gradient that should favor diffusion of small molecules. The concentration of carcinoembryonic antigen (CEA), for example, can be 10–1000 times greater within cyst fluid than in serum (17). As tumor invades the cyst wall, antigen would be shed into the abundant lymphatic vessels and capillaries within the ovary before the tumor had actually metastasized beyond the confines of the organ. To provide an effective screening test for occult cancer, tumor-associated antigen(s) must be shed into serum at a time when the tumor is still amenable to conventional treatment by surgical resection or radiation therapy. If tumor-associated antigens are, in fact, shed at an early stage of tumor growth, a second requirement for an effective screening test is a high degree of immunochemical specificity. Antibodies incorporated in the test must recognize an epitope that is expressed on shed tumor-associated antigen, but which is not found in nonmalignant adult tissue or shed into the serum of normal adults. Given the extraordinary specificity of many monoclonal reagents, hybridomas might be used to generate antibodies that could recognize an appropriate epitope.

For other applications less specific reagents might suffice. Antibodies that recognize organ-specific differentiation antigens should prove valuable in monitoring patients with known disease, imaging tumor nodules with radionuclides and treating residual disease with serotherapy. The initial management of ovarian carcinoma generally involves excision of all normal ovarian tissue, as well as the fallopian tubes and uterus. Following surgical excision of the ovaries and all Müllerian duct derivatives, any ovarian or Müllerian differentiation antigens would only be associated with residual malignant tissue. Despite the potential utility of heteroantisera directed against normal tissue differentiation antigens, remarkably little attention has been given to developing antibodies that react with normal ovary or adult tissue derived from the Müllerian duct (17-19). Useful monoclonal reagents might react either with tumor-specific or tumor-associated differentiation antigens.

MONOCLONAL ANTIBODIES AGAINST HUMAN OVARIAN CARCINOMA

A murine monoclonal IgG_1 antibody designated OC125 was developed against a human epithelial ovarian carcinoma cell line, OVCA433, that has been established from a serous cystadenocarcinoma (20). BALB/c mice were immunized with intact viable OVCA433 cells. Hybridomas were prepared using Kennett's modification (21) of the techniques of Köhler and Milstein (22). Supernatants from clones were screened by indirect immunofluorescence using viable intact cells. Antibodies were chosen that would react with OVCA433 but not with an Epstein-Barr virus-transformed auto logous B-lymphocyte line or with enzymatically dissociated cells from a normal adult ovary. Use of the autologous B-cell line permitted the elimination of antibodies that would react with Ia or HLA determinants that might be expressed by OVCA433. Promising antibodies were subsequently screened against ovarian and nonovarian tumor cell lines and cryopreserved ovarian carcinomas.

Monoclonal antibody OC125 reacted with each of six epithelial ovarian carcinoma cell lines and with cryopreserved tumor tissue from 12 of 20 ovarian cancer patients (20). In a subsequent study, the spectrum of reactivity of OC125 with different human ovarian tumors was defined by testing cryostat tissue sections from 60 selected ovarian tumors by indirect immunofluorescence (23). Antibody OC125 failed to react with mucinous tumors, but bound to 7 of 7 benign and borderline serous ovarian tumors, 19 of 23 (83%) serous adenocarcinomas, 2 of 2 mixed serous and endometrioid carcinomas, 2 of 3 endometrioid carcinomas, 1 of 4 clear cell carcinomas, and 2 of 2 undifferentiated carcinomas. No reactivity was found with 11 sex cord, Brenner, germ cell, or hematopoietic tumors that involved the ovary. In neoplastic tissue, indirect immunofluorescence was most intense on the luminal surface and subadjacent cytoplasm. Cells in solid sheets showed peripheral staining, although both antigen-positive and antigen-negative cells could be found intermixed within tumor clumps. Expression of OC125 reactivity did not appear related to the grade of the tumor judged by conventional pathological criteria.

Monoclonal antibody OC125 reacted with 1 of 14 tumor cell lines established from a variety of nonovarian neoplasms. The nonovarian tumor cell line to which OC125 bound had been established from a malignant melanoma. The antibody did not, however, react with 3 other melanoma lines tested, nor did it react with any of 12 nonovarian tumors in cryostat sections. Extensive studies utilizing indirect immunofluorescence failed to detect reactivity of OC125 with any normal adult tissue (20). Peripheral blood leukocytes, hematopoietic and lymphoreticular populations were amenable to study by flow cytometry, whereas a variety of solid tissues could only be examined in cryostat section. Of particular significance, no binding was observed to the surface epithelium of normal adult ovary from which the epithelial ovarian carcinomas are thought to arise.

In subsequent studies of fetal tissues utilizing a biotin–avidin peroxidase technique, OC125 bound to epithelial cells in structures derived from the Müllerian duct, including the fallopian tubes, endometrium, endocervix, and upper vagina (24). Staining was also observed along the embryonic peritoneum, pleura, and pericardium, but not on the surface epithelium of normal ovary. Other fetal structures, including intestinal mucosa, failed to react with OC125. When examined with the more sensitive biotin–avidin technique, traces of antigen were also found in normal adult fallopian tube, endometrium, and endocervix, but not on the surface of normal adult ovary.

Biochemical characterization of the antigen(s) to which OC125 binds is still preliminary. Surface structures of OVCA433 have been labeled with ^{125}I using iodogen or lactoperoxidase. After immunoprecipitation with OC125, a glyco-protein of $> 500,000$ daltons can be demonstrated on polyacrylamide gel electro-phoresis under reducing and nonreducing conditions (25).

The antigen recognized by OC125 is not likely to be carcinoembryonic antigen. Antibody OC125 has failed to precipitate ^{125}I-labeled CEA in the presence of zirconyl phosphate gel (20). Moreover, in histological studies, mucinous tumors consistently lacked reactivity with OC125, but seven of eight mucinous adenomas and adenocarcinomas bound a monoclonal antibody against CEA (23). Lack of reactivity with mucinous tumors also differentiates OC125 from antibodies that recognize OCAA or OCAA-1. OC125 does not appear to recognize NB/70K, in that each of six epithelial ovarian carcinoma cell lines bind OC125, but only two bind a heteroantiserum with specificity for NB/70K (26).

A second murine monoclonal IgG_1 antibody that reacts with malignant ovarian tumors of mucinous histology has recently been reported by Bhattacharya et al. (27). BALB/c mice were immunized with a saline extract from an undifferent-iated ovarian carcinoma. A priming injection was administered subcutaneously in Freund's complete adjuvant and a second injection was given intraperitoneally in saline. Hybridomas were prepared and antibodies screened for their ability to bind to tissue extracts that had been used to coat plastic microtiter wells. Binding of antibody was detected by incubation with ^{125}I-labeled rabbit anti-mouse immuno-globulin. Antibodies were selected that bound to extracts of the ovarian tumor used for immunizing the spleen cell donors, but not to extracts of normal ovary or to human serum.

Clones ID_3 and ID_5 produced immunoglobulins that reacted with 12 of 72 ex-tracts from ovarian epithelial cancers. All of the tumors with which the antibodies reacted were of mucinous histology. Overall, 12 of 14 mucinous cystadenocar-cinomas contained the antigen(s) recognized by these antibodies. Benign mucin-ous tumors did not react, nor did nonepithelial ovarian carcinomas or a variety of malignant neoplasms from different primary sites. Using a radioimmunoassay, antigen could not be detected in a number of adult tissues, although fetal intes-tine did exhibit significant reactivity with the products of both clones. Quanti-tative absorptions confirmed significant activity in mucinous cystadenocarcinomas and fetal intestine. In addition, adsorption with a homogenate of normal ovary produced slight inhibition of antibody binding, but was less than 1/20 as active as an extract of mucinous cystadenocarcinoma. Tissue sections were not exam-ined either by indirect immunoflourescence or by immunoperoxidase techniques. Consequently, reactivity with cell-surface epithelium cannot be excluded.

The antigens recognized by ID_3 and ID_5 did not seem to be related to CEA, normal (colonic) glycoprotein, normal serum components, or human ABO blood groups. Restriction of reactivity to mucinous cystadenocarcinomas set these anti-bodies apart from those that react with OCAA, which is found in two-thirds of serous and mucinous cystadenocarcinomas, as well as OCAA-1, which is found in 90% of all gynecological tumors and which occasionally can be detected in colon, breast, and pancreatic tumors.

Attempts to develop monoclonals against glycoproteins associated with human ovarian carcinomas have produced antibodies that react with a 48,000-dalton antigen that is associated with a variety of human cancers (28). Bhattacharya et al. have partially purified glycoproteins from a saline extract of ovarian carcinoma using Sephadex G200 gel filtration, diethylaminoethyl cellulose ion exchange, and concanavalin-A–Sepharose affinity chromatography. The glycoprotein fraction that was retained on concanavalin-A–Sepharose and eluted with alpha-methylmannose was used to immunize BALB/c mice. Hybridomas were prepared and immunoglobulins screened in an indirect solid-phase radioimmunoassay for reactivity with the immunizing material and for lack of reactivity with similar fractions prepared from pooled normal adult ovary or human serum. An IgG_1 murine monoclonal antibody reacted with 90% of ovarian carcinomas and 60% of benign and malignant tumors from other sites. A 48,000-dalton glycoprotein was detected by immunoprecipitation and sodium dodecyl sulfate-polyacrylamide gel electrophoresis. Quantitative immunoprecipitation indicated that the glycoprotein was also present in some normal adult tissues, as well as fetal intestine, liver, and kidney. Higher concentrations were, however, present in many ovarian tumors.

Development of monoclonal antibodies to tumors from other primary sites has produced reagents that react with ovarian carcinomas. DU-PAN-2 is a murine monoclonal IgM antibody developed by Metzgar et al. (29) against a human pancreatic cell line HPAF. Clones had been selected that produced antibody which would bind to intact HPAF cells, but not to T- or B-lymphoblastoid cell lines in an ^{125}I-labeled antiglobulin binding assay. During initial characterization DU-PAN-2 reacted with four of five pancreatic carcinoma cell lines, as well as with two of four cell lines derived from colon carcinoma and one of two lung carcinoma cell lines. The antibody failed to react with normal skin fibroblasts, A and B erythrocytes, and enriched T and B lymphocytes from 10 different donors. DU-PAN-2 did react with ductal epithelial cells from normal adult pancreas, but could not be detected in a variety of other adult tissues using immunoperoxidase staining of acetone-fixed cryostat sections. In the fetus the antibody bound to secretory cells of the small intestine and salivary gland, but not to fetal pancreas. During initial screening, DU-PAN-2 failed to react with 18 nonpancreatic tumors from 9 different primary sites. In subsequent studies reactivity with ovarian, breast, and colon carcinomas has been detected (30). The antigen is associated with cell membrane and is observed near the apical portion of columnar adenocarcinoma cells.

Exclusion of the antigen on Sepharose 6B is consistent with a molecular weight in excess of 10^6. Antigen activity is destroyed by the treatment of cells with neuraminidase, suggesting that sialic acid residues contribute to the epitope recognized by DU-PAN-2. Antigen in ascites fluid from patients with ovarian and pancreatic carcinoma will inhibit binding of DU-PAN-2 to the insolublized antigen. Using this assay, antigen activity has been detected in the serum of patients with ovarian, breast, and colon cancer. No inhibition was observed with CEA, sialic acid, or blood group antigens. Serial studies of antigen levels in the serum of patients with ovarian carcinoma appeared to be correlated with disease state. Although the pattern of reactivity with ovarian tumors of different histological type has not been well defined, antigen activity has been detected in the serum of at least one patient with endometrioid carcinoma.

CLINICAL APPLICATION OF MONOCLONAL ANTIBODIES REACTIVE WITH HUMAN OVARIAN CARCINOMA

Whether or not any of the monoclonal reagents that are now available will prove useful in detecting or monitoring occult carcinoma must be resolved by future studies. Antigens that can be detected in normal adult tissues are, in general, not promising markers for screening. Müllerian differentiation antigens might be one exception to this generalization, in that they could ordinarily be shed into the lumen of the fallopian tube or the endometrial cavity rather than into the lymphatics or venous circulation. Appearance of Müllerian differentiation antigens in blood could reflect the ectopic release of these substances by invasive or exophytic ovarian neoplasms.

Reagents for monitoring, imaging, or treating previously diagnosed ovarian neoplasms could react with tumor-specific, oncofetal, or organ-specific differentiation antigens. Conventional heteroantisera against CEA have already been used for imaging primary and metasatic ovarian carcinomas (31). Antibodies are now available that react with mucinous (27) and nonmucinous tumors (20, 29). A family of monoclonal antibodies may be required to recognize differentiation antigens associated with all of the epithelial tumor types. In addition to developing monoclonal antibodies against ovarian carcinomas of different phenotypes, a more conscious attempt might be made to develop monoclonal reagents that bind to normal ovarian or Müllerian differentiation antigens which are also expressed on ovarian neoplasms. Monoclonal reagents to differentiation antigens are likely to prove useful in determining the origin of tumor cells in malignant ascites when the site of the primary tumor is uncertain. To develop organ- or tumor-specific reagents, it is now apparent that promising antibodies must be screened by histochemical as well as immunochemical techniques for reactivity with ovarian carcinoma and for lack of reactivity with nonovarian tumors or nonmalignant tissues.

Lack of reactivity with normal tissues may be particularly important in selecting monoclonals for serotherapy. The toxicity of antibodies and conjugates may relate, at least in part, to their deposition at sites not involved by tumor. Metastases often occur on the surface of the peritoneum. Consequently, the intraperitoneal administration of monoclonals could encourage close contact between residual tumor nodules and antibody. In a murine model, intraperitoneal administration of conventional polyclonal heteroantiserum can eliminate at least 10^5 tumor cells growing within the abdominal cavity (32–34). Intraperitoneal serotherapy can be potentiated by the concomitant administration of an immunostimulant such as *Corynebacterium parvum* (35, 36). Doses, routes, and schedules of *C. parvum* administration that potentiate serotherapy also attract and activate peritoneal macrophages which can participate more effectively in antibody-dependent cell-mediated cytotoxicity (ADCC) than can resident peritoneal cells (36). Silica can abrogate the anti-tumor activity of antibody and *C. parvum* in vivo as well as the ADCC activity of peritoneal cells in vitro (37). Taken together, these data suggest that large numbers of activated peritoneal effectors for ADCC may be required for optimal intraperitoneal serotherapy. In clinical studies, the intraperitoneal administration of *C. parvum* has reduced ascites (38, 39) and produces regression of small ovarian tumor nodules that had failed to respond completely to combination chemotherapy (40). Intraperitoneal administration of *C. parvum* augments the ability of human peritoneal cells to mediate ADCC (40). The administration of *C. parvum* or another immunostimulant capable of augmenting ADCC might potentiate serotherapy mediated by monoclonal antibodies against human ovarian carcinoma.

Recent studies suggest an alternative method for attracting mononuclear cells to sites of ovarian tumor growth. Antibodies OC125 and OC133 have been conjugated with the chemotactic polypeptide f-Met–Leu–Phe (41). The conjugate retains the ability to bind to human epithelial ovarian-carcinoma cell lines in vitro and can mediate chemotaxis of human peripheral blood and peritoneal mononuclear cells. Similar conjugates could be introduced within the peritoneal cavity, possibly in combination with agents capable of augmenting monocyte functions after they respond to the chemotactic stimulus.

If murine monoclonal antibodies are to be used for serotherapy, the subclass may be critical in determining interactions with human effector mechanisms. Each of the monoclonals described to date that react with human ovarian carcinoma is either IgG_1 or an IgM. Although some murine IgM antibodies can lyse human cells in the presence of human complement, neither IgM nor IgG_1 antibodies cooperate efficiently with human effectors for ADCC. Antibody OC125, for example, is an IgG_1 immunoglobulin that does not lyse human ovarian carcinoma cells in the presence of human complement. The antibody can mediate lysis of human epithelial ovarian tumor cell lines in the presence of *C. parvum*-activated murine peritoneal cells, but will not mediate lysis of the same cell lines in the presence of human peripheral blood mononuclear cells or human peritoneal cells from normal or *C. parvum*-treated donors. Recent studies suggest that murine IgG_2 antibodies can lyse ovarian epithelial cell lines in the presence of human peripheral blood effectors.

Antibodies of the IgG_1 subclass might be well suited to the preparation of conjugates with drugs, toxins, or isotopes. Direct access to the peritoneal cavity should permit the administration of conjugates in high concentration. Administration by the intraperitoneal route should minimize the toxicity of conjugates in a manner analogous to that achieved with "belly baths" of more conventional cytotoxic drugs (42). Occlusion of diaphragmatic lymphatics by metastatic tumor might slow the outflow of macromolecular conjugates sufficiently to permit prolonged interaction of conjugates with peritoneal implants before their eventual absorption or withdrawal by lavage. Development of appropriate monoclonal conjugates should soon permit an evaluation of this approach to immunotherapy.

CONCLUSION

Several murine monoclonal antibodies have been developed that react with human ovarian carcinomas (20, 27, 28, 29). Each antibody appears to recognize a different determinant, although critical comparative studies have not yet been performed. Two reagents, ID₃ (27) and OC125 (20), recognize epitopes expressed by mucinous and nonmucinous tumors, respectively. Discrimination of histological subtypes using immunochemical markers lends credence to conventional histopathological analysis. OC125 binds to a Müllerian differentiation antigen that can be also be detected in trace amounts within the epithelium of the fallopian tubes, endometrium, and endocervix (24). Thus different ovarian carcinomas resemble tissues derived from the Müllerian duct both immunochemically and histologically. Studies with additional monoclonals may better define the development of normal and abnormal gynecological tissues. Monoclonal reagents might also define prognostic groups that are not readily characterized by conventional histology and could permit identification of the primary source of tumor cells in ascites fluid when this was not readily apparent.

Reliable tests for detecting and monitoring the growth of ovarian carcinoma would facilitate management of this disease. The unique biology of epithelial ovarian carcinoma should lend itself to the development of such assays, provided that tumor or organ-specific epitopes can be identified. Intraperitoneal administration of monoclonal antibodies or their conjugates may assure contact with metastases on the peritoneal surface. This may provide an optimal setting in which to test combinations of antibody with immunostimulants or to evaluate antibodies conjugated with cytotoxic drugs, toxins, or radioisotopes.

ACKNOWLEDGMENTS

The authors are most grateful to Nancy Coppedge and Helen Thurman for excellent secretarial assistance.

REFERENCES

1. C. T. Griffiths, in *Cancer Medicine* (J. F. Holland and E. Frei III, eds.), Lea and Febiger, Philadelphia, 1982, p. 1958.

2. R. C. Young, R. C. Knapp, and C. A. Perez, in *Cancer: Principles & Practice of Oncology* (V. T. DeVita, Jr., S. Hellman, and S. A. Rosenberg, eds.) Lippincott, Philadelphia, 1982, p. 884.
3. R. J. Mayer, R. S. Berkowitz, and C. T. Griffiths, *Cancer 41*:776 (1978).
4. M. Bhattacharya and J. J. Barlow, *Int. Adv. Surg. Oncol. 2*:155 (1979).
5 J. R. Van Nagell, Jr., E. S. Donaldson, M. B. Hanson, E. C. Gay, and E. J. Pavlik, *Cancer 48*:495 (1981).
6. R. C. Bast, Jr., and R. C. Knapp, in *Gynecological Malignancy I* (C. T. Griffiths and A. Fuller, eds.), Nijhoff, The Hague, 1983, p. 187.
7. N. Imamura, T. Takahashi, K. O. Lloyd, J. L. Lewis, and L. J. Old, *Int. J Cancer 21*:570 (1981).
8. K. O. Lloyd, in *Compendium of Assays for Immunodiagnosis of Human Cancer* (R. B. Herberman, ed.), Elsevier/North-Holland, Amsterdam, 1978, p. 533.
9. S. Knauf and G. I. Urbach, *Am. J. Obstet. Gynecol. 138*:1222 (1980).
10. S. Chow, W. Chiang, and P. Wei, *Int. J. Gynaecol. Obstet. 14*:280 (1976).
11. L. Stolbach, A. Pitt, L. Gandbhir, B. Dorsett, H. Barber, and H. Ioachim, in *Compendium of Assays for Immunodiagnosis of Human Cancer* (R. B. Herberman, ed.), Elsevier/North-Holland, Amsterdam, 1979, p. 553.
12. M. Bhattacharya and J. J. Barlow, *Cancer 42*:1616 (1978).
13. M. Bhattacharya and J. J. Barlow, in *Compendium of Assays for Immunodiagnosis of Human Cancer* (R. B. Herberman, ed.), Elsevier/North-Holland, Amsterdam, 1979, P. 527.
14. S. Knauf and G. I. Urbach, *Am. J. Obstet. Gynecol. 127*:705 (1977).
15. S. Knauf and G. I. Urbach, *Am. J. Obstet. Gynecol. 131*:780 (1978).
16. S. Knauf and G. I. Urbach, *Cancer Res. 41*:1351 (1981).
17. J. R. Van Nagell, E. S. Donaldson, E. C. Gay, R. M. Sharkey, P. Rayburn, and D. M. Goldenberg, *Cancer 41*:2335 (1978).
18. C. E. Bailye, T. N. Evans, L. M. Weiner, and K. S. Moghissi, *Am. J. Obstet. Gynecol. 114*:639 (1972).
19. J. Bara, A. Malarewicz, F. Loisillier, and P. Burtin, *Br. J. Cancer 36*:49 (1977).
20. R. C. Bast, Jr., M. Feeney, H. Lazarus, L. M. Nadler, R. B. Colvin, and R. C. Knapp, *J. Clin. Invest. 68*:1331 (1981).
21. R. H. Kennett, K. A. Denis, A. S. Tung, and N. R. Klinman, *Curr. Top. Microbiol. Immunol. 81*:77 (1978).
22. G. Köhler and C. Milstein, *Nature 256*:495 (1975).
23. S. E. Kabawat, R. C. Bast, Jr., W. R. Welch, R. C. Knapp, and R. B. Colvin, *Am. J. Clin. Pathol. 79*:98 (1983).
24. S. Kabawat, R. C. Bast, Jr., A. Bhan, W. Welch, R. C. Knapp, and R. C. Colvin, *Int. J. Gyn. Pathol.* (in press).
25. Y. Masuho, D. Sang, H. Lazarus, R. C. Knapp, and R. C. Bast, Jr., manuscript in preparation.
26. H. Lazarus, B. Malone, R. C. Bast, Jr., and R. C. Knapp, manuscript in preparation.

27. M. Bhattacharya, S. K. Chatterjee, J. J. Barlow, and H. Fuji, *Cancer Res.* *42*:1650 (1982).

28. M. Bhattacharya, S. K. Chatterjee, J. J. Barlow, and H. Fuji, *Proc. Am. Assoc. Cancer Res.* *23*:276 (1982).

29. R. S. Metzgar, M. T. Gaillard, S. J. Levine, F. L. Tuck, E. H. Bossen, and M. J. Borowitz, *Cancer Res.* *42*:601 (1982),

30. V. N. Daasch, P.D. Fernsten, and R.S. Metzgar, *Proc. Am. Assoc. Cancer Res.* *23*:266 (1982).

31. J. R. Van Nagell, Jr., E. Kim, S. Casper, F. S. Primus, S. Bennett, F. H. Deland, and D. M. Goldenberg, *Cancer Res.* *40*:502 (1980).

32. S. E. Order, V. Donahue, and R. Knapp, *Cancer 32*:573 (1973).

33. S. E. Order, R. Kirkman, and R. Knapp, *Cancer 34*:175 (1974).

34. R. C. Bast, Jr., R. C. Knapp, V. C. Donahue, J. G. Thurston, A. R. Mitchell, M. Feeney, and S. F. Schlossman, *J. Nat. Cancer Inst.* *64*:365 (1980).

35. R. C. Knapp and R. S. Berkowitz, *Am. J. Obstet. Gynecol.* *128*:782 (1977).

36. R. C. Bast, Jr., R. C. Knapp, A. K. Mitchell, J. G. Thurston, R. E. V. Tucker, and S. F. Schlossman, *J. Immunol.* *123*:1945 (1979).

37. R. C. Bast, Jr., M. Knapp, J. Thurston, and R. C. Knapp, manuscript in preparation.

38. H. E. Webb, S. E. Oaten, and C. P. Pike, *Br. Med. J.* *1*:338 (1978).

39. A. Mantovani, C. Sessa, G. Peri, P. Allvena, M. Introna, N. Polentarutti, and C. Mangioni, *Int. J. Cancer 27*:437 (1981).

40. R. C. Bast, Jr., J. S. Berek, R. Obrist, C. T. Griffiths, R. Berkowitz, N. F. Hacker, L. Parker, L. D. Lagasse, and R. C. Knapp, *Cancer Res.* *43*:1395 (1983).

41. R. Obrist, R. Reilly, T. Leavitt, H. Lazarus, R. C. Knapp, and R. C. Bast, Jr., *Int. J. Immun. Pharacol.* *5*:307 (1983).

42. J. L. Speyer, J. M. Collins, R. L. Dedrick, M. F. Brennan, A. R. Buckpitt, H. Londer, V. T. DeVita, Jr., and C. E. Meyers, *Cancer Res.* *40*:567 (1980).

10 MONOCLONAL ANTIBODIES TO PROSTATE ADENOCARCINOMA ANTIGENS

James J. Starling, Mary Lou Beckett, and George L. Wright, Jr. /
Eastern Virginia Medical School, Norfolk, Virginia

INTRODUCTION

Cancer of the prostate is the most common male genitourinary malignancy, and its incidence is steadily increasing. It ranks as the second leading cause of death by cancer among the U.S. male population. By the end of 1982, it has been estimated that over 73,000 newly diagnosed cases of prostate carcinoma and more than 23,000 deaths will be reported in the United States (1). The incidence of prostate carcinoma is exceeded only by carcinoma of the lung. Prostate carcinoma increases with advancing age and autopsy studies have revealed the presence of previously unsuspected malignant foci in 50-80% of males who have survived to age 80 (2). It can be anticipated that with improved diagnostic techniques and greater longevity, the diagnosis of prostate cancer will be made more frequently and the problem of treatment of a malignancy in the aged population will be of increasing concern. The present problem with diagnosis of prostate carcinoma is that there is no procedure that can detect early localized disease, which is curable with current treatment modalities. Diagnosis is usually made when the disease becomes symptomatic and the malignancy is in the advanced state. The rectal examination remains the mainstay for detecting prostate tumors (2); however, the unequivocal diagnosis can only be made on histological examination of biopsied tissue. Only in this way can causes for induration of the prostate, such as prostatic calculi, granulomatous prostatitis, and nodular prostatic hypertrophy, be differentiated from a malignant tumor. Still, only 10–20% of the cases with localized disease can be detected by rectal examination. The small, localized stage A carcinoma is entirely unsuspected by any parameters on physical examination, serum tumor markers, or radiographic examination but is found incidentally on pathological examination of the prostate, surgically excised for presumed benign prostate hyperplasia (BPH). Pathologically, prostate tumors present a variable pattern of histological manifestations, ranging from well-differentiated to undifferentiated cell morphology, making it difficult to correlate histology with the clinical course of the disease. Because of the variable stages of prostate carcinoma, there are many divergent opinions as to the best approach for treating prostate cancer (3). For primary treatment, surgery, interstitial implantation of ^{125}I seeds (4), and external beam radiation (5), used singly or in various combinations, have afforded a reasonable opportunity to obtain a 5-10 year disease-free interval and possible cure for localized prostate cancer (2). For example, the 5-year survival for stage B carcinoma (tumor confined to the prostate gland) treated with external beam radiotherapy or ^{125}I implants is approximately 75%, whereas the 5-year survival for stage C disease (tumor extended beyond the confines of the prostate gland) following radiation therapy is 45%. Unfortunately, 40% of patients with cancer of the prostate have distant metastasis at the time of diagnosis, which makes them no longer amenable to "definitive" surgical or radiation treatment (6). Most patients will have an initial favorable response to hormonal manipulation, the mainstay of treatment for patients with advanced prostate carcinoma (7, 8). However, the relapse rate is high, presumably because those tumor cells that are resistant to the hormones continue to proliferate, resulting in progression and ultimate death (2).

The foregoing discussion on the clinical and pathological manifestations of prostate carcinoma suggests that malignant tumors are treatable with the current therapeutic modalities as long as the tumor is diagnosed when it is confined to the prostate gland. A sensitive, specific, and reproducible procedure or assay for early diagnosis of localized prostate carcinoma is presently unavailable. One approach to aid early diagnosis and in monitoring the effectiveness of therapy has been the search for specific prostate tumor markers. The purpose of this chapter is to present a brief review of the advantages and disadvantages of two prostate tumor markers that have been shown to be of some value in diagnosis and treatment management, namely, prostatic acid phosphatase (PAP) and the more recently discovered marker prostate antigen (PA), and then to review the generation and characterization of monoclonal antibodies prepared in our laboratory and those produced by other investigators to delineate new prostate tumor antigens. The need for developing a panel of well-characterized monoclonal antibodies for effective early diagnosis, for improving histological classification and staging, and for the selection and monitoring treatment will be discussed.

TUMOR MARKERS CURRENTLY USED IN THE DIAGNOSIS AND MONITORING OF PROSTATE CANCER

Prostatic Acid Phosphatase

Prostatic acid phosphatase (PAP) was discovered by Gutman et al. (9) in 1939, and is still the most common marker used in the diagnosis of prostate cancer. The initial assay system for PAP measured acid phosphatase catalytic activity in the patients' serum or bone marrow; however, the accurate determination of prostatic-specific acid phosphatase activity was fraught with difficulties owing to contamination by serum phosphatase of nonprostatic origin and instability of the enzyme's catalytic activity (10). The prostate-specific acid phosphatase (i.e., the number 2 isoenzyme of acid phosphatase) only recently was purified and demonstrated to be a 100,000-dalton glycoprotein produced in the cytoplasm of the ductal epithelial cell of the prostate gland (11,12). Antisera raised against the purified PAP made it possible to develop sensitive immunoassays for measurement of PAP (12-17). Several different types of immunoassays have been developed, including counterimmunoelectrophoresis (12, 16), radioimmunoassays (13-15), and a solid-phase fluorescent immunoassay (17), all of which appear to be superior to the colorimetric enzyme assays in terms of sensitivity, specificity, and reproducibility (18-23). The most widely adopted immunoassay used for the measurement of serum PAP is the radioimmunoassay (RIA). The wide acceptance of RIA has been largely due to the availability in the past few years of commercial RIA PAP kits (24). Unfortunately, there is a plethora of data resulting from many different RIAs for PAP stemming from clinical overoptimism, which has resulted in much confusion and uncertainty of the utility of the RIA in the diagnosis of prostate carcinoma. Although in patients with obvious bony metastases, the sensitivity has increased from 60-80% with enzymatic assays to 95% with RIAs, the RIAs can accurately identify only 8-44% of the cases with localized carcinoma of the prostate (19, 21, 22, 25). However, in all fairness, the wide range of positive PAP values for patients with localized disease (stages A and B) may reflect (a) differences in the RIAs, (b) the source of purified PAP, (c) the purification method, (d) the population of patients studied, (e) whether the patient had received treatment at the

time of the blood test, and especially (f) the criteria used in staging (i.e., surgical
versus clinical). There is not sufficient data available at present to determine if
the immunoassays will offer any additional diagnostic value over the enzymatic
assays. The increased sensitivity of the RIAs has also brought decreased specificity. The false positive rate is at least 8% in patients with BPH (19, 20, 25). The
best correlation with increased serum PAP has been found in patients with less
differentiated primary prostate tumors. Although a few studies indicate the RIA
was more effective than the enzyme assay for detecting prostate cancer, most studies to date show that the RIA can provide a reliable measurement of PAP, but
that the RIA is not more effective than the enzymatic assay for screening and in
the diagnosis of prostate cancer in its early stages (18-26). The evaluation of the
application of serum PAP levels, by immunoassay procedures, for monitoring the
efficacy of treatment is just in its initial phases. It is too early to determine
whether serial monitoring will benefit better treatment management of the prostate cancer patient, although some encouraging results have been demonstrated
with disseminated disease (22, 27-28).

Several reports using enzymatic assays have indicated that measuring bone marrow PAP levels improves the accuracy in detecting disseminated disease, that is,
bony metastases (29, 30). However, the clinical utility in measuring bone marrow
PAP has recently been reevaluated using the sensitive immunochemical assays, with
most reports stating that bone marrow PAP levels provided no additional value
over serum levels in predictin bony metastases (22, 30-32). Immunohistochemical identification of PAP is also being assessed for its value to identify metastatic
prostate carcinoma, to correlate the histological grade with PAP production in
tissue sections of patients with prostatic carcinoma and to monitor effectiveness
of therapy (33-40). Basically, these studies showed a more intense and uniform
staining in well-differentiated tumors and less intense and more variable staining
in poorly differentiated and metastatic tumors. Monoclonal antibodies to PAP
have been produced and recently evaluated immunohistochemically (36, 37).
These studies found that some but not all monoclonal anti-PAP antibodies could
be used for detection of PAP in tissue sections. Those prostate tissues that did
not stain with monoclonal antibody, however, did stain with conventional polyclonal antiserum. By using a mixture of several monoclonal antibodies, the detection of PAP in tissue sections was enhanced (36). Whether monoclonal antibodies will be better reagents than polyclonal antisera for the detection of PAP
remains to be determined, although these two studies would suggest that they will
not improve on the detection of PAP in tissues. Monoclonals, however, should
be very useful for studying the biology of PAP.

In summary, the present status of PAP as a marker for prostate carcinoma is
that elevated serum PAP levels in patients at risk may signify the presence of tumor (41). The use of PAP as a marker for detecting localized prostate carcinoma
is doubtful, as is its use for screening unsuspected cancer in the general population,

because of the large number of false positives (42). Serial monitoring of serum PAP levels may prove to be a good marker for objective measurement of response to therapy. Immunochemical techniques may also aid the identification of metastatic disease. Further evaluation of serum PAP is required before full clinical potential in the diagnosis and follow-up of prostate carcinoma can be made.

Prostate Antigen

Prostate antigen (PA) is a new marker (also referred to as prostate-specific antigen) that is biochemically and immunologically distinct from PAP (43). Prostate antigen is a 34,000-dalton glycoprotein of cytoplasmic origin identified in the epithelium of normal, BPH, and malignant prostate tissues. No other tissues or cells contain this prostate antigen as determined by RIA and immuno-histochemical procedures (44-46). Using a sensitive enzyme immunoassay, Kuriyama et al. (47) showed that 371 of 442 patients with prostate cancer and 13 of 19 patients with BPH had elevated PA levels. No quantitative differences in PA levels were observed between patients with BPH and early-stage prostate carcinoma, although elevated levels were observed in patients with advanced stages of prostate cancer. Another study showed that pretreatment values of serum PA levels in patients with advanced stages of prostate carcinoma may be of prognostic value with regard to patient survival following therapy, in that lower levels were accompied by longer survival times (48). Recent studies using immunohistochemical staining techniques have shown PA to be localized at the epithelial lining of the prostate gland and ducts, as well as in prostatic secretions and concretions, and to be primarily of cytoplasmic origin (44, 46). One study reported that only tumors of prostate origin, both primary and secondary, were found to express PA (42). In fact, in this report, PA was detected in 100% (73 primary and 49 metastatic) of the prostate tumor tissue sections tested. None of 78 nonprostatic malignancies stained positive for PA. The results are comparable with what these investigators previously reported for PAP, that is, all known prostate tumors stained positive for PAP and all nonprostate malignancies were negative for PAP (36). However, in two recent reports (E. P. Allhoff et al. and B. S. Stein et al., both in Abstracts of the Annual Meeting of the American Urology Association, Inc., 1982), PAP and PA were not found in all prostate tumor tissues examined by the immunoperoxidase technique. In the former study (Allhoff et al.), PAP and PA were evaluated on serial tissue sections of the same tumor. They found that nine prostate tumor tissues, in which the cell type was in doubt, stained for PA, whereas only seven stained positive for PAP. Similarly, not all metastatic tissues stained positive by either marker. Further heterogeneity was demonstrated on some tissue sections where tumor areas would stain for both markers and another area was stained for only one of the markers. In the latter study (Stein et al.), 80% of 30 prostate carcinoma tissues were positive for PA. The six prostate tumor tissues that did not stain positive for PA were all poorly differentiated tumors. As ex-

pected, all 52 BPH tissues stained for PA in the acinar cells. These latter two reports indicate the possible heterogeneity in expression of both PAP and PA, especially in poorly differentiated, undifferentiated, and metastatic tumors. Therefore these markers must be carefully evaluated with standardized reagents before
the reliability of either or both of these markers for histological classification and
accurate identification of occult tumors can be made. A monoclonal antibody
against PA used in an immunoperoxidase technique also demonstrated staining
heterogeneity that was most striking in poorly differentiated adenocarcinomas
of the prostate but significant enough for differential diagnosis of these tumors
(49).

In summary, the most promising markers for prostate cancer at present are
prostatic acid phosphatase and the recently identified prostate antigen. Although
several clinical studies using sensitive immunoassays for measuring these markers
in body fluids and tissues have become available, conflicting data exists, especially
in the detection rate at which these markers are found elevated in patients with
localized prostate carcinoma, making it presently difficult to determine the precise value of these markers in the clinical management of prostate cancer. A
recent report suggests that the simultaneous measurement of both PAP and PA
can be of added value in the immunodiagnosis of prostate carcinoma (50). However, even in this study, only 58% of the patients with stage A and B (localized prostate adenocarcinoma) had elevated levels of either or both markers, while 10% of
the BPH patients had positive serum levels of these markers. It must be pointed
out that both of these markers are tissue- or organ-specific proteins of the prostate gland and originate in the cytoplasm of the ductal epithelial cells and therefore
presumably cannot be of value for screening purposes because they cannot differentiate benign prostate hyperplasia from malignant prostate disease. Probably
the most important clinical application of PAP and PA immunoassays at the present stage of development is for monitoring treatment management of prostate
cancer. Monoclonal antibodies to these markers are just beginning to be evaluated;
whether they will uncover new specificities that will improve the clinical utility
of these markers in diagnosis remains to be determined. In any case, the cytoplasmic location of these markers may limit their usefulness as a target antigen
for in vivo localization of micrometastasis with radiolabeled antibody or for therapy
using immunotoxins. Several additional markers, including PAP and PA, for prostate cancer are presented in two excellent reviews (51, 52).

MONOCLONAL ANTIBODIES TO PROSTATE TISSUE ANTIGENS

Problems Associated with Generating Monoclonal Antibodies to Prostate Antigens

It is clear from the above discussion of the presently available prostate tumor
markers that a continued search for new and more specific markers of prostate

carcinoma is essential. Most studies have concentrated on prostate tumor markers associated with the cell cytoplasm. Although very little is known about the structure and composition of the plasma membrane of prostate tumor cells, it is clear that immunochemical characterization of cell-surface components and isolation of antibodies specific for membrane antigens that can specifically delineate the neoplastic condition will be invaluable in further immunological studies to improve diagnosis, monitoring, and therapy of prostate cancer. The application of the lymphocyte hybridoma technique for producing monoclonal antibodies to identify new antigen specificities, especially membrane antigens on prostate carcinoma cells, would appear to be a promising approach in view of the many reports that describe the identification of surface tumor-associated antigen (TAA) on several different human tumors using monoclonal antibodies (53–62).

Perhaps one of the most important considerations to be made in order to produce monoclonal antibodies to prostate tumor antigens is the selection of an adequate immunogen. This appears to be important for prostate cancer when compared to some other human tumors, such as malignant melanomas, since the failure to detect prostate TAA may be attributed to the lack of a stable and reliable source of prostate tumor cell antigens (63). One of the problems in obtaining a reliable antigen source has been the limited success in establishing prostate adenocarcinoma cell lines when compared to other tumors such as malignant melanoma (54). Recent advances in cell culture techniques have resulted in the establishment of eight prostate cell lines (64), but at present only three of these lines, DU145 (65), PC-3 (66), and LNCaP (67), have been sufficiently characterized for us to be confident that they have been derived from human prostate carcinoma cells. The important biological characteristics of these three lines are shown in Table 1. All three prostate adenocarcinoma cell lines were established from metastatic tissue (Table 1), which could present a problem if the antigen specific for the primary tumor is absent from the metastatic cell as a result of antigenic modulation (70). The prostate cell lines claimed to have been derived from primary prostate carcinoma are either contaminated with HeLa cell chromosome markers (71, 72), have finite growth span (73), grow poorly in culture (67), or have not been sufficiently characterized to consider them stable lines at this time (64). All of these features are, of course, important considerations in selecting the most appropriate cell line to be used as a reliable source of immunogen. Even then, the mere fact that the cells are grown and maintained under in vitro culture conditions applies considerable selective pressure on antigen expression and stability. For example, it is not usually possible to know if the antigen is expressed on either high, low, or both high and low cell passage number before initiating the hybridoma experiments. One also has to take into account that the selective pressures of cell culture may have resulted in derivation of a cell that is malignant by the criteria applied but which does not maximally express tumor antigens. Optimal antigen expression may also be cell cycle dependent. Most established cell lines have not been cloned

Table 1 Characteristics of Prostate Adenocarcinoma Cell Lines

Cell line	Originator	Source	Cultivation	Morphology	Karyology	Markers	HL-A	Tumorigenicity
DU145	Stone et al. (1978)	M^a brain moderately differentiated	Confluent monolayer, 20% bovine serum, soft agar, multinucleates (68) poor plating efficiency, hormone independent and insensitive, little to no PAP produced, no PA produced[e]	E^b	MN^c64	Y, 3 marker chromosomes (no HeLa markers)	A3, B17 (69), no Ia	NM^d
PC-3	Kaighn, et al. (1979)	M bone poorly differentiated	Confluent monolayer, 20% fetal bovine serum, soft agar, multinucleates (68), hormone independent and insensitive no PAP or PA produced[e]	E	MN58	11 marker chromosomes (no HeLa markers)	ND^d	NM

| LNCaP | Horoszewicz et al. (1979) | M lymph node moderately differentiated | No uniform mono-layers, 15% fetal bovine serum, low anchorage potential, slow growth (5–7 days), hormone insensitive and independent, PAP and PA produced[e] | E | MN80–95 | Y, 7 marker chromosomes (no HeLa markers) | ND | NM |

[a]M, metastatic tumor.
[b]E, epithelial cell.
[c]MN, modal number.
[d]ND, not determined; NM, nude mice.
[e]PAP produced when cells cultured in chemically defined media (E. Kaighn, personal communication).

and therefore contain a heterogeneous mixture of cell types. In this case, the "minor" cell type could overgrow the "major" cell type and prevent adequate immunization against the antigens expressed on the "major" cell type. Despite these apparent problems in using established tumor cell lines as immunogens for the hybridoma technique, several reports have described the successful use of established cell lines for generating monoclonal antibodies that bind to membrane antigens on both cell lines and tumor tissue (53, 54, 56, 57). The binding of the cell line-generated monoclonal antibodies to tumor tissue is essential; otherwise they would have presumably no clinical utility. Futhermore, monoclonal antibodies that specifically bind to both cell lines and tumor tissue make the cell line even more invaluable for purposes of specificity testing and as a source of antigen for purification. The latter would be especially valuable where the amount of tumor tissue obtainable is small, such as in the case of primary prostate tumor tissue.

The use of surgical tissue as a source of prostate tumor antigens is also fraught with problems. Because radical surgery is a less common form of treatment for prostate carcinoma, large quantities of primary prostate tumor tissue obtained by prostatectomy usually are not available. What are available are small quantities of tissue obtained by transurethral resection, in which 80% of the transurethral resection tissue chips may contain either normal or hyperplastic tissue without any malignant tissue (63). Furthermore, many of the transurethral resection chips often appear burned or "cooked," which can result in antigen denaturation. Prostate carcinoma tissue available after therapy usually has been altered by radiation or fulguration. Surgical acquisition of metastatic tissue is confined to lymph nodes at the time of surgical staging following radiotherapy, and in most cases the lymph nodes contain few cancerous cells. Metastatic tissues in other organs, such as bone and soft tissues, are usually only obtainable at autopsy.

Monoclonal Antibodies Produced with Prostate Tissue as Immunogen

Because of the problems associated with the procurement of appropriate primary prostate tumor tissue for immunization, attempts have been made to use benign prostate hyperplasia (BPH) tissue cell membranes (74) or cytoplasmic extracts (75) to generate monoclonal antibodies that might detect antigens expressed on malignant prostate tumors as well as on BPH, but at a greater concentration Murine monoclonal antibodies against membrane-enriched fractions of BPH tissues were prepared by Frankel and co-workers (74). After extensive screening by radioimmunoassay and immunoperoxidase staining of tissue sections, they could phenotype the antibody reactivity into three types: prostate epithelium specific, polyepithelial, and stroma specific. Although these investigators claimed to have isolated two monoclonal antibodies that are prostate specific, cross-reactivity to other human tissues (particularly breast and salivary glands) was demonstrated for each of these antibodies. These antibodies could not differentiate BPH from malignant prostate tumors, although they were not cross-reactive with PAP or PA.

A monoclonal antibody was recently described by Clarke et al. (75) that was produced against a cytoplasmic antigen extract of BPH cells. The primary objective of their study was to provide a marker to identify acinar cells in culture and to follow their development and/or differentiation with time. They evaluated the reactivity of their monoclonal antibody by indirect immunofluorescence on frozen tissue sections and by an immunoperoxidase technique on formalin-fixed tissue. The antigen detected was located primarily in the perinuclear region of acinar cells, similar to the location of PAP and PA. They determined that the antigen detected by their antibody was not PAP or PA by RIA, blocking assays, and absorption experiments. The antigen was also found in the first fraction ejaculate, which has a high concentration of prostatic secretory products, and in epithelial cell outgrowth from prostate explants maintained in culture. They concluded that this monoclonal antibody is directed against antigens that are characteristic of differentiated prostatic acinar cells.

Both these studies only presented preliminary data on the reactivity of their monoclonal antibodies. No data was presented on the potential clinical utility of these antibodies. The data presented would suggest that these antibodies do not react with either PAP or PA, but that they react to antigens expressed by prostate ductal epithelial cells and in this way are similar to PAP and PA. Intensive specificity testing is required by both groups of investigators in order to determine if any of these monoclonals will be any more clinically useful than PAP or PA.

Monoclonal Antibodies Produced Against Established Prostate Adenocarcinoma Cell Lines as Immunogen

At present two reports describing the production of monoclonal antibodies to prostate carcinoma membrane antigens using established prostate adenocarcinoma cells lines have been published. The first study was by Ware et al. (76), who described a monoclonal antibody (αPro 3) that was produced against the well-established human prostate adenocarcinoma cell line PC-3 (66). Using RIA combined with absorption and immunoaffinity chromatography, they showed that αPro 3 reacted strongly with the immunizing cell line PC-3, but was found to have little reactivity against another prostate carcinoma cell line, DU145 (Table 1; Ref. 61). They reported that although the antigen detected by αPro 3 was present in extracts of normal, BPH, and malignant prostate tissue, as well as in extracts of normal and malignant nonprostatic tissue, the highest concentration of the antigen was associated with malignant prostate tissue. The strongest reactivity of this monoclonal antibody was against tissue extracts of poorly differentiated prostatic carcinoma and testicular tumors. αPro 3 was also shown to compete with prostate carcinoma patient serum immunoglobulin for binding to a 54-kilodalton protein antigen present in extracts of primary prostate carcinoma tissue. Further specificity testing of αPro 3 is required in order to determine the potential clinical significance of this monoclonal antibody.

Initial attempts to produce monoclonal antibodies to prostate tumor antigens in our laboratory utilized the established prostatic adenocarcinoma cell line DU145 to generate the 83.21 monoclonal antibody (77). The specificity of this monoclonal antibody and a second monoclonal antibody designated 6.2 (produced against the PC-3 prostate carcinoma cell) will be described.

Production and Reactivity of 83.21 and 6.2 Monoclonal Antibodies: The 83.21 monoclonal antibody was produced from a fusion of spleen cells from BALB/c mice hyperimmunized with DU145 cells and the P3-x63-Ag8 murine myeloma cell line. The 6.2 monoclonal antibody resulted from fusing spleen cells from mice hyperimmunized with the PC-3 prostate cell line and the P3-x63 NS-1 murine myeloma cell line. The resulting hybridoma supernatants from both fusion experiments were initially screened for antibody binding activity to the immunizing cell line and to a human lung cancer cell line, CALU-1, using a solid-phase RIA. Hybrid cultures that demonstrated preferential binding to the immunizing cell line were cloned and recloned by limiting dilution and the supernatant again tested for reactivity and specificity by RIA, membrane immunofluorescence (IF), and a complement-dependent cytotoxicity (CDC) assay. It was felt necessary to employ more than one type of immunoassay in order to accurately assess the specificity of the monoclonal antibodies.

Monoclonal antibody 83.21 demonstrated strong binding to the immunizing prostate adenocarcinoma cell line DU145, but reacted weakly with the PC-3 and HPC-36 prostate carcinoma cell lines by RIA (Table 2). However, both PC-3 and DU145 were bound by monoclonal antibody 83.21, as demonstrated by membrane immunofluorescence and complement-dependent cell cytotoxicity assay, whereas neither HPC-36 nor another prostate carcinoma cell line, LNCaP, were positive by these assays (Table 2). Considerable cross-reactivity of this monoclonal antibody was also observed with several urinary bladder cell lines (Table 2). No detectable cross-reactivity was demonstrated to a variety of nonprostate or nonbladder malignant cell lines or to normal human fibroblasts or blood cells (Table 3).

As shown in Table 4, 6.2 monoclonal antibodies reacted strongly to the immunizing cell line PC-3, but did not react to two other prostate adenocarcinoma cell lines. Although this antibody did not react to the T24 and 639V bladder carcinoma cell lines, as was observed with the 83.21 monoclonal antibody, it did bind to three bladder transitional cell carcinoma lines (647V, 575A, and RT4). Also in contrast to monoclonal antibody 83.21, the 6.2 antibody reacted with kidney, colon, and breast carcinoma cell lines and a hepatoma cell line. This cross-reactivity suggested a wider distribution for the antigen detected by antibody 6.2 than for the antigen detected by antibody 83.21. The 6.2 antibody had no apparent reactivity against melanoma, astrocytoma, neuroblastoma, osteosarcoma, or lung carcinoma, or to several normal human fibroblast cell lines (Table 4).

Table 2 Reactivity of Hybridoma 83.21 Monoclonal Antibodies to Prostate and Urinary Bladder Cell Lines as Measured by RIA, Membrane IF, and CDC[a].

Target cell	RIA, binding ratio[b]	IF percentage of positive cells[c]	CDC percentage of specific lysis[d]
Prostate tumor lines			
DU145	10	80	82
PC-3	2	33	48
LNCaP	NT[e]	0	0
HPC-36	1	0	0
Bladder tumor lines			
T-24	12	67	34
RT4	3	21	46
639V	7	23	23
575A	2	0	0
HCV-29 (benign)	NT	0	0

[a]RIA, membrane IF, and CDC assays are described in detail in Ref. 33.

[b]Total number of cell-bound counts using a hybridoma supernatant divided by the number of cell-bound counts using P3-X63-Ag8 myeloma supernatant.

[c]The percentage of cells showing positive fluorescence out of 300 cells counted.

[d]CDC values by 83.21 antibodies are significantly different from myeloma spent culture medium control values (P < .05 to P < .001); the mean of two to four.

[e]NT, not tested.

Significance of Cross-Reactivity of Monoclonal Antiprostate Antibodies with Urinary Bladder Carcinoma Cells: The cross-reactivity of the monoclonal antibodies described above with urinary bladder carcinoma cell lines raises the possibility of a common urogenital surface antigen present on both prostate and bladder tumor cells. The possibility that 83.21 detects a urogenital cell differentiation antigen is attractive, since both the urinary bladder and prostate originate from the urogenital sinus during embryological development (Fig. 1). The uroepithelium of the bladder and the glandular epithelium of the prostate gland both originate from the endoderm. The majority of the malignant tumors found associated with these organs originate from these two cell types. The assumption would be that the 83.21 antigen functions at some stage of development of these urogenital epithelial cells that becomes repressed in the adult cell, only to become re-expressed as a result of neoplastic transformation. If this assumption is valid, it should be possible to detect this antigen on fetal prostate and bladder epithelial cells. Such studies are in progress.

Monoclonal antibody 6.2 also cross-reacts with urinary bladder carcinoma cell lines, but with an opposite pattern of reactivity when compared to 83.21 (Table 5). For example, T24 was strongly bound by 83.21, but was not bound by 6.2

Table 3 Lack of Reactivity of Hybridoma 83.21 Monoclonal Antibodies to Various Normal and Malignant Human Cell Lines

Target cell	RIA, binding ratio[a]	Immunofluorescence, percentage of positive cells[a]	CDC, percentage of specific lysis[a]
Malignant cell lines			
769P (RCC)[b]	3	0	0
CAKI-2 (RCC)	2	0	0
A498 (RCC)	2	0	0
MG-178 (glioblastoma)	2	0	0
MCF-7 (breast)	2	0	0
CALU-1 (lung)	2	0	0
WM9 (melanoma	2	0	0
A101D (melanoma)	2	0	0
WM56 (melanoma)	2	0	0
G292 (osteosarcoma)	1	0	0
IMR32 (neuroblastoma)	1	0	0
SW 1116 (colon)	2	0	0
Normal fibroblast lines			
IMR90 (fetal lung)	1	0	0
FLOW 4000 (fetal kidney)	2	0	0
WI 38 (embryonic lung)	1	0	0
HEL 299 (fetal lung)	1	0	0
Other normal cells			
A Erythocytes	1	0	0
B Erythocytes	1	0	0
AB Erythocytes	1	0	0
Lymphocyte panel (six donors)	2	0	0

[a]Terms are defined in Table 2.

[b]Renal cell carcinoma.

using two different immunoassays (immunofluorescence and RIA), whereas the exact opposite was recorded for the 575A transitional cell carcinoma cell line. An intermediate reaction with the RT4 cell line was obtained with both antibodies. Since the 6.2 antigen is found on other malignant cells (i.e., breast and kidney), it is likely that this antigen may be expressed on a number of cell types and therefore does not represent a urogenital differentiation antigen. The different patterns of reactivity with both prostate and bladder tumor cell lines may also be the result of antigen density, cell cycle dependency, or different subpopulations of tumor cells. The possibility that 83.21 and 6.2 detect different determinants on the same anti-

Table 4 Reactivity of Monoclonal Antibody NSPC-3-6.2.1 in a Fixed Cell Radioimmunoassay[a]

Cell origin	Cell Line	NSPC-3-6.2.1
Prostate carcinomas		
Bone metastasis	PC-3	4447
Brain metastasis	DU145	1574
Lymph node metastasis	LNCaP	661
Primary	HPC-36	421
Urinary bladder carcinomas		
Primary	575A	5912
Primary	647V	4136
Primary	RT4	4136
Primary	T24	792
Primary	639V	563
Lymph node metastasis	253J	451
Other malignancies		
Kidney, primary	A498	639
Kidney, skin metastasis	CAKI-1	1260
Kidney, primary	CAKI-2	1822
Breast, pleura	MCF-7	3673
Hepatoma, ascites	SK-HEP-1	1224
Colon, primary	SW948	2268
Colon, primary	SW1116	1899
Melanoma, lymph node metastasis	WM9	740
Melanoma, primary	H1477	634
Astrocytoma, primary	A1088	718
Neuroblastoma	IMR-32	781
Lung, pleura	CALU-1	753
Osteosarcoma	G292	829
Normal		
Fetal lung fibroblasts	HEL 299	651
Fetal lung fibroblasts	WI 38	730
Fetal lung fibroblasts	IMR90	386
Fetal skin fibroblasts	GM 10	452
Fetal kidney fibroblasts	FLOW 4000	524

[a]Fixed cell radioimmunoassay was used as described (77). Data presented as cpm. Background (cpm in presence of P3-x68-Ag) myeloma culture supernatant) varied for each cell line listed and ranged between 450 and 750 cpm.

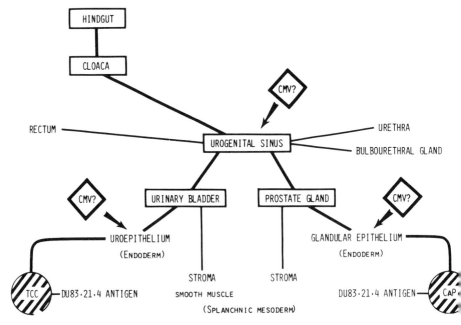

Figure 1   Flow diagram to illustrate the embryonic origin of the prostate gland and urinary bladder. Both the uroepithelium of the urinary bladder and the ductal epithelium of the prostate gland originate from the endoderm derived from the urogenital sinus. It is from these epithelial sites that the majority of the prostate and urinary carcinomas originate. The DU83.21.4 antigen detected on the surface of some bladder (TCC) and prostate carcinomas (CaP) suggests that this antigen may represent a urogenital differentiation antigen. Cellular transformation following infection by cytomegalovirus (CMV) may have resulted in the expression of the DU83.21.4 antigen on the tumor cells.

gen that is preferentially expressed by some cell lines but not by others cannot be overlooked as a possible explanation for the different patterns of reactivity. Preliminary immunohistochemical studies (described later) suggest that these antibodies are detecting antigens expressed on two different urinary bladder tumor cell populations.

Significance of the Cross-Reactivity of Monoclonal Antibodies with Cells Transformed by Cytomegalovirus: The evidence for a direct relationship between herpesvirus infection and human cancer is quite strong, particularly for the associations between Epstein-Barr virus and both Burkitt's lymphoma and nasopharyngeal carcinoma (78); the association between herpesvirus type II and cervical carcinoma (79); and the most recent implication of an association between cytomegalovirus (CMV) (a member of the herpesvirus group) and Kaposi's sarcoma (80, 81) and cancer of the prostate (82, 83). Evidence in support of a CMV association with the etiology

Table 5 Comparison of the Binding of Monoclonal Antibodies DU83.21.4 and NSPC-3 6.2.1 to Human Cell Lines

Cell line	DU83.21.4 binding activity		NSPC-3-6.2.1 binding avtivity	
	RIA (BR)[a]	IF (%)[b]	RIA (BR)	IF (%)
Prostate				
DU145	10	80	2	9
PC-3	2	33	7	95
Bladder				
T24	12	67	2	0
RT4	3	21	9	45
575A	2	0	18	60
CMV transformed				
CMV-Mj-HEL-1	21	29	2	3
BH-21	16	33	3	2
7E	11	17	5	8
Other				
CALU-1	2	0	1	0
HEL 299	2	0	1	0

[a]Binding ratio (see Table 2).
[b]Percent fluorescing cells (see Table 2).

of prostate adenocarcinoma is that (a) CMV antigens can be detected in the nucleus and on the membranes of human prostate tumor cells (82), (b) the detection of new antigens induced on the surface of CMV-infected and -transformed human and animal cells (82), (c) the demonstration that CMV isolated from human prostate tissue transforms human cells in vitro and that these transformed cells can induce tumors in nude mice (82), (d) the observation that significantly more prostatic cancer as well as urinary bladder cancer patients have high titers of antibodies to CMV than do patients with other malignancies or normal individuals (84), and (e) the demonstration that the human seminal tract can be a repository for CMV. Although the exact relationship between CMV infection and prostate cancer remains unknown, it is becoming clear that this virus has certain properties that resemble those of the known oncogenic herpesviruses.

Because of the evidence suggesting a possible association of CMV and prostate cancer, we decided it would be important to test our monoclonal antibodies with cells transformed by CMV. Monoclonal antibody 83.21 was extensively tested against a variety of virally transformed cell lines. The data in Table 6 show that antibody 83.21 reacted with 10 of 10 CMV-transformed human cell lines while demonstrating no reactivity to other herpesvirus-transformed, SV40 virus-transformed, CMV-infected, or nontransformed human and rodent cell lines. In con-

Table 6   Reactivity of 83.21 Monoclonal Antibodies with Virus-Transformed and Nontransformed Cell Lines

Cell line	RIA, binding ratio[a]	IF, percentage of positive cells[a]	CDC, percentage of specific lysis[a]
CMV-transformed			
CMV-Mj-HEL-1[b]	18	21	48
BH-19[c]	8	17	46
BH-21[c]	16	33	52
BH-47[c]	10	36	44
LH-1[d]	8	31	34
LH-2[d]	11	33	28
LH-5[d]	14	27	22
6H[e]	7	17	16
5B[e]	9	20	18
7E[e]	11	17	34
CMV-infected			
WI 38	0	0	0
HEL 299	0	0	0
Herpes-transformed			
333.8.9[f]	3	0	0
EB-3[g]	1	0	0
SV40-transformed			
SV40 hp[h]	2	0	0
SV80[i]	2	0	0
Nontransformed			
HEL 299	2	0	0
WI 38	1	0	0

[a]Assays are described in Table 2; results expressed are the mean of three to six experiments.

[b]CMV-transformed human embryonic cell (HEL 299).

[c]Towne strain CMV DNA fragment-transformed human fibroblast.

[d]Towne strain CMV-transformed human fibroblast.

[e]Strain BT 1757 CMV-transformed human fibroblast.

[f]Herpes virus-transformed hamster fibroblast.

[g]Epstein-Barr virus-transformed human lymphocyte.

[h]SV40 virus-transformed rat hepatocyte.

[i]SV40 virus-transformed human fibroblast.

trast, 6.2 does not react or reacts weakly with CMV-transformed cells (Table 5). Since herpesvirus-infected cells possess IgG Fc receptors (85, 86), the possibility that antibody 83.21 bound to Fc receptors rather than to a TAA was addressed. Although both CMV-infected and CMV-transformed cells were shown to have IgG Fc-like receptors for human and rabbit IgG by immunofluorescence and rosette assays, binding of 83.21 to CMV-transformed cells could not be blocked by prior incubation of the transformed cells with mouse, rabbit, or human IgG. Similarly, 83.21 could not block the binding of human IgG to Fc receptors (Table 7). From these experiments, it was concluded that 83.21 binds to a membrane antigen distinct from Fc-like receptors (G. L. Wright, Jr. et al., unpublished data). Further studies have shown that 83.21 was not reactive with CMV-coded proteins in the nucleus, cytoplasm, or membranes of CMV-infected human fibroblasts at the immediate early, early, or late stages of infection. These results suggest that transformation by CMV leads to expression of a cell-surface, nonviral protein that cross-reacts with an antigen on the membrane of prostate and bladder tumor cells. The antigen recognized by 83.21 may be a transforming antigen or reexpression of urogenital differentiation antigen as a result of infection and transformation of normal uroepithelium by CMV (Fig. 1). Further studies will be required to elucidate the nature of this interesting antigen.

Immunohistochemical Evaluation of the Monoclonal Antibodies: The binding of monoclonal antibodies 83.21 and 6.2 to established human cell lines indicated a restricted pattern of reactivity. Still to be determined was whether these monoclonal antibodies reacted with antigens present in tissue specimens. Absorption experiments, in which the monoclonal antibodies were absorbed with increasing concentrations of membrane extracts, suggested that both 83.21 and 6.2 antigens were present in extracts of malignant prostate tissues (both primary and metastatic) but not in extracts prepared from benign prostate hyperplastic tissue. The binding of either monoclonal antibody to prostate tumor cells could not be reduced after absorption of the antibodies with membrane extracts of nonprostate tumor and normal tissues.

To further define the reactivity and specificity of these two monoclonal antibodies, we elected to use the immunoperoxidase staining procedure because of several advantages offered by this technique, such as (a) the presence of normal tissue elements that serve as a specificity control for each abnormal tissue examined; (b) the identification, localization, and determination of the number of positively stained cells; (c) the capability of screening a large number of tissues in a short period of time; (d) the potential of performing retrospective studies, if the antigen is present in fixed and embedded tissue sections; and (e) the feasibility of long-term storage of the stained tissue sections. Both frozen and formalin-fixed tissues were examined. Although the antigens detected by 83.21 and 6.2 were detected in both frozen and formalin-fixed tissues, the most consistent and reproducible results were obtained with the formalin-fixed, paraffin-embedded tissues. This permitted immediate access to a large number of tissue blocks. The immunoperoxidase pro-

Table 7 Evidence That Monoclonal Antibody DU83.21 Does Not Bind to Fc-Like Receptors

Blocking Agent	Primary Antibody	Percent positive fluorescing cells[a,b]						
		DU145	PC-3	T24	CMV-Mj-HEL-1	CALU-1	HEL 299	CMV infected (72 hr) HEL 299
None	83.21	70	20	64	63	NEG	NEG	NEG
P3-x 63-Ag8 supernatant	83.21	68	25	93	58	NEG	NEG	NEG
Normal rabbit sera	83.21	88	14	66	66	NEG	NEG	NEG
Normal mouse sera	83.21	78	22	73	58	NEG	NEG	NEG
Normal human sera	83.21	77	17	68	63	NEG	NEG	NEG
CMV human sera	83.21	72	24	66	63	NEG	NEG	NEG
Human IgG	83.21	74	20	70	52	NEG	NEG	NEG
Human IgM	83.21	80	22	64	55	NEG	NEG	NEG
Monoclonal anti-PAP	83.21	81	23	66	70	NEG	NT	NT
None	Human IgG	23	46	44	57	NEG	NEG	NEG
Normal rabbit sera	Human IgG	2	1	8	4	NEG	NEG	NEG
83.21	Human IgG	26	52	48	63	NEG	NEG	NEG

[a]The membrane immunofluorescent assays were used as described (see Table 2).
[b]Identification of cell lines is given in Tables 2, 3, and 6.

cedure used for these experiments was the avidin–biotin immunoperoxidase kit purchased from Vector Laboratories, Burlingame, Calif. (a detailed description of this
method can be found in Ref. 87). The first section of each tissue block was stained with hematoxylin–eosin for histological examination. Subsequent serial sections
were reacted with either control antibodies, 83.21, or 6.2. Prostate tissue sections
were also reacted with antibodies to prostatic acid phosphatase (PAP) or prostate
antigen (PA). The tissue sections which reacted with antibody were evaluated
according to staining intensity and number of tumor cells stained.

The reactivity of monoclonal antibodies 83.21 and 6.2 to a variety of malignant,
benign, and normal tissues is shown in Table 8. Using 10 μg of antibody per tissue
section, the percent of positive primary prostate carcinomas was 63% (12 of 19)
for 83.21 and 74% (14 of 19) for 6.2. When the results obtained by both antibodies
were combined, 17 of 19 or 89% of the primary prostate tumors were positive. In
addition to the observation that some tumors were stained by one but not the
other monoclonal antibody, it was also observed that not all tumor cells stained in
many of the positive primary tumors [Fig. 2 (Plate 3, facing page 274)]. The
positive tumor cells in these tissue sections range from a low of 12% to a high of
100%. Furthermore, in many of the primary prostate tumor sections, tumor
cells in one area were stained but tumor cells in another area of the tumor tissue

Table 8 Immunoperoxidase Staining of Fixed Human Tissue Sections with
Monoclonal Antibodies DU83.21.4 and NSPC-3-6.2.1

Tissue type	Number of positive/total number tested			
	DU83.21.4		NSPC-3-6.2.1	
Prostate				
Primary carcinoma	12/19	(63%)	14/19	(74%)
Metastatic carcinoma	2/7	(29%	5/7	(71%)
Benign prostate hyperplasia	0/12	(0%)	2/12	(17%)
Bladder				
Carcinoma	4/8	(50%)	6/8	(75%)
Normal	0/6	(0%)	0/6	(0%)
Nonprostate, nonbladder carcinomas	0/10[a]	(0%)	6/10	(60%)
Normal	0/27[b,c]	(0%)	0/27[b,c]	(0%)

[a]Adenocarcinomas of lung, liver, colon, breast, melanoma, kidney, and pancreas; squamous
cell carcinomas of esophagus and larynx.

[b]Normal tissues: lung, breast, heart, spleen, liver, kidney, colon, pancreas, testes, and vas
deferens.

[c]Pale staining of some cells in convoluted tubules (kidney) and hepatocytes (liver).

did not stain. This staining heterogeneity was often observed even within the same area of tumor cells, where a negatively stained cell was observed next to a cell that stained positive for the specific TAA [Fig. 2 (Plate 3)]. Positive staining of primary prostate tumor tissue did not appear to be influenced by how well differentiated the tumor appeared, since all pathological types (well differentiated, poorly differentiated, and undifferentiated) scored positive [Fig. 2A, (Plate 3)]. The percentage of metastatic prostate tumors that were reactive also varied for the two monoclonal antibodies; 29% (2 of 7) were positive with 83.21 and 71% (5 of 7) were positive with 6.2. The two metastatic lesions positive with 83.21 were both draining (obturator) lymph nodes. Those positive with 6.2 were lymph nodes, urinary bladder, skin, and liver. The staining heterogeneity observed in the positive primary prostate tumor tissue sections was also evident in the positive metastatic prostate tissue sections [Fig. 2E, (Plate 3)]. The positive staining reaction in all malignant prostate tissues appeared to be restricted to the tumor cells; no apparent staining was observed in the normal ductal epithelium stroma, blood vessels, or lymphocytes [Fig. 2A, B, D-G (Plate 3)]. In approximately one-quarter of the well-to-moderately-well differentiated primary prostrate adenocarcinomas, positively stained cells were found in the lumen of some ducts, and some concretions also stained positive. Not all positive tumors resulted in the same staining reaction. The patterns of reactivity observed were membrane staining [Fig. 2B, F (Plate 3)], or diffuse cytoplasmic staining [Fig. 2A, G (Plate 3)]. Of the 12 benign prostate hyperplasia tissues tested, none were positive with 83.21 and 2 showed positive staining with 6.2. The positive reactions in these two BPH specimens were confined to a few weakly stained cells present in the lumen of a few ducts. The ductal epithelial cells did not stain. Whether this reaction represents a premalignant situation or a nonspecific reaction will require

Figure 2 Immunoperoxidase staining of formalin-fixed, paraffin-embedded tissue sections of prostate and bladder tumors. (A) Undifferentiated prostate adenocarcinomas reacted with 6.2: positively stained tumor cells (T) and negatively stained stroma (S) (×400). (B) Poorly differentiated prostate adenocarcinoma reacted with 83.21: Note the positively stained tumor cells (T) surrounded by negative tumor cells (t); the stroma (S) is negative (×200). (C) Benign prostate hyperplasia reacted with monoclonal anti-PAP: Note the diffuse cytoplasmic staining of the ductal epithelium (E) and lack of staining in the stroma (S) (×200). (D) Serial section of same tissue as (C), but reacted with 83.21: Note the lack of staining in both the ductal epithelium (E) and stroma (S) (×200). (E) Prostate tumor metastasis of the liver reacted with 6.2: Note the positive staining of some tumor cells in two metastatic foci (T) and the negative staining of most of the tumor cells in the other two foci (t); and of hepatocytes (H) (×100). (F) Higher magnification of one of the positively stained metastatic foci shown in (E): Note the intense membrane staining and diffuse cytoplasmic staining of the positive tumor cells (T) interspersed among negative tumor cells (t) within the metastatic foci; hepatocytes (H) are negative (×400). (G) Prostate tumor metastasis of the lymph node reacted with 83.21: diffuse cytoplasmic staining of most of the tumor cells (T); negative staining of lymphocytes (L) (×400). (H) Transitional cell carcinoma of the urinary bladder reacted with 6.2: intense membrane staining of tumor cells (T); the muscle (M) and stroma (S) are not stained (×400).

Plate 3

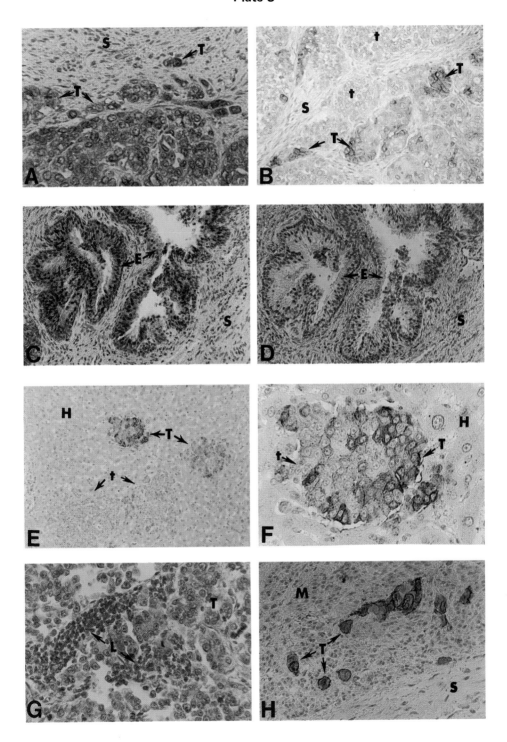

extensive evaluation. Monoclonals 83.21 and 6.2 were also tested for reactivity to nonprostate tumor and normal tissues. Neither antibody reacted to any of the following normal tissues: lung, colon, breast, heart, spleen, liver, pancreas, testes, vas deferens, and urinary bladder. Both 83.21 and 6.2 did, however, react with the proximal convoluted tubules of normal kidney specimens. The tubules stained a yellowish orange that was definitely above background but different from the reddish brown reaction observed for positively stained tumor cells. This reaction in kidney tissues with mouse monoclonal antibodies has been observed by others (59, 74). The nature of this reaction remains to be determined.

Monoclonal 6.2 showed cross-reactivity with six of eight transitional cell carcinomas of the urinary bladder, two of three adenocarcinomas of the breast, one of two adenocarcinomas of the lung, and one of two adenocarcinomas of the pancreas (Table 8). In contrast, 83.21 was found to cross-react only with urinary bladder carcinoma tissue (Table 8). The reactivity of both antibodies to a variety of neoplastic tissues is currently being studied to determine the precise range of the observed cross-reactivity, especially for 6.2. It is interesting to note that a strong correlation existed between the reactivity observed for the tumor cell lines and that recorded with the tissue specimens, which could have made it possible to predict the outcome of the tissue reactivity. Because of the possibility that one (83.21) or both monoclonals are detecting common urogenital TAAs on prostate and urinary bladder carcinomas, as previously described, we are in the process of an extensive evaluation of the cross-reaction with urinary bladder tissue and cytological specimens. The data collected thus far has shown 6.2 to react with 75% (six of eight) and 83.21 with 50% (four of eight) of the bladder tissue sections (Table 8). Two specimens positive with 83.21 were not positive with 6.2. Similarly, two other specimens positive with 6.2 were not positive or weakly positive with 83.21. Neither antibody reacted with any of the six specimens of normal bladder tissue tested. Although substantially more data are required, it presently appears that 83.21 reacts with a small, less pleomorphic bladder neoplastic cell than the cell that stains positive with 6.2 [Fig. 2H (Plate 3, facing page 274)]. The cell that binds 6.2 is a large cell displaying a large hyperchromatic nucleus typical of the malignant transitional epithelium cell [Fig. 2H (Plate 3)]. Preliminary membrane immunofluorescent studies of the cells contained in bladder washings from bladder cancer patients has confirmed the tissue observations. Whether the cell detected by 83.21 is a different (i.e., subtype) neoplastic cell than the one detected by 6.2 or the same cell but at a different stage of cell differentiation remains to be determined.

The immunoperoxidase procedure was used to compare the reactivity of 83.21 and 6.2 with the reactivity of antibodies to two established prostate tumor markers, PAP and PA, on tissue sections of prostate tumors. The reactivity with the four antibodies could be placed into several distinct groups (Table 9). Reaction to all four antibodies was demonstrated in 5 of 10 (50%) primary prostate tumors, ·

Table 9 Comparison of Immunoperoxidase Staining of Fixed Tissue Sections of
Prostate Adenocarcinoma, Benign Prostate Hyperplasia, and Normal Prostate with
Monoclonal Antibodies DU83.21.4 and NSPC-6.2.1 and Antibodies to PAP and PA

Prostate tissue specimen	Staining intensity of tumor cells (or normal ductal epithelium)[a]			
	DU83.21.4	NSPC-6.2.1	Anti-PAP[b]	Anti-PA[c]
Primary tumor (pathology)[d]				
1 (W)	3	3	3	3
2 (W)	3	3	1	2
3 (W)	1	2	1	1
4 (P)	NEG	2	NEG	NEG
5 (P)	2	NEG	NEG	2
6 (W)	3	2	2	2
7 (U)	NEG	3	NEG	NEG
8 (M)	3	1	2	1
9 (W)	NEG	2	3	2
10 (U)	NEG	NEG	NEG	NEG
Metastic tumor (site)[e]				
1 (B)	2	3	2	2
2 (S)	NEG	2	3	3
3 (L)	NEG	2	NEG	NEG
4 (L)	NEG	1	NEG	NEG
5 (LN)	NEG	3	2	3
6 (LN)	NEG	1	NEG	2
Benign prostate hyperplasia				
1	NEG	1[f]	2	3
2	NEG	1[f]	3	3
3	NEG	NEG	1	3
4	NEG	NEG	2	3
5	NEG	NEG	2	2
6	NEG	NEG	3	3
7	NEG	NEG	2	2
8	NEG	NEG	3	3
9	NEG	NEG	1	3
10	NEG	NEG	3	1
11	NEG	NEG	3	3
12	NEG	NEG	2	3

[a]A biotin-avidin immunoperoxidase procedure (Vector Laboratories, Inc., Burlingame, Calif.),
was used on formalin-fixed, paraffin-embedded tissues (81): 3, strong staining; 2, moderate
staining; 1, weak staining; NEG, no staining.

while one of the six (17%) metastatic prostate tumors was positive by all four antibodies. Only one primary and none of the metastatic prostate tumors were negative by all four antibodies. The 83.21 antigen was detected in 6 of 10 (60%), the 6.2 antigen in 8 of 10 (80%), and both antigens were present in 5 of 10 (50%) of the primary prostate tissues. Prostate acid phosphatase was detected in 6 of 10 (60%) of the primary prostate tumors. Two of the primary prostate tumor tissues negative for PAP, PA, and 83.21 were positive for 6.2. The ability to detect PAP or PA in some of the primary prostate tumors apparently was related to how well differentiated the tumor appeared. The three tumors negative for PAP or PA were either poorly differentiated or undifferentiated. The 83.21 antigen was found in only one of six (17%) of the metastatic prostate tumors, while all six (100%) stained with 6.2. Prostate acid phosphatase was detected in three of six (50%) and PA was detected in four of six (67%) of the metastatic prostate tumors. This latter result is in contrast to some immunoperoxidase studies that found PAP or PA in all metastatic prostate tumors (36, 46). Tumor cell heterogeneity included variation in intensity and location of the staining reaction (membrane or cytoplasmic) for 83.21 and 6.2 as previously described. The staining intensity also varied for PAP and PA, usually demonstrating a diffuse granular pattern confined to the cytoplasm. None of the 12 BPH specimens were positive for 83.21 [Fig. 2D (Plate 3, facing page 274)], whereas 2 of 12 (17%) were positive for 6.2. As expected, all 12 BPH tissues were positive for PAP and PA, with the reaction confined to the ductal epithelium [Table 9; Fig. 2C (Plate C)]. The results from this study suggest a diverse pattern of antigen expression in prostate tumors, where antigen expression may be dependent on the state of tumor cell differentiation, cell cycle, subpopulations or mixed populations of tumor cells, and antigen density or concentration. Results from studies such as these should, however, be interpreted with caution, since the results could be influenced by antibody concentration and antibody affinity. Both 83.21 and 6.2 appear to be low-affinity IgM antibodies. Not only can low-affinity antibodies plague immunoperoxidase experiments, but IgM antibodies can often be "sticky," resulting in nonspecific binding, especially to collagen and elastic tissues, which cannot be adequately blocked without interfering with the specific reaction, thereby resulting in a high background. New fusion experiments are in progress to generate

---

[b]The anti-PAP antibody is a monoclonal antibody purchased from Hybritech, Inc., San Diego, Calif.

[c]The anti-PA antibody is a polyclonal (rabbit) antibody (Dako) purchased from Accurate Chemical and Scientific Corp., Westbury, N.Y.

[d]W, well differentiated; M, moderately differentiated; P, poorly differentiated; and U, undifferentiated.

[e]B, urinary bladder; S, skin; L, liver; LN, draining lymph node.

[f]Cell-like material (not secretion or concretion) stained inside lumen of a few ducts (less than 5%).

high-affinity IgG monoclonal antibodies to the 83.21 and 6.2 antigens. Nevertheless, what has emerged from this study is that 83.21 and 6.2 can apparently be used
to differentiate between benign and malignant prostate tumors, which is not possible with PAP and PA. Furthermore, 6.2 may be a better marker than either PAP
or PA for the detection of metastatic prostate tumors. These data suggest that a
panel of monoclonal antibodies to well-defined prostate TAA will enhance the
detection rate of primary prostate tumors.

Characterization of Prostate TAA: Competitive binding, direct binding, absorption,
and blocking immunoassays have shown that both 83.21 and 6.2 monoclonals are
not directed against PAP, PA, carcinoembryonic antigen, alpha-fetoprotein, HLA
(A, B, C) antigen, HLA-DR antigens, beta-2-microglobulin, or fibronectin (77). Immunoaffinity chromatography and sodium dodecyl sulfate gel electrophoresis, utilizing Nonidet P40 detergent extracts of $[^3H]$ glucosamine-labeled DU145 prostate
carcinoma cells, has shown that the antigen recognized by the 83.21 monoclonal
antibody is a membrane glycoprotein consisting of a complex of a 60- and a 30-
kilodalton molecule (Fig. 3). By comparison, PAP is a 100,000-dalton protein and
PA is a 34,000–36,000 dalton glycoprotein present in the cytoplasm of prostate
epithelial cells. Also, the glycoprotein detected by 83.21 does not appear to be
similar to any of the CMV protein antigens described to date (88). Characterization
of the antigen detected by 6.2 has only recently been initiated.

FUTURE DEVELOPMENTS

The studies described above would suggest that additional antigen specificities
will need to be identified by monoclonal antibodies in order to address the
diverse antigen expression found on prostate tumors. What is the best way to proceed in light of the existence of only three well-characterized prostate adenocarcinoma cell lines and the availability of only small quantities of tumor tissue as the
source of prostate TAA? One way is to repeat the fusion experiments with splenocytes from mice immunized with the same cell lines. However, second- and even
third-generation fusion experiments have often failed to uncover new antigen speci-
ficites (Z. Steplewski, personal communication). One then must resort to tumor
tissue as the source of prostate TAA. The small amount of surgically removed primary tumor tissue, which most often contains a heterogeneous mixture of normal,
benign, and tumor cells, even when pooled, has not, in our laboratory, resulted in
the successful generation of murine monoclonal antibodies to prostate TAAs at
this time. Metastatic prostate tissue, in sufficient quantity, is usually available
only at autopsy, which presents an additional problem of autolytic denaturation
of the antigen before the tissue can be processed in the laboratory.

How does one proceed to obtain a better source of prostate antigen? Because
of the difficulties in deriving primary as well as established prostate tumor cell lines

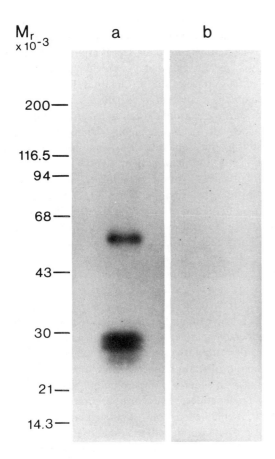

Figure 3 Autoradiogram of the affinity-purified 83.21 antigen. Extracts prepared from [^{3}H] glucosamine-labeled cell lines were passed over a monoclonal 83.21 affinity chromatographic column, the eluted fractions subjected to sodium dodecyl sulfate gel electrophoresis, and the gels developed by fluorography: (a) DU145 prostate adenocarcinoma eluted fraction and (b) CALU-1 lung adenocarcinoma eluted fraction (M_r, molecular weight markers). Note the 60- and 28-kilodalton components eluted from the DU145 cell extract that were not eluted from the lung carcinoma cell extract.

from either primary or metastatic prostate carcinoma tissue, we have elected to look at several alternatives for the procurement of prostate tumor tissue. One approach that we are presently exploring is the procedure of aspiration biopsy using the Franzen needle (89, 90), which has been used for approximately 15 years in Europe but which has not been routinely endorsed in the United States. This procedure can be well tolerated by the patient and is less invasive than punch biopsy or transurethral resection. Because the patient can tolerate this procedure, repeat aspiration biopsies can be periodically taken to monitor the course of therapy, providing an additional advantage of this procedure. One disadvantage of this procedure is that only a small number of cells (10^5) can be obtained; another disadvantage is that it takes a great deal of experience to distinguish if the aspirated cell is malignant or normal. Since the cell number would be inadequate for hyperimmunizing mice, we are currently evaluating the possibility of using the aspirated cells to immunize mouse splenocytes or human lymphocytes (prostate tumor patient's lymph node or peripheral blood lymphocytes, or normal tonsillar lymphocytes) in vitro and the fusing the immunized lymphocytes with a myeloma or lymphoblastoid fusion partner. The theory and methods for in vitro production of monoclonal antibodies can be found in an excellent review by Reading (91). Repeat aspiration biopsies from the same and different patients, including frozen or fixed tissue sections, would be used for antibody screening and specificity testing. Because of the potential importance of the cross-reactivity observed with bladder tumors with monoclonals 83.21 and 6.2, there is a need to generate monoclonal antibodies to bladder carcinoma cells used as immunogen to help elucidate the nature and diversity of antigen specific for prostate from those specific for bladder tumor and those that coexist on both types of tumors. Although a considerable number of established bladder tumor cell lines exist as a potential source of antigen, the same problem exists as for prostate tumors, that is, only small amounts of tumor tissue are readily available as an antigen source. The possibility of using bladder washings to obtain bladder tumor cells for in vitro immunization, in a manner described above for prostate tumor cells obtained by aspiration biopsy, should be explored. Although preference has been given to the use of malignant prostate tumor cells as immunogen, in our laboratory and that of Ware et al. (76) studies should continue to generate and evaluate monoclonal antibodies that are produced to membrane antigens on benign prostate hyperplasia (74) and prostatic fluid as the source of immunogen. Such studies might identify a membrane antigen found in high concentration in malignant prostate tissues, possibly analogous to PAP or PA. Hopefully the studies briefly outlined above will provide a panel of monoclonal antibodies that can be used to define the antigens expressed on different cell stages of prostate adenocarcinoma and possibly bladder tumors.

POTENTIAL CLINICAL APPLICATION OF MONOCLONAL ANTIPROSTATE ANTIBODIES

The generation and clinical utility of monoclonal antiprostate antibodies has not progressed as far as for some other human solid neoplasms, such as malignant melanoma (92, 93) and colorectal tumors (94–96). However, once monoclonal antibodies to well-defined prostate membrane TAAs have been defined, it is possible that these monoclonal antibodies will find utility for purification of the TAA, classification of prostate tumors, monitoring treatment management, diagnosis, radioimmunological localization of micrometastatic foci, and serotherapy. They may also be used as immunological probes to study the biology of antigen expression and diversification of tumor cell types and to facilitate the evaluation of the oncogenesis of prostate carcinoma at the membrane level. The immunohistochemical data suggest that monoclonal antibodies 83.21 and 6.2 may be recognizing useful markers that will aid the development of a more meaningful pathological classification of prostate tumors, especially when used in a panel that includes antibodies to PAP and PA. Presently it is impossible to correlate the histopathology of prostate tumors with the patient's clinical status. A classification scheme that included immunochemical and functional markers as well as chemical and morphological aspects of the tumor cells could provide more direct information to aid the pathologist and urologist in diagnosis, selection and monitoring treatment management, detection of early recurrent tumor, and predicting the prognosis of the prostate cancer patient. In this context, the aspiration biopsy would appear to be a valuable procedure for repeat cell sampling of the prostate gland before, during, and after treatment without seriously traumatizing the patient. An unexpected application of 83.21 and 6.2 might turn out to be their utility in the diagnosis and monitoring of urinary bladder carcinomas. Unlike prostate cancer, there are yet no definable tumor markers for bladder cancer. The presence or absence of A, B, and H antigens on bladder tumor cells is at present the only potential candidate tumor marker for bladder cancer. The loss of A, B, and H antigens appears to indicate that the tumor will be more invasive (97); however, the routine measurement of A, B, and H antigens has not at present gained wide acceptance for treatment management or as a prognosticator of bladder cancer. If the initial immunohistochemical observations can be confirmed by more extensive evaluation, both 83.21 and 6.2 may have similar clinical applications for bladder cancer as described above for prostate cancer. Maximum application could be in diagnosis and screening of bladder cancer, specifically the detection of bladder tumor cells present in bladder washings or urine specimens. The nature of the antigens detected by 83.21 and 6.2, especially related to the cross-reactivity with bladder tumor cells (i.e., urogenital cell differentiation antigen) will require extensive evaluation. Temporarily excluding the nature of the antigens detected by these monoclonals, 83.21 and 6.2 appear to be good candidate tumor markers for both prostate and urinary bladder carcinomas.

CONCLUSIONS

Studies of prostate carcinoma-associated antigens have concentrated on antigens or tumor markers associated with the cell cytoplasm, and only recently have studies been initiated to search for membrane TAAs on prostate cells. Much of the impetus to study membrane antigens has been stimulated by the development of the lymphocyte hybridoma technique. The application of the hybridoma technique to produce monoclonal antibodies to prostate TAAs has only recently begun. The few reports available already suggest that this technique will uncover new antigen specificities that will have clinical application. The membrane antigens detected by monoclonal antibodies described by other investigators await extensive analyses; therefore the clinical potential of any of these monoclonals remains unknown. Two monoclonal antibodies, 83.21 and 6.2, produced in our laboratory, appear to be useful for facilitating the identification and location of tumor cells in tissue specimens of both prostate and urinary bladder tumor specimens. Both of these monoclonals were produced using established prostate adenocarcinoma cell lines. Although only three well-characterized prostate tumor cell lines exist, some TAAs present on prostate tumor tissue cells are also expressed on the cell lines, making these cell lines a valuable source of these TAAs. The cross-reactivity of these anti-prostate tumor monoclonal antibodies with urinary bladder tumors is intriguing and suggests that at least one of these antibodies (83.21) is directed to a common urogenital differentiation antigen that is expressed on these tumor cells as a result of neoplastic transformation. Whether the antigen detected by this cross-reaction is present on fetal prostate and bladder cells (i.e., oncofetal antigen) remains to be determined. The binding of 83.21 to the surface of human cells transformed by cytomegalovirus (CMV) may be an important observation in view of the possible association of CMV with prostate cancer. An in-depth study to elucidate these interesting cross-reactivities is underway. Considerable heterogeneity of both antigen expression and antigen concentration was observed between and within various histological grades of prostate and bladder tumors. This coupled with the inability to obtain a positive staining reaction of all prostate tumors suggests that it will be necessary to identify additional TAA specificities in order to develop a panel of monoclonals that will detect all stages and subpopulations of prostate tumor cells. It is most likely that new specificities will be produced using tumor tissue as a source of antigen rather than cell lines, owing to the fact that few prostate tumor cell lines currently exist. It should, however, be possible to now use both 83.21 and 6.2 in a panel to study the dynamics of both prostate and bladder neoplasia and to assess the clinical value of these antibodies.

ACKNOWLEDGMENT

The studies performed with monoclonals 83.21 and 6.2 were done in collaboration with Paul F. Schellhammer, Susan Sieg, Leopoldo Ladaga, and Ann Campbell, and we also thank Patty Wirth, Zeinab Wahab, Margaret Lewis, and Paula Thompson for excellent technical assistance. The cytomegalovirus-transformed cell lines were kindly supplied by Dr. Fred Rapp of the Department of Microbiology at Pennsylvania

State University and Dr. E.- S. Huang of the Cancer Research Center at the University of North Carolina. These studies were supported in part by grants from the National Institutes of Health (CA-27623), the National Prostatic Cancer Project, the National Cancer Institute (CA-26659), an American Cancer Society Institutional Grant, and the Immunology Program of Eastern Virginia Medical School.

REFERENCES

1. E. Silverberg, *Ca 31*:13 (1981)
2. G. P. Murphy, *Ca 31*:96 (1981).
3. R. J. Boxer, *Urol. Surv. 27*:75 (1977)
4. W. Barzell, M. A. Bean, B. S. Hilaris, and W. F. Whitmore, Jr., *J. Urol. 118*:278 (1977).
5. C. E. Carlton, Jr., P. T. Hudgins, W. G. Guerriero, and R. Scott, Jr., *J. Urol. 116*:206 (1976).
6. Veterans Administration Cooperative Urological Research Group, *Surg. Gynecol. Obstet. 124*:1011 (1967).
7. C. Huggins and C. V. Hodges, *Cancer Res. 1*:298 (1941).
8. C. E. Blackard, *Cancer Chemother. Rep. 59*:225 (1975).
9. E. B. Gutman, E. E. Sproul, and A. B. Gutman, *Am. J. Cancer 28*:485 (1936).
10. R. Y. Kirdani, J. P. Karr, G. P. Murphy, and A. A. Sandberg, in *Clinics in Andrology*, Vol. 6 (E. S. E. Hafez and S. Sprinz-Mills, eds.) Nijhoff, Boston, 1981, p. 79.
11. T. M. Chu, W. Ostrowski, M. J. Varkarakis, C. Marrin, and G. P. Murphy, *Cancer Chemother. Rep. 59*:97 (1975).
12. T. M. Chu, M. C. Wang, W. W. Scott, R. P. Gibbons, D. E. Johnson, J. D. Schmidt, S. A. Leoning, G. R. Prout, and G. P. Murphy, *Invest. Urol. 15*:319 (1978).
13. J. F. Cooper, A. G. Foti, and P. W. Shank, *J. Urol. 119*:392 (1978)
14. W. D. Belville, H. D. Cox, D. E. Mahan, J. P. Olmert, B. T. Mittenmauer, and A. W. Bruce, *Cancer 41*:2286 (1978).
15. P. Vihko, L. Sanjanti, L. Peltonen, and R. Vihko, *Clin. Chem. 25*:1915 (1978).
16. A. N. Romas, K. C. Hsu, P. Tomashefsky, and M. Tannenbaum, *Urol. 12*:79 (1978).
17. C. L. Lee, C. S. Killian, G. P. Murphy, and T. M. Chu, *Clin. Chim. Acta 101*: 209 (1980).
18. W. D. Belville, H. D. Cox, D. E. Mahan, R. E. Stutzman, and A. W. Bruce, *J. Urol. 121*:442 (1979).
19. G. R. Quinones, T. J. Rohner, Jr., J. R. Drago, and L. M. Demers, *J. Urol. 125*:361 (1981).
20. A. W. Bruce, D. E. Mahan, L. D. Sullivan, and L. Goldenberg, *J. Urol. 125*: 357 (1981).
21. P. Vihko, O. Lukkarinen, M. Kontturi, and P. Vihko, *Cancer Res. 41*:1180 (1981).
22. P. F. Schellhammer, S. S. Warden, G. L. Wright, Jr., and S. M. Sieg, *J. Urol. 127*:66 (1982).

23. G. L. Wright, Jr., P. F. Schellhammer, S. M. Sieg, D. N. Brassil, and M. S. Leffell, *Urology* 14:351 (1982).
24. G. L. Wright, Jr., P. F. Schellhammer, D. N. Brassil, S. M. Sieg, and M. S. Leffell, *Clin. Chem.* 27:1747 (1981).
25. J. C. Griffiths, *Clin. Chem.* 26:433 (1980).
26. S. L. Goldenberg, H. K. B. Silver, L. D. Sullivan, M. J. Morse, and E. L. Archibald, *Cancer* 50:1847 (1982).
27. C. S. Killian, F. P. Vargas, N. H. Slack, G. P. Murphy, and T. M. Chu, *Clin. Chem.* 27:1064 (1981).
28. C. S. Killian, F. P. Vargas, E. J. Pontes, S. Beckley, N. H. Slack, G. P. Murphy, and T. M. Chu, *Prostate* 2:187 (1981).
29. D. T. Chua, R. J. Veenema, R. J. Muggia, and A. Graff, *J. Urol.* 103:462 (1970).
30. J. E. Pontes, S. W. Alcorn, A. J. Thomas, and J. M. Pierce, Jr., *J. Urol.* 114: 422 (1975).
31. J. R. Drucker, C. W. Moncure, C. L. Johnson, M. J. Smith, and W. W. Kootz, *J. Urol.* 119:94 (1978).
32. J. E. Pontes, B. K. Choe, N. R. Rose, and J. M. Pierce, *J. Urol.* 119:772 (1978).
33. J. E. Pontes, B. K. Choe, and N. R. Rose, *J. Urol.* 117:459 (1977).
34. C. Li, W. K. W. Lam, and L. Y. Yam, *Cancer* 46:706 (1980).
35. J. E. Pontes, N. R. Rose, C. Ercole, and J. M. Pierce, Jr., *J. Urol.* 126:187 (1981).
36. M. Nadji and A. R. Morales, *Ann. N.Y. Acad. Sci.* 390:133 (1982).
37. W. Y. Naritoku and C. R. Taylor, *J. Histochem. Cytochem.* 30:253 (1982).
38. A. -C. Jöbsis, G. P. DeVries, A. E. F. H. Meijer, and J. S. Ploem, *Histochem. J.* 13:961 (1982).
39. R. J. Bates, C. M. Chapman, G. R. Prout, Jr., and C. W. Lin, *J. Urol.* 127: 574 (1982).
40. M. Lippert, H. Bensimon, and N. Javadpour, *J. Urol* 128:1114 (1982).
41. J. E. Pontes, *J. Urol.* 125:375 (1981).
42. R. A. Watson and D. B. Tang, *N. Engl. J. Med.* 303:497 (1980).
43. M. C. Wang, L. Valenzuela, G. P. Murphy, and T. M. Chu, *Invest. Urol.* 17: 159 (1979).
44. L. D. Papsidero, M. Kuriyama, M. C. Wang, J. S. Horoszewicz, J. Leong, L. A. Valenzuela, G. P. Murphy, and T. M. Chu, *J. Nat. Cancer Inst.* 66:37 (1981).
45. L. D. Papsidero, M. C. Wang, L. A. Valenzuela, G. P. Murphy, and T. M. Chu, *Cancer Res.* 40:2428 (1980).
46. M. Nadji, S. Z. Tabei, A. Castro, T. M. Chu, G. P. Murphy, M. C. Wang, and A. R. Morates, *Cancer* 48:1229 (1981).
47. M. Kuriyama, M. C. Wang, L. D. Papsidero, C. S. Killian, T. Shimano, L. A. Valenzuela, T. Nishiura, G. P. Murphy, and T. M. Chu, *Cancer Res.* 40:4658 (1980).
48. M. Kuriyama, M. C. Wang, C. Lee, L. D. Papsidero, C. S. Killian, H. Inaji, N. H. Slack, T. Nishiura, G. P. Murphy, and T. M. Chu, *Cancer Res.* 41:3874 (1981).

49. L. D. Papsidero, G. A. Croghan, M. C. Wang, M. Kuriyama, E. A. Johnson, L. A. Valenzuela, and T. M. Chu, *Hybridoma* 2:139 (1983).

50. M. Kuriyama, M. C. Wang, C. L. Lee, C. S. Killian, L. D. Papsidero, H. Inaji, R. M. Loor, M. F. Lin, T. Nishiura, N. H. Slack, G. P. Murphy, and T. M. Chiu, *J. Nat. Cancer Inst.* 68:99 (1982).

51. J. E. Pontes, in *Markers for Diagnosis and Monitoring of Human Cancer* (M. I. Colnaghi, G. L. Buragi, and M. Ghione, eds.), Academic, London, 1982, p. 198.

52. T. M. Chu, M. C. Wang, C. L. Lee, C. S. Killan, M. Kuriyama, L. D. Papsidero, L. A. Valenzuela, and G. P. Murphy, in *Human Cancer Markers* (S. Sell and B. Wahren, eds.), Humana, New Jersey, 1982, p. 179.

53. H. Koprowski, Z. Steplewski, D. Herlyn, and M. Herlyn, *Proc. Nat. Acad. Sci. U.S.A.* 75:3405 (1978).

54. R. G. Woodbury, J. P. Brown, M. Y. Yeh, I. Hellström, and K. E. Hellström, *Proc. Nat. Acad. Sci. U.S.A.* 77:2183 (1980).

55. J. Ritz, J. M. Pesando, J. Notis-McConarty, H. Lazarus, and S. F. Schlossman, *Nature* 283:583 (1980).

56. R. H. Kennett and F. Gilbert, *Science* 203:1120 (1979).

57. J. F. Schnegg, A. C. Diserens, S. Carrel, R. S. Accolla, and N. Tribolet, *Cancer Res.* 41:1209 (1981).

58. D. Colcher, P. Horan Hand, M. Nuti, and J. Schlom, *Proc. Nat. Acad. Sci. U.S.A.* 78:3199 (1981).

59. F. Cuttitta, S. Rozen, A. F. Gazdar, and J.D. Minna, *Proc. Nat. Acad. Sci. U.S.A.* 78:459 (1981).

60. M. J. Embleton, B. Gunn, V. S. Byers, and R. W. Baldwin, *Br. J. Cancer* 43:582 (1981).

61. R. S. Metzgar, M. T. Gaillard, S. J. Levine, F. L. Tuck, E. H. Bossen, and M. J. Borowitz, *Cancer Res.* 42:601 (1982).

62. R. Veda, S. -I. Ogata, D. M. Morrissey, C. L. Finstad, J. Szkudlarek, W. F. Whitmore, H. F. Oettgen, K. O. Lloyd, and L. J. Old, Proc. Nat. Acad. Sci. *U.S.A.* 78:5122 (1981).

63. G. L. Wright, Jr., P. F. Schellhammer, R. J. Faulconer, J. W. Reid, D. N. Brassil, and S. M. Sieg, *Prostate* 2:121 (1981).

64. R. D. Williams, *Invest. Urol.* 17:359 (1980).

65. K. R. Stone, D. D. Mickey, H. Wunderli, G. Mickey, and D. F. Paulson, *Int. J. Cancer* 21:274 (1978).

66. M. E. Kaighn, K. S. Narayan, Y. Ohnuki, J. F. Lechner, and L. W. Jones, *Invest. Urol.* 17:16 (1979).

67. J. S. Horoszewicz, S. S. Leong, T. M. Chu, Z. L. Wajsman, M. Friedman, L. Papsidero, U. Kim, L. S. Chai, S. Kakati, S. K. Arya, and A. A. Sandberg, in *Progress in Clinical and Biological Research*, Vol. 37 (G. P. Murphy, ed.), Alan R. Liss, New York, 1980, p. 115.

68. K. D. Somers and M. M. Murphey, *Cancer Res.* 42:2575 (1982).

69. A. -K. Ng, M. A. Pellegrino, K. Imai, and S. Ferrone, *J. Immunol.* 127:443 (1981).

70. E. A. Weiler, *Exp. Cell Res. Suppl.* 7:244 (1959).

71. J. E. Pontes, J. M. Pierco, Jr., B. K. Choe, and N. R. Rose, *In Vitro* 15:469 (1979).

72. W. A. Nelson-Rees and R. R. Flandermeyer, *Science 191*:96 (1976).
73. M. E. Kaighn, J. F. Lechner, M. S. Babcock, M. Marnell, Y. Ohnuki, and K. S. Narayan, in *Progress in Clinical and Biological Research*, Vol. 37 (G. P. Murphy, ed.), Alan R. Liss, New York, 1980, p. 85.
74. A. E. Frankel, R. V. Rouse, and L. A. Herzenberg, *Proc. Nat. Acad. Sci. U.S.A. 79*:903 (1982).
75. S. M. Clarke, D. J. Merchant, and J. J. Starling, *Prostate 3*:203 (1982).
76. J. L. Ware, D. F. Paulson, S. F. Parks, and K. S. Webb, *Cancer Res. 42*:1215 (1982).
77. J. J. Starling, S. M. Sieg, M. L. Beckett, P. F. Schellhammer, L. E. Ladaga, and G. L. Wright, Jr., *Cancer Res. 42*:3084 (1982).
78. J. Tooze, *DNA Tumor Viruses, Molecular Biology of Tumor Viruses*, 2nd ed., Cold Spring Harbor Laboratory, New York, 1981, p. 766.
79. A. J. Nahmias and B. Norrild, in *Oncogenic Herpesviruses*, Vol. 2 (F. Rapp, ed.), CRC Press, Boca Raton, Fl., 1980, p. 25.
80. G. Giaraldo, E. Beth, and E. S. Huang, *Int. J. Cancer 26*:23 (1980).
81. I. Boldogh, E. Beth, E. S. Huang, S. K. Kyalwazi, and G. Giraldo, *Int. J. Cancer 28*:469 (1981).
82. L. Geder, E. J. Sanford, T. J. Rohner, and F. Rapp, *Cancer Treat. Reps. 61*:139 (1977).
83. E. Sanford, L. Geder, A. Laychock, T. Rohner, and F. Rapp, *J. Urol. 118*:789 (1977).
84. A. M. Laychock, L. Geder, E. J. Sanford, and F. Rapp, *Cancer 42*:1766 (1978).
85. A. A. Rahman, M. Teschner, K. K. Sethi, and H. Brandis, *J. Immunol. 117*:253 (1976).
86. R. Keller, R. Peitchel, J. N. Goldman, and M. Goldman, *J. Immunol. 116*:722 (1976).
87. S. M. Hsu, L. Raine, and H. Fanger, *J. Histochem. Cytochem. 29*:577 (1981).
88. M. F. Stinski, *J. Virol. 23*:751 (1977).
89. S. Franzen, G. Giertz, and J. Zajick, *J. Urol. 32*:193 (1960).
90. P. L. Esposti, and S. Franzen, *Scand. J. Urol. Nephrol. Suppl. 55*:49 (1980).
91. C. L. Reading, *J. Immunol. Methods 53*:261 (1982).
92. J. J. Thompson, M. F. Herlyn, D. E. Elder, W. H. Clark, Z. Steplewski, and H. Koprowski, *Am. J. Pathol. 107*:357 (1982).
93. H. J. Garrigues, W. Tilgen, I. Hellström, W. Franke, and K. E. Hellström, *Int. J. Cancer 29*:511 (1982).
94. H. F. Sears, M. Herlyn, B. D. Villano, Z. Steplewski, and H. Koprowski, *J. Clin. Immunol. 2*:135 (1982).
95. P. A. Farrans, A. C. Perkins, M. V. Pimm, J. D. Hardy, M. J. Embleton, R. W. Baldwin, and J. D. Hardcastle, *Lancet 2*:397 (1982).
96. J. L. Magnani, M. Brockhaus, D. F. Smith, V. Ginsburg, M. Blaszcyk, K. F. Mitchell, Z. Steplewski, and H. Koprowski, *Science 212*:55 (1981).
97. P. H. Lange, C. Limms, and E. E. Fraley, *J. Urol. 124*:124 (1980).

11 DISSECTION AND CHARACTERIZATION OF HUMAN TUMOR-ASSOCIATED MACROMOLECULES USING MONOCLONAL ANTIBODIES

Herbert Z. Kupchik / Boston University School of Medicine, The Hubert H. Humphrey Cancer Research Center, Boston University, and The Mallory Institute of Pathology, Boston, Massachusetts

INTRODUCTION

The argument often expressed that cancer is difficult to cure because it is not one disease but a hundred different diseases might provide an analogy for the relative inability to identify human tumor-specific markers that are diagnostically accurate. The innate heterogeneity of individual tumors implies that conventional antisera produced to extracts, cell suspensions, or other immunizing preparations will characteristically be heterogeneous, containing a wide variety of antibodies of differing specificities, affinities, and avidities. Since the tumor cells are likely to originate from normal stem cells, the frequency of normal cell products that are identical or immunochemically similar to those produced by tumor cells will be significant.

Antisera raised to such tumor cells have not been tumor specific. Attempts to eliminate from antisera those antibodies that react with "normal products" by absorption with normal tissues have not been successful. Many explanations could be advanced for such results, including the possibility that there are no totally tumor-specific markers (widely believed by many investigators) or perhaps that the tumor markers do not exhibit "immunopotent" antigenic determinants. Since the specificity of the immune response is capable of great diversity, there is obviously a selection of determinants in any given situation. In 1969, Sela (1) coined the term *immunopotent* to describe those determinants that could provoke the formation of specific antibodies in high concentration. Thus one could imagine a scenario in which a marker specific for a particular tumor might be present in an immunizing preparation but would not exhibit an immunopotent determinant. The resulting antiserum might contain some antibodies that identify the tumor-specific site, but such antibodies would be in low concentration and not capable of surviving the gross challenge of absorption. With the advent of somatic cell fusion (2) it is now feasible to hybridize lymphocyte cell populations that are capable of recognizing such specific antigens or determinants. The antibodies produced by the resulting "hybridomas" could then be used to select the antigen directly out of the myriad of immunogens. Alternatively, one might use the "cascade" approach (described below) in which immunopotent antigens are sequentially removed by immunoabsorption with their corresponding antibodies until the lesser immunopotent antigens become the principal immunizing force in the immunogen preparation.

Perhaps more germane to this chapters is the situation where putative tumor-specific markers are found to lack qualitative specificity relative to tumor versus benign or normal tissue of origin or, as in most instances to date, both. If the conventional antisera raised against the "purified" markers are used to define the marker, the heterogeneous antisera will not discriminate among tumor-specific determinants, determinants common to both tumor and normal products, and determinants that overlap various disease states. Tumor specificity would therefore not be seen and those who insist that such specificity does not exist are further encouraged. An analogous situation was recently described by Schröder (3) when he studied the hormones human chorionic gonadotropin (HCG), luteinizing hormone, and follicle-stimulating hormone. All of these consist of an identical α chain and a partially identical β chain. Owing to their heterogeneity, most conventional antisera raised against any of these hormones or their subunits show cross-reactivity with all of the others. However, the β chain of HCG contains a unique carboxyl terminus not found in the β subunits of the other hormones. A monoclonal antibody against this specific segment of HCG would show no cross-reactivity with the others. If specific moieties also exist on tumor markers, they too could result in specific monoclonal antibodies. The real issue, then, is whether or not the tools and approaches used to date have been adequate to prove or dismiss the specificity of any human tumor marker. Monoclonal antibodies now offer the possibility to not only use a new approach to identify tumor-specific markers, but to go back and examine the nature and specificity of those already being evaluated or used at the clinical level.

This chapter will refrain from classifying as antigens those human tumor-associated macromolecules that are discussed, since there have been no definitive studies to date demonstrating their immunogenicity in patients; rather, they will be referred to as tumor markers (whether specific or associated) or macromolecules.

Although each monoclonal antibody is specific for a single determinant, differing antigens that contain the same determinant may cross-react. Such cross-reactivity could and would be absorbed out of conventional antisera, but cannot be eliminated from monoclonal antibody preparations. This property can be used to advantage in demonstrating shared determinants that are indicative of structural similarities, which, in turn, may identify functional relationships between macromolecules.

This chapter will attempt to present some approaches that may be applied to the dissection and characterization of tumor markers such as carcinoembryonic antigen (CEA) and alpha-fetoprotein (AFP) through the use of monoclonal antibodies. The unique specificity of such antibodies for a specific determinant may help identify species of such markers more related to malignancy and/or tissue of origin than is presently available.

SOURCES OF HETEROGENEITY OF TUMOR MACROMOLECULES

The heterogeneity attributed to the two human tumor markers, CEA and AFP will be reviewed. These markers are perhaps the most widely studied in clinical use today and serve as excellent examples when considering how monoclonal antibodies may serve to increase their clinical utility by dissecting out specific variants.

Carcinoembryonic Antigen

Carcinoembryonic antigen (CEA) is a glycoprotein of approximately 200,000 daltons and was first described by Gold and Freedman (4, 5) as an antigen present exclusively in adenocarcinoma of the human digestive tract and in digestive organs from fetuses of 2–6 months gestation. In 1969, a radioimmunoassay for CEA in the serum of patients was described (6). Circulating levels greater than 2.5 ng/ml of serum were reported in 35 of 36 patients with adenocarcinoma of the colon, and "insignificant" levels were found in the serum of patients with nongastrointestinal malignancies or benign diseases. These initial findings, plus the disappearance of CEA from the circulation of patients following complete surgical removal of tumor, offered the promise of an early diagnostic procedure for patients with digestive system cancer. Studies from many laboratories have now established that whereas a positive CEA assay may be a good indicator of invasive colonic cancer, and particularly of metastases to the liver, CEA elevation occurs in less than 50% of patients with localized disease (Duke's stage A) (7, 8). The circulating

CEA level apparently depends upon several factors, including the pathological stage and degree of differentiation of the primary tumor; the presence of invasion of lymphatics, blood vessels, or perineural spaces; the extent of distant spread of tumor and the total mass of CEA-producing tumor (9). The involvement of the liver and its functional status is believed to be of special importance (10). Additionally, CEA has been identified and measured in the circulation and body fluids of patients with numerous nongastrointestinal malignancies, patients with gastrointestinal benign diseases, and normal individuals using assays with conventionally produced antisera (7,11).

This lack of specificity has been attributed both to heterogeneity of purportedly purified CEA and to its variable intramolecular antigenicity (12). It is also possible that some individual antigenic determinants identified in present CEA assays are associated with CEA molecules synthesized by normal gastrointestinal tissues and are only quantitatively distinct in the presence of malignancy.

Although most investigators agree that CEA isolated from gastrointestinal tumors or from plasma of patients with such tumors has a molecular weight of approximately 200,000, the CEA in plasma of patients with other malignancies has been shown to have a molecular weight of approximately 370,000 (13, 14). The carbohydrate-to-protein ratio can range from 1:1 in preparations from colonic tissue to 5:1 in those from gastric cancer tissue, and differences have been noted on polyacrylamide gel electrophoresis and on isoelectric focusing of preparations from different sources (15, 16). Numerous studies have confirmed that much of the apparent heterogeneity of CEA is a reflection of differences in the carbohydrate portion of the molecule. A widely varying sialic acid content probably accounts for a good deal of the heterogeneity seen during gel electrophoresis.

Although protein sequence studies on CEA have been hampered by the high (approximately 50%) carbohydrate content and the relatively large number of amino acids (over 600), recent studies have shown that polypeptide fragments can be obtained by limited proteolysis (17, 18). These studies indicated that the polypeptide chain of CEA is reproducible from preparation to preparation and contains the tumor-associated antigenic site recognized by conventional heteroantisera.

Several studies have indicated that the CEA-like antigens identified as nonspecific cross-reacting antigen (NCA), normal glycoprotein (NGP), colonic carcinoembryonic antigen-2, breast carcinoma glycoprotein, colon carcinoma antigen III (CCA III), and tumor-associated antigen may be identical and that they do not cross-react in radioimmunoassays for CEA performed on perchloric acid extracts (19). Newman et al. (19) show that a significant portion of the CEA-reactive antibodies in antisera developed against purified CEA detected an antigenic determinant shared by CEA and CCA III, but this common determinant on CEA was stereochemically different from that on CCA III. Recent studies of their amino acid sequences suggested that the protein component of CEA and such CEA-like molecules are closely related (20). These authors proposed that the protein backbone is under control of related genes from a common evolutionary origin.

Antisera obtained from monkeys immunized with CEA were more specific for CEA than those produced by sheep or rabbits (21). The monkey antisera did not react against the CEA–NCA common site determinants. The authors suggested that monkeys have a normally occurring antigen similar to NCA. Kuroki et al. (22) purified and characterized a number of CEA-related antigens isolated from normal adult feces. Using a variety of conventional antisera that were prepared against CEA and cross-reacting antigens and that were treated by absorptions designed to eliminate other CEA-reactive species, they determined that CEA and normal fecal antigens can be divided into four antigenic determinants having various degrees of commonality and specificity among at least five different molecules. Rogers and Keep (23) have shown that normal colon CEA-active glycoprotein is largely a heat-labile material that does not bind to concanavalin A (Con A) but which shares an antigenic determinant with colonic tumor CEA. Colon tumor CEA, on the other hand, contains, in addition to this determinant, one that is heat stable. Certain conventional anti-CEA antisera are clearly able to react with both determinants. Whether or not CEA assays are able to measure both components has not been established. These studies suggest that with the availability of more highly specific monoclonal antibodies, it may be possible to even further define CEA and CEA-related substances, with the hope of eliminating the heterogeneity present today and enhancing the specificity of clinical assays.

Alpha-Fetoprotein

Alpha-fetoprotein (AFP) is a glycoprotein of 65,000–70,000 daltons first identified by Bergstrand and Czar (24) in 1956 as X component in human cord blood. In 1963, Abelev et al. (25) demonstrated that this embryonal alpha-globulin was not only detected in normal pregnant mice and the sera of newborn mice, but also in mice bearing hepatocellular carcinomas. Subsequently, in 1964, Tatarinov (26) identified AFP in the sera of patients with primary liver tumors. It now appears that AFP is first produced in the yolk sac and later in the liver of the embryo. Alpha-fetoprotein synthesis in the liver subsides or is depressed after birth and can be found in only extremely small amounts in the adult, except in the presence of hepatomas or teratomas. Albumin and AFP have similar chemical properties and their concentrations in serum are high and inversely related (27). This coupled with the additional evidence that there is a homologous sequence of amino acids in AFP and albumin suggests that these two proteins have a common ancestor (28). Circulating levels of AFP can be used to diagnose and monitor treatment of patients with primary liver cancers and germ cell tumors. More recently, the measurement of AFP in maternal serum and in amniotic fluid during pregnancy has been useful for the prenatal diagnosis of spina bifida and congenital nephrosis (29). Although more homogeneous and reproducible than CEA, AFP has been shown to exist as molecular variants that are indistinguishable by conventional antisera. In 1970, Purves et al. (30) used starch electrophoresis to demonstrate microheterogeneity of human AFP. These findings were confirmed in 1971 by Alpert et al. (31) using extended agarose electrophoresis and isoelectrofocusing. More recently, Ruoslahti et al. (32) prepared three different variants of human AFP from fetal serum and amniotic fluid by Con A–Sepharose chromatography. Their results suggested that the AFP synthesized by the liver and by the yolk sac tissue are glycosylated differently. Breborowicz et al. (33) recently described the heterogeneity of AFP identified in the sera of 76 patients by lectin affinoimmuno-electrophoresis. They were able to identify two AFP variants by means of differences in binding to Con A and three variants based on binding to lentil lectin. Furthermore, they demonstrated 14 AFP profiles that could be used to categorize the different patient populations.

Despite such reports regarding the apparent chemical heterogeneity of AFP, no significant immunological differences have been identified using conventional antisera to date. Again, one must consider the possibility that monoclonal antibodies might elucidate the chemical heterogeneity and exploit differences in the AFP variants associated with benign liver disorders, hepatomas, yolk sac tumors, and liver metastases of cancer. Such antibodies might also be extremely useful in elucidating factors that regulate AFP production and lead to an understanding of the pathogenesis of AFP-producing tumors.

Other tumor markers currently under investigation will surely show similar heterogeneity, since many have been defined with conventional antisera. An example of such a marker appears to be the pancreatic oncofetal antigen originally described by Banwo et al. in 1974 (34). In an attempt to reproduce the work of Banwo et al., other investigators have identified markers that appear similar to pancreatic oncofetal antigen but which lack the original specificity described for it. Monoclonal antibodies may be able to correct this situation, especially since there are bound to be numerous antigenic determinants on this molecule(s) of $8 \times 10^5 - 1 \times 10^6$ daltons.

METHODOLOGY SUGGESTED FOR DISSECTION AND CHARACTERIZATION

The unique specificity of monoclonal antibodies has opened up a whole new field of methodology. Access to a panel of monoclonal antibodies prepared against the identical immunogen provides the opportunity to examine any number of determinants and/or variants of the molecule in question. Such studies have been either impractical or too cumbersome when attempted with conventional polyclonal antisera. This is not to say that monoclonal antibodies do not present problems when used as reagents to examine tumor markers. Individual monoclonal antibodies may not agglutinate or fix complement and are, in general, poor immunoprecipitating agents, since they bind only one determinant on a monomeric antigen and cannot cross-link extensively. The new methodology currently being devised is providing ways of circumventing such difficulties while at the same time providing a better understanding of the nature of the macromolecules being examined.

Many of these methods are fairly straightforward and logical when one considers that the investigator is freed of the constraints imposed by the use of conventional antisera. Titration curves of monoclonal antibodies reacting with radio- or enzyme-labeled ligands can provide information relative to the specificity of different antibodies, the number of different determinants recognized by various antibodies, and/or the number of variants present in the ligand preparation. Similar information can be obtained by examining competitive effects of ligand binding among the various monoclonal antibodies created to an immunogen, as well as the ability of such monoclonal antibodies to block part or all of the binding seen between a conventional antiserum and the ligand. The latter is important when evaluating tumor markers that have been previously defined by their reactivity with conventional antisera. Such studies can be extended one step further by developing two-site sandwich immunoassay systems in which one monoclonal antibody is immobilized and acts as an immunoadsorbent and another monoclonal antibody is labeled with enzyme or radioisotope (35, 36). This type of system can be used to determine the similarity or proximity of determinants on an antigen and can be used to identify variants that may possess one but not both determinants.

Potocnjak et al. (37) recently described a new immunoradiometric assay based on inhibition of the interaction between monoclonal antibodies by an antigen. One antibody (attached to a solid support) is specific for the antigen in question and the second antibody (radiolabeled) is specific for the idiotype of the first antibody. One requirement of the system is that the idiotype site on the first antibody be close to its antigen combining site. This type of procedure may prove valuable in dissecting and characterizing tumor markers, since only one epitope is required on the marker, the marker does not have to be purified, and the system is extremely sensitive and may be ideal for looking at weak immunogens.

Several investigators have used a technique that combines immunoprecipitation with sodium dodecyl sulfate–polyacrylamide gel electrophoresis (SDS–PAGE) to identify variants of molecules that react with their monoclonal antibodies. Here labeled or unlabeled antigen, cell membranes, or cells are incubated with the hybridoma supernatants or monoclonal antibodies and the immune complexes precipitated with a precipitating agent such as formalin-fixed, heat-inactivated *Staphylococcus aureus* (38) or rabbit anti-mouse IgG-coated *S. aureus* Cowan I (39). The antigen can then be eluted from the antibody and applied to SDS-PAGE. After electrophoresis, the gel can be stained and/or the isotope autoradiographed or counted to visualize and quantitate the reactive molecules. This provides a measure of the molecules within a preparation that are reactive with the monoclonal antibody used, as well as information regarding the size and relative mobility, and can be used to compare different marker preparations. An alternative electrophoretic procedure has arisen from the technique developed by Southern (40) for the analysis of DNA. In this technique, proteins are first subjected to electrophoresis in SDS–PAGE and then electrophoretically blotted on nitrocellulose paper (41). The method permits detection and quantitation of radiolabeled proteins by autoradiography, but more importantly, proteins immobilized on the nitrocellulose paper can be detected by immunological procedures. Nonprecipitating monoclonal antibodies can be applied to the immobilized protein followed by a second antibody directed against the monoclonal antibodies. The second antibody can be radiolabeled or conjugated to fluorescein or an enzyme such as peroxidase. Towbin et al. (41) report detecting 100 pg of protein using a peroxidase-conjugated second antibody in this technique. This technique has many obvious advantages and will surely be a powerful tool in dissecting tumor markers with monoclonal antibodies.

Monoclonal antibodies can also be used as specific immunoadsorbents that can select and isolate reactive variants from tumor marker preparations. The purified monoclonal immunoglobulin can be attached to a solid support such as Sepharose 4B and mixed with the marker preparation or the marker preparation applied to a column consisting of the immunoadsorbent. Relatively mild conditions (e.g., 4 mol/liter urea in 0.1 ml/liter Tris-HCl at pH 7.4) can be used to elute the bound marker (3). This is another very obvious approach for using already prepared monoclonal antibodies to evaluate tumor marker preparations. This procedure can be taken one step further as a means of isolating all the components of a tumor marker preparation if an appropriate panel of monoclonal antibodies is not available. Removal from the immunizing preparation of previously recognized determinants (presumably more immunopotent) with monoclonal antibodies in a sequential manner will restrict the immunizing stimulus to previously unrecognized (less immunopotent) determinants. Thus a "cascade" consisting of alternating cell hybridization and immunoabsorption will ultimately produce a complete library of monoclonal antibodies against the total immunogen population (42, 43).

CHARACTERIZATION OF CEA USING MONOCLONAL ANTI-CEA ANTIBODIES

Efforts to improve the specificity of CEA assays by alternative approaches for purification of the marker (44), absorption of conventional antisera with CEA-like components (22, 45), or synthesis of an antigenic moiety of CEA (46) have met with only partial success. A number of investigators have prepared monoclonal antibodies to CEA in order to separate out the heterogeneity and increase the clinical utility of CEA assays.

One such monoclonal antibody, designated 1E9, was examined in the context of its ability to bind the purified CEA used in clinical radioimmunoassays (47). A double-antibody solid-phase assay (47) was used to titrate and compare the binding of 1E9 antibody to $[^{125}I]$ CEA with that achieved using commercially available goat anti-CEA antiserum (G-As; Roche Diagnostics, Nutley, N.J.) As shown in Table 1, 1E9 antibody could bind a maximum (above background T_0)

Table 1 Comparative Maximum Binding by 1E9 Antibody and G-As to [^{125}I] CEA Preparations Using Double-Antibody Solid-Phase Assay

	1E9		G-As	
[^{125}I] CEA treatment	$T_0{}^a$	Maximum percentage $(-T_0)^b$	T_0	Maximun percentage $(-T_0)$
No treatment	2.0	45.5	2.0	69.8
Immunoadsorbed	4.8	60.5	3.9	77.0
Nonadsorbable	5.7	7.9	5.5	24.6

^{a}Percentage of [^{125}I] CEA precipitated nonspecifically in the absence of antibody.

^{b}Maximum percentage of total [^{125}I] CEA bound at any dilution of antibody (background subtracted).

Source: Modified from Ref. 47.

of 45.5% of the [^{125}I] CEA added, while G-As bound 69.8%. In an attempt to increase the total binding of 1E9 antibody to the labeled CEA, the labeled CEA was adsorbed on an affinity column containing the monoclonal 1E9 antibody conjugated to cyanogen bromide-activated Sepharose 4B. The 1E9 antibody could bind a maximum of 60.5% of the labeled CEA eluted from the immunoadsorbent column. Although improved, this was still lower than the 77% bound by G-As. A portion of the nonadsorbable labeled CEA that passed through the affinity column without binding to the antibody could be bound by G-As, but not by 1E9 antibody.

To determine the relationship of the species of [^{125}I] CEA bound by the monoclonal antibody and the G-As, an excess of G-As was incubated with immunoadsorbed labeled CEA, and the immune complexes were precipitated with donkey anti-goat IgG (DAG) conjugated to Kynar (polyvinylindene fluoride) floccules. The remaining unbound labeled CEA in the supernatant was then incubated with an excess of 1E9 antibody, and these complexes were precipitated with goat anti-mouse IgG (GAM) conjugated to Kynar floccules. The reverse procedure was also carried out.

Labeled CEA was also incubated with both G-As and 1E9 antibody simultaneously, and either DAG or GAM was used for specific precipitation, as shown in Table 2. The goat antiserum bound all available labeled CEA if added first, and the monoclonal antibody could bind only 62% of the total bound (63%) by both antibodies. There was no apparent competition between the antibodies when both were added simultaneously; that is, they still bound approximately the same amounts as when added first in the previous experiments. However, when G-As was incubated for 18 hr with treated labeled CEA, followed by addition of 1E9 antibody to the mixture and another 18-hr incubation period, and then the

Table 2 Competitive Binding of $[^{125}I]$ CEA by 1E9 Antibody and G-As Using the Double-Antibody Solid-Phase Assay[a]

	Percentage of $[^{125}I]$ CEA bound $-T_0$[b,c]		
Anti-CEA	DAG	GAM	Total
G-As then 1E9	71.2	→ 0.9[d]	72.1
1E9 then G-As	24.9	← 39.1[d]	63.0
G-As + 1E9[e]	73.3	35.9	
G-As→1E9[f]	73.8	27.7	
1E9→G-As[f]	72.9	36.9	

[a]DAG- or GAM-conjugated Kynar suspension were used for G-As or 1E9, respectively.
[b]$[^{125}I]$ CEA was immunoadsorbed.
[c]In experiments where two antibodies were used, the T_0 control contained the antibody not precipitated by a Kynar conjugate.
[d]Arrows indicate the sequence of specific precipitations.
[e]Antibodies added together to $[^{125}I]$ CEA incubation and complexes precipitated with DAG or GAM.
[f]Arrows indicate the sequence of antibody addition. Each antibody was incubated for 18 hr at 20°C.
Source: Ref. 47.

immune complexes were precipitated with DAG or GAM, less labeled CEA was available for binding by 1E9 (27.7%) than in the reverse experiment (36.9%) or when both antibodies were added simultaneously (35.9%).

These data could be interpreted to suggest the presence of at least three variants of CEA present within the initial labeled preparation, with two of the variants, in equilibrium with each other, remaining after immunoadsorption. For example, if the equation

$$CEA_{total} = (CEA_A \rightleftharpoons CEA_B) + CEA_C$$

is considered, G-As might bind all three variants in the initial preparation (100%), while 1E9 antibody might bind only CEA_A as 65% of the total (Table 1, first row). During immunoadsorption, CEA_B and CEA_C are removed. The specifically adsorbed CEA_A, when eluted, generates additional CEA_B and again there is equilibrium between CEA_A and CEA_B in a ratio of approximately 4:1, respectively (i.e., 79:21 as calculated from Table 1, second row). Using this ratio, it can be estimated that the original untreated CEA preparation might have consisted of approximately 65% CEA_A, 16% CEA_B, and 19% CEA_C.

Inhibition studies were undertaken to determine if the selectivity of the 1E9 monoclonal antibody applied to unlabeled purified CEA as well. The monoclonal 1E9 ascitic fluid was used at 1:1 ($\times 10^6$) or 1:3 ($\times 10^6$) final dilution in the double-antibody solid-phase assay with treated or untreated [^{125}I] CEA, respectively. Similarly, Roche G-As was diluted 1:5 ($\times 10^5$) or 1:3 ($\times 10^5$). Figure 1 shows that when untreated CEA was used to inhibit the binding between untreated labeled CEA and G-As (curve a) or 1E9 (curve b), 1E9 was about 2.8 times less sensitive to CEA inhibition than was G-As as determined by the concentration of CEA required for 50% inhibition. Treatment of the radiolabeled CEA did not improve the inhibition sensitivity of 1E9 antibody for untreated unlabeled CEA, but improved that of G-As by approximately

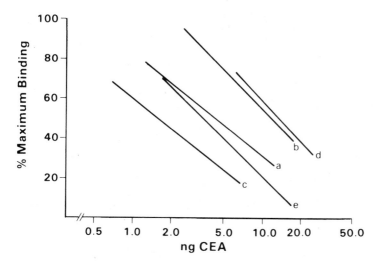

Figure 1 Comparative inhibition curves. Curves are drawn based on linear regression analysis and represent maximum percentage of binding of [^{125}I] CEA by antibody in the presence of increasing concentrations of unlabeled purified CEA

$$\text{Percentage of maximum binding} = \frac{X - T_0}{B_0 - T_0} \times 100$$

where X is the experimental percentage bound, T_0 is background in the absence of antibody, and B_0 is binding in the absence of inhibitor. Curves a and b are inhibition curves when untreated CEA and [^{125}I] CEA were used with G-As and 1E9, respectively. Curves c and d are inhibition curves when untreated CEA and immunoadsorbed [^{125}I] CEA were used with G-As and 1E9, respectively. Curves c and e are inhibition curves when both unlabeled and labeled CEA, which had been immunoadsorbed, were used with G-As and 1E9, respectively. Curve c represents two curves, since quantitation of the immunoadsorbed CEA was done using the untreated CEA as a standard. (From Ref. 47.)

2.7-fold. Treatment of both labeled and unlabeled CEA preparations significantly enhanced the inhibition sensitivity of 1E9 antibody for CEA (approximately 3.5-fold). Immunoadsorption of either the labeled or unlabeled CEA did not result in any apparent changes in the immunological identity of the antigen preparations as recognized by the respective antibodies. This is shown by the similar slopes of inhibition for curves a and c, and curves b, d and e, respectively. Thus treatment of labeled and unlabeled CEA could improve the binding and inhibition curves of 1E9 antibody, but might not result in an inhibition sensitivity comparable to that for G-As if two variants (CEA_A and CEA_B) are present. The lower inhibition sensitivity of the 1E9 antibody for CEA limits its use in a conventional radioimmunoassay since the same degree of sensitivity as that commercially available with G-As cannot be obtained. However, the 1E9 antibody may be quite useful, since it appears to have an increased selectivity for a specific CEA variant. When CEA adsorbed on a 1E9 antibody affinity column is inserted into the assay system, the inhibition sensitivity of the goat antiserum for treated or untreated CEA is enhanced without affecting the apparent immunological identity of the antigen as seen by the antiserum. If such an increase in sensitivity were accompanied by increased clinical specificity, clinical assays for CEA might be significantly improved.

Similar studies in other laboratories have also shown an ability of the monoclonal antibodies to selectively bind certain species of CEA. Newell et al. (48) produced monoclonal antibodies that could be grouped in three different classes: (a) those that reacted with CEA, meconium antigen (MA), and NCA; (b) those that reacted with CEA and MA; and (c) those that reacted with CEA only. Their findings showed that the first two types of monoclonal antibody could bind similar amounts of labeled CEA as could conventional anti-CEA or anti-NCA antisera, while the third type could bind only 50% of the labeled CEA bound by the conventional goat antiserum. They suggested that their monoclonal antibodies defined at least four separate determinants on CEA; one shared by CEA, MA, and NCA: two others shared by CEA and MA, and a fourth specific for a subpopulation of CEA molecules.

Accolla et al. (49) were able to identify two different monoclonal anti-CEA antibodies (one IgG_1 and the other IgG_2) after screening 400 hybrids from seven fusions. The IgG_1 antibody could bind up to 80% of their purified [^{125}I] CEA and 0.4 ng of purified CEA could inhibit this binding. The IgG_2 antibody could bind up to 65% of the labeled antigen, but was 70 times less sensitive than the IgG_1 antibody in inhibition studies. Neither antibody showed any significant reactivity with the cross-reacting antigen NGP (50). Verification of the specificity of these two monoclonal antibodies was provided by immunohistochemical localization of CEA on frozen sections of human colon carcinoma and on the surface of colon carcinoma cell lines (51). Differences in the relative affinities (1.4×10^8 and 1.1×10^7 M^{-1}, respectively) for these two antibodies were suggested as the reason for differences in sensitivity.

Lindgren and Bang (52) reported the production of four monoclonal anti-CEA antibodies that did not react with NGP and had affinities high enough for radio-immunoassay. Another four monoclonal antibodies were specific for CEA but had low affinities, and two others cross-reacted with NGP. Lockhart et al. (53) reported the production of a hybridoma anti-CEA antibody that could bind up to 70% of ^{125}I-labeled CEA and was completely blocked by unlabeled CEA. No additional specificity studies were reported.

Rogers et al. (54) recently described a murine monoclonal antibody that could bind weakly to CEA in perchloric acid extracts of tumors, but strongly to CEA in perchloric acid extracts of serum, and presented preliminary assay results which suggested their monoclonal antibody detected a different spectrum of cancer than conventional antisera. Their monoclonal antibody could only bind a maximum of 27% of the radiolabeled CEA, as compared to 70% binding by conventional antiserum, and approximately 200 times as much standard unlabeled CEA was required for 50% inhibition of labeled CEA and monoclonal antibody bindings as compared to that with conventional antiserum. Their monoclonal antibody recognized a determinant on both heat-labile and heat-stable CEA but, like conventional anti-CEA antisera, was unable to distinguish different chemical forms of CEA as separated by Con A affinity chromatography.

Additional studies by Rogers et al. (54) suggested that their monoclonal antibody might be specific for a unique subpopulation of CEA molecules of possible fetal CEA characteristics and that this CEA was predominant in the sera of patients owing to chemical modification and/or degradation or alteration of tumor CEA by the liver or other mechanisms. A double-antibody radioimmunoassay that incorporated their monoclonal antibody showed a relatively high specificity for a CEA component in untreated sera from patients with various cancers (Table 3).

Oehr et al. (55) developed a monoclonal anti-CEA antibody that, when inserted into a radioimmunoassay, gave virtually identical results obtained with a con-

Table 3 Assay Results on Untreated Sera from Cancer Patients and Normal Individuals

Patients	#15 u/ml[a]	Percentage positive
Colonic cancer	30/102	29
Rectal cancer	16/42	38
Gastric cancer	16/31	51
Prostatic cancer	12/34	35
Normal	1/144	< 1

[a]Here 1 u is equivalent to 86 ng of standard CEA.
Source: Data from Ref. 54.

ventional guinea pig antiserum in a comparable assay. They suggested that their monoclonal antibody binds a common site of the heterologous CEA and that the monoclonal antibody should replace the conventional antiserum, since it can effect better reproducibility, specificity, titer, and binding properties and because the monoclonal antibody is homogeneous in structure whereas polyclonal antisera are heterogeneous.

CHARACTERIZATION OF AFP USING MONOCLONAL ANTI-AFP ANTIBODIES

Tsung et al. (56) showed that their monoclonal antibody to AFP was of the IgG_1 subclass. Association-dissociation kinetics demonstrated rapid and complete association kinetics as compared to anti-AFP antisera from both an early bleed (10 weeks) and a late bleed (18 months) of a goat immunized with purified AFP. The monoclonal antibody was also of very high avidity with little dissociation and was comparable to the hyperimmunized goat antiserum in that regard. They suggested that the monoclonal antibody would serve as an ideal reagent in classic radio-immunoassays for AFP, immunohistological studies, and for localizing AFP-producing tumors in patients. No studies on the specificity of the monoclonal antibody were reported.

Uotila et al. (57) reported that the IgG_1 monoclonal anti-AFP antibody they produced was capable of binding the same amount (approximately 90%) of labeled AFP as could conventional antisera, and showed that nanogram amounts of unlabeled AFP could inhibit the binding of monoclonal antibody to $[^{125}I]$ AFP. The several monoclonal antibodies they produced could not differentiate between the Con A or other possible variants of AFP. In addition, assays based on mono-clonal anti-AFP antibody appeared to have a clinical specificity and sensitivity similar to their assay using conventional antisera when normal sera, sera and amniotic fluid from pregnant women, sera from patients with teratocarcinoma or hepatoblastoma patients, or international AFP standards were tested.

These investigators also showed that simplified sandwich assays in which one AFP monoclonal antibody is immobilized and another is labeled can be used to determine similarity or "closeness" of epitopes on AFP (35).

Van Heyningen et al. (58) produced three monoclonal antibodies to AFP that could bind radiolabeled AFP in a polyethylene glycol-dependent precipitation assay. When combinations of two or all three were used, the "cooperativity" helped generate antibody dilution or inhibition curves.

Schröder (59) studied the characteristics of the IgG_1 anti-AFP antibody produced by one of several clones developed in his laboratory. In his hands, significant inhibition of binding between the monoclonal antibody and $[^{125}I]$ AFP required approximately 10 times more purified AFP than necessary when conventional goat antiserum was used in a comparable assay system. However, analyses of serum and amniotic fluid samples for AFP concentrations showed no systematic differences between assays utilizing the two antibodies. He concluded that the monoclonal antibody offered no advantages over conventional antisera in the radioimmunoassay. Schröder (3) did demonstrate, however, that the monoclonal antibody could be useful for affinity purification of AFP using mild reagents for elution.

CONCLUSIONS

It is obvious that this review can only provide a preliminary and incomplete description of some methods that utilize monoclonal antibodies which have been used for the dissection and characterization of human tumor-associated macromolecules, as exemplified by CEA and AFP. In addition, an attempt has been made to suggest additional methods that can and surely will be used to this end. The availability of large amounts of reproducibly homogeneous monoclonal antibodies specific for single antigenic determinants, coupled with a rapidly expanding technology in which such antibodies play a principal role, assures that only the tip of the iceberg can be seen at this time.

It is appropriate that the human tumor markers CEA and AFP are among the first to undergo scrutiny with monoclonal antibodies. These markers have become extremely useful at the clinical level, but their value would increase dramatically if specific determinants could be identified and exploited. Rogers et al. (54) have described "the first monoclonal antibodies with a high specificity for circulating CEA." Whether their preliminary assay results can be expanded or improved upon with their antibodies or by other investigators such as Oehr et al. (55) remains to be determined. Uotila et al. (35, 57) have developed highly sensitive radioimmunoassays and a new sandwich enzyme-linked immunospecific assay in which monoclonal antibodies to AFP are used advantageously to effect rapid, simple, and sensitive clinical tests. Although the monoclonal antibodies to AFP produced by them and others do not appear to differentiate the variants of AFP described to date, studies in that direction are continuing. Whether or not monoclonal antibodies to CEA and AFP can find their way directly into clinical assays, it is apparent that they will be extremely useful in preparing more homogeneous standards and ligands for such assays.

The use of monoclonal antibodies to human tumor markers for immunodetection and therapy is described elsewhere in Chapters 12 and 13 of this volume. Suffice it to say that such applications will also require in-depth examination of the specificities of such monoclonal antibodies as they relate to the variants, cross-reacting molecules, and differing antigenic determinants of the corresponding marker preparations.

ACKNOWLEDGMENTS

The secretarial assistance of Ms. Suzette Witschi is gratefully acknowledged.

REFERENCES

1. M. Sela, *Science* 166:1365 (1969).
2. G. Köhler and C. Milstein, *Nature* 256:495 (1975).
3. J. Schröder, *Med. Biol.* 58:140 (1980).
4. P. Gold and S. O. Freedman, *J. Exp. Med.* 121:439 (1965).
5. P. Gold and S. O. Freedman, *J. Exp. Med.* 121:467 (1965).
6. D. M. P. Thomson, J. Krupey, S. O. Freedman, and P. Gold, *Proc. Nat. Acad. Sci. U.S.A.* 64:161 (1969).
7. H. Z. Kupchik, N. Zamcheck, and C. A. Saravis, *Nat. Cancer Inst. Monogr.* 52:413 (1979).
8. N. Zamcheck, T. L. Moore, P. Dhar, and H. Z. Kupchik, *N. Engl. J. Med.* 286:83 (1972).
9. N. Zamcheck, W. G. Doos, R. Prudente, B. B. Luria, and L. S. Gottlieb, *Human Pathol.* 6:31 (1975).
10. M. S. Loewenstein and N. Zamcheck, *Gastroenterology* 72:161 (1977).
11. N. Zamcheck and H. Z. Kupchik, in *Manual of Clinical Immunology* (N. R. Rose and M. Friedman, eds.), American Cancer Society, Washington, D.C., 1980, p. 919.
12. A. Fuks, C. Banjo, J. Shuster, S. O. Freedman, and P. Gold, *Biochim. Biophys. Acta* 417:123 (1974).
13. Q. Pletsch and D. M. Goldenberg, *J. Nat. Cancer Inst.* 53:1201 (1974).
14. B. Herzog, J. C. Hendrick, and P. Franchimont, *Eur. J. Cancer* 12:657 (1976).
15. C. Banjo, J. Shuster, and P. Gold, *Cancer Res.* 34:2114 (1974).
16. A. H. Rule and C. Golesky-Reilly *Immunol. Commun.* 2:213 (1973).
17. J. E. Shively, C. W. Todd, V. L. W. Go, and M. L. Egan, *Cancer Res.* 38:503 (1978).
18. N. Ariel, M. Krantz, S. Inoue, and P. Gold, *Protides Biol. Fluid Proc. Colloq.* 27:37 (1979).
19. E. S. Newman, S. W. Petras, A. Georgiadis, and H. J. Hansen, *Cancer Res.* 34:2125 (1974).
20. J. E. Shively, J. N. S. Glassman, E. Engvall, and C. W. Todd, in *Carcinoembryonic Proteins*, Vol. 1 (E. G. Lehman, ed.) Elsevier/North-Holland, New York, 1979, p. 9.
21. F. Ruoslahti, E. Engvall, M. Vuento, and H. Wigzell, *Int. J. Cancer* 17:358 (1976).
22. M. Kuroki, Y. Koga, and Y. Matsuoka, *Cancer Res.* 41:713 (1981).
23. G. T. Rogers and P. A. Keep, *Eur. J. Cancer* 16:127 (1980).
24. C. G. Bergstrand and B. Czar, *Scand. J. Clin. Lab. Invest.* 8:174 (1956).
25. G. I. Abelev, S. D. Perova, N. I. Khramkove, Z. A. Postnikova, and I. S. Irlin, *Transplantation* 1:174 (1963).
26. Y. Tatarinov, *Vopr. Med. Khim.* 10:90 (1964).
27. M. Kekomälä, C. Ehnholm, A. L. Schwartz, and K. Raivic, *Int. J. Cancer* 8:250 (1971).
28. E. Ruoslahti and W. D. Terry, *Nature* 260:804 (1976).
29. E. Ruoslahti, A. Pekkala, D. E. Comings, and M. Seppälä, *Br. Med. J.* 2:768 (1979).

30. L. R. Purves, E. van der Merwe, and I. Bersohn, *Lancet 2*:464 (1970).
31. E. Alpert, J. Drydale, K. Isselbacher, and P. Schur, *J. Biol. Chem. 237*:3792 (1972).
32. E. Ruoslahti, E. Engvall, A. Pekkala, and M. Seppälä, *Int. J. Cancer 22*:515 (1978).
33. J. Breborowicz, A. Mackiewicz, and D. Breborowicz, *Scand. J. Immunol. 14*:15 (1981).
34. O. Banwo, J. Versey, and J. R. Hobbs, *Lancet 1*:643 (1974).
35. M. Uotila, E. Ruoslahti, and E. Engvall, *J. Immunol. Methods 42*:11 (1981).
36. G. S. David, R. Wang, R. Bartholomew, E. Dale Sevier, T. H. Adams, and H. E. Greene, *Clin. Chem. 27*:1580 (1981).
37. P. Potocnjak, F. Zavala, R. Nussenzweig, and V. Nussenzweig, *Science 215*:1637 (1982).
38. J. P. Brown, P. W. Wright, C. E. Hart, R. G. Woodbury, K. E. Hellström, and I. Hellström, *J. Biol. Chem. 255*:4980 (1980).
39. K. F. Mitchell, J. P. Fuhrer, Z. Steplewski, and H. Koprowski, *Proc. Nat. Acad. Sci. U.S.A. 77*:7287 (1980).
40. E. M. Southern, *J. Mol. Biol. 98*:503 (1975).
41. H. Towbin, T. Staehelin, and J. Gordon, *Proc. Nat. Acad. Sci. U.S.A. 76*:4350 (1979).
42. C. Milstein, *Proc. R. Soc. London B. 211*:393 (1981).
43. T. Springer, *J. Biol. Chem. 256*:3833 (1981).
44. E. F. Plow and T. S. Edington, *Int. J. Cancer 15*:748 (1975).
45. J. Shuster, S. O. Freedman, and P. Gold, *Am. J. Clin. Pathol. 68*:679 (1977).
46. R. Aron, N. Novik, J. Haimovich, and S. Chaitchik, *Isr. J. Med. Sci. 13*:1022 (1977).
47. H. Z. Kupchik, V. R. Zurawski, J. G. R. Hurrell, N. Zamcheck, and P. H. Black, *Cancer Res. 41*:3306 (1981).
48. K. D. Newell, D. M. Goldenberg, and F. J. Primus, *Fed. Proc. 41*:830 (1982).
49. R. S. Accolla, S. Carrel, and J. P. Mack, *Proc. Nat. Acad. Sci. U.S.A. 77*:563 (1980).
50. J. P. Mack and G. Pusztaszeri, *Immunochemistry 9*:1031 (1972).
51. R. S. Accolla, S. Carrell, M. Phan, D. Heumann, and J. P. Mack, *Protides Biol. Fluid Proc. Colloq. 27*:31 (1979).
52. J. Lindgren and Bang, paper presented at the *Eighth Meeting of the International Society of Oncodevelopmental Biology and Medicine*, Tallinn, U.S.S.R., September 15–19, 1980.
53. C. G. Lockhart, R. S. Stinson, H. W. Margraf, C. W. Parker, and G. W. Philpott, *Fed. Proc. 39*:928 (1980).
54. G. T. Rogers, G. A. Rawlins, and K. D. Bagshawe, *Br. J. Cancer 43*:1 (1981).
55. P. Oehr, H -D. Adolphs, A. Wustrow, and G. Derigs, *Tumor Diagnostik, 2*: 189 (1981).
56. Y -K. Tsung, A. Milunsky, and E. Alpert, *J. Immunol. Methods 39*:63 (1980).
57. M. Uotila, E. Engvall, and E. Ruoslahti, *Mol. Immunol. 17*:791 (1980).
58. V. van Heyningen, D. Crichton, S. Lawrie, L. Barron, and D. J. H. Brock *Br. J. Cancer 43*:566 (1981).
59. J. Schröder, personal communication, 1980.

12 MONOCLONAL ANTIBODIES FOR RADIOIMMUNODETECTION OF CANCER

F. James Primus*, Frank H. DeLand, and David M. Goldenberg*/ University of Kentucky and Veterans Administration Medical Centers, Lexington, Kentucky

INTRODUCTION

The advent of monoclonal antibodies has resulted in a renewed interest in the use of antibodies for targeting diagnostic or therapeutic agents to tumors (1-9). This work is based upon a long history of the use of conventional anti-tumor antibodies for in vivo cancer detection and therapy, particularly when labeled with a gamma-emitting radionuclide. It is therefore appropriate that this earlier work concerned with the application of radiolabeled antibodies for tumor imaging be reviewed in order to present the use of monoclonal antibodies in proper perspective.

EARLY STUDIES OF CANCER RADIOIMMUNODETECTION WITH POLYCLONAL ANTIBODIES

Pioneering studies on the method of detecting and treating tumors with radio-labeled anti-tumor antibodies were performed by Pressman and Korngold (10) and Bale et al. (11,12). They discovered that antibody to fibrin or fibrinogen localized

---

*Present affiliation: Center for Molecular Medicine and Immunology, University of Medicine and Dentistry of New Jersey, Newark, New Jersey.

certain growing neoplasms, and in subsequent clinical studies tumor localization was observed by external scintigraphy in 65% of the cases given ^{125}I-labeled anti-fibrin antibody (13,14). In 1965, Mahaley and Day (15) localized human gliomas with anti-glioma antibody, but Bagshawe et al. (16) were not sucessful in imaging a pulmonary metastasis of choriocarcinoma in a patient given anti-human chorionic gonadotropin (HCG) antibody. This was in contrast to earlier work that showed increased accretion of anti-HCG antibody in human choriocarcinomas growing in hamsters (17).

We initiated in 1972 localization studies in a human colon tumor–hamster host model (18) using goat polyclonal antibodies against the carcinoembryonic antigen (CEA). The paired-label method introduced by Pressman et al. (19) was used to compare tissular localization of specific antibody and control irrelevant IgG in the same animal. Selective tumor uptake of antibody to CEA was demonstrated by this technique, with tumor localization ratios increasing with time after administration of the radiolabeled IgG mixture (18). Subsequent studies revealed that this selective antibody uptake in tumors was sufficient to allow them to be specifically imaged several days after injection of radiolabeled antibody (20). These findings were confirmed by Mach et al. (21), who also showed specific uptake of radiolabeled anti-CEA antibodies in CEA-producing human tumor xenografts. Prior to establishing clinical studies, we purified our anti-CEA antibody preparation by affinity chromatography that resulted in about three- to four-fold improvement in immunoreactivity and tumor localization in the xenograft model (22).

Initial clinical studies by Reif et al. (23) and Mach et al. (24) failed to show tumor localization with anti-CEA antibodies. Our own clinical studies of CEA radioimmunodetection began in 1977, employing an affinity-purified antibody preparation that had an immunoreactivity with CEA of more than 70% (25) and a binding constant of 1.6×10^{12} M^{-1}. Antibody was labeled with ^{131}I by the chloramine-T procedure to a specific activity of $5-20$ $\mu Ci/\mu g$. The patients received intravenous injections of $2-3$ $\mu g/kg$ body weight of the radioiodinated antibody, delivering a total body dose of about $2-2.5$ mCi of [131]I.

Radionuclide images of the anterior, posterior, and lateral views of the chest and abdomen were obtained routinely with a gamma scintillation camera at 24 and 48 hr after administration of the radioantibody. To compensate for background radioactivity, $Na^{99m}TcO_4$ (0.5 mCi) and ^{99m}Tc-labeled human serum albumin (0.5 mCi) were administered intravenously 30 and 5 min, respectively, before each imaging session. The scans were stored in a minicomputer that generated digital images of the radioiodinated antibody alone at an energy of 364 keV, of the Tc components alone, at 140 keV, and of the ^{131}I radioactivity minus that of [99m]Tc. This subtraction technology has been refined further for the liver by using a liver-specific radionuclide, such as ^{99m}Tc-sulfur colloid, by which the liver image made with the colloid is extracted from the region of interest and then the ^{99m}Tc radioactivity is subtracted from that of [131]I. A similar treatment is made for the lungs, except that this organ is outlined electronically before being processed by the usual subtraction method. It is important to note that at the time of the interpretation

Table 1 Carcinoembryonic Antigen Radioimmunodetection Results with Polyclonal Antibodies by Tumor Sites in 173 Patients

Primary diagnosis	Number of patients	Sensitivity (true positive rate)			
		Primary site	Secondary site	Total	Percent
Colorectal cancer	51	10/12	49/53	59/65	91
Ovarian cancer	19	10/10	11/14	21/24	88
Lung cancer	30	18/25	5/8	23/33	70
Mammary cancer	6	2/5	7/9	9/14	64
Pancreatic cancer	6	3/6	1/2	4/8	50
Cervical cancer	15	6/8	13/13	19/21	90
Other uterine cancers	5	3/3	6/7	9/10	90
Gastric cancer	4	2/3	3/3	5/6	83
Unknown origin	9	NA[a]	8/9	8/9	89
Miscellaneous cancers	26	9/21	8/9	17/30	57
Lymphoma	2	0/2	0/2	0/4	0

[a]NA, not applicable.

of these images, the nuclear medicine observer is not aware of any clinical information or of the antibody preparation used.

Table 1 provides a summary of our results for CEA radioimmunodetection in the first studies of our series. The method appears to have a high true positive rate for detecting the major tumor types expressing CEA, such as colorectal, ovarian, lung, and cervical carcinomas. An overall true positive detection rate of up to 91% was found for colorectal cancer, based upon the sites of tumor disclosed in the first 51 cases (26). Only two presumptively false positive findings were obtained, constituting a false positive rate of less than 4% in this series. A false positive rate ranging between 9 and 14% was also determined on a tumor site basis (26). Perhaps the most important observation in this study of CEA radioimmunodetection in colorectal cancer was that occult cancer could be localized in 11 of the 51 patients, and subsequently confirmed by other methods (26). It was found, as in previous studies (25, 27), that radioimmunodetection was less reliable in demonstrating tumors less than 2 cm in diameter or when the lesion was devoid of CEA.

Of major concern in such studies with tumor-localizing antibodies is the specificity of the antibody–antigen reaction. Radioactivity eluted from surgical tumor specimens after radioimmunodetection studies with CEA antibodies indicated that CEA–antibody complexes were formed in the tumors (28). Using the paired-label method, a selective

accretion of radioactive CEA antibody was found in colorectal tumors when compared to radioactive normal goat IgG (29). Additionally, we studied the specificity
of CEA radioimmunodetection in 142 cancer patients by analyzing 116 nonneo-
plastic disease sites, and found that only an empyema and a diverticulosis showed
evidence of abnormal radioactivity, representing a false positive rate in these conditions of less than 2% (27). Radiolabeled normal goat IgG administered to 22
cancer patients resulted in only 4 of 32 tumor sites showing some evidence of
increased radioactivity, 3 of which were large tumors that measured more than 10
cm in diameter (27). Thus it appears that imaging of smaller tumors by means of
radiolabeled anti-tumor antibodies is due to specific binding of the antibody to
antigen at the tumor.

Based on these studies with CEA radioimmunodetection, we have now extended
the approach to the use of radioactive alpha-fetoprotein (AFP) and HCG antibodies
for cancer detection. Of 22 cancer sites known to be present in 12 patients with
testicular embryonal carcinoma, ovarian endodermal sinus tumor, or hepatocellular
carcinoma, radioimmunodetection with radioactive AFP antibodies revealed 21, or
95%, of these tumors (30,31). Our experience in the first 13 testicular cancers
studied with HCG antibodies showed that all 10 patients with proven cancer at the
time of our study had their sites revealed by radioimmunodetection (32,33).
The three patients without recent evidence of tumor were found to be correctly
negative by imaging. Of the 14 tumor sites revealed by radioimmunodetection in
10 testicular cancer patients, it is noteworthy that 4 were occult at the time of our
examination and then verified later on by other techniques (33). These findings
are thus similar to our experience with CEA radioimmunodetection in detecting
occult tumors, but since testicular cancers are responsive to chemotherapy, it
appears that radioimmunodetection may come to play an important role in the
management of patients with this tumor type.

RADIOIMMUNODETECTION OF CANCER WITH MONOCLONAL
ANTIBODIES

The development of the hybridoma technology has added another dimension
to the study of antibody-directed diagnostic and therapeutic agents, particularly
as a result of the immunospecific nature and production advantages that monoclonal
antibodies (MAs) have over polyclonal antibodies. The ease of antibody purification
and the reproducibility of the purified preparation, both in protein type and specificity, that can be achieved with MAs far exceeds that possible with conventional
antisera. Monoclonal antibodies also offer the obvious advantage of identifying
potential targetable antigenic constituents and/or determinants on tumor cells
that might not be revealed by conventional approaches. Even if it is possible to
obtain similar antibodies in an antiserum, irrespective of their titer, extensive purification procedures are necessary to remove irrelevant IgG and antibodies reacting
with normal tissue antigens. Other advantages of MAs for tumor localization are

less clear. It is anticipated in clinical use that problems with host sensitization to foreign protein would be inherent to both polyclonal antibodies and MAs raised in nonprimate animal species. The severity and type of immune complex diseases induced by reaction of antibody with circulating antigen, especially after multiple antibody injections, might differ between polyclonal antibodies and MAs owing to the nonrepetitive nature of epitopes recognized by MAs. The possibility that an MA may target better than a polyclonal one rests on the rationale, as we view it, that antibody against the targetable epitope(s) can only be produced in sufficient concentrations with MAs. On the basis of current knowledge suitably prepared polyclonal antibodies should be equally effective as targeting agents as MAs. In fact, the restricted epitope specificity of MAs could even pose a limitation on their localizing efficacy if heterogeneity in expression of the epitope occurs between primary and metastatic cancer or between tumors of different patients. Thus expectations that MAs will alleviate several of the limitations already encountered in the radioimmunodetection of tumors with polyclonal antibodies, for example, requirements for background subtraction, will likely be unfulfilled, although in certain instances they may provide alternative approaches to this area that were not feasible with conventional antisera. It is the purpose of the following discussion to review briefly the experience to date with MA localization of tumors and to focus, where possible, on the comparative localization properties of MAs and polyclonal antibodies.

Most of the studies of the radiolocalization qualities of MAs have used those of murine origin and applied to investigations in syngeneic or xenogeneic animal models as well as in human cancer. With the exception of one study (34), all others have shown that MAs, like their conventional counterparts, will preferentially localize in tumors in an antigen-specific fashion to a degree that allows tumor detection by scintigraphic techniques (1-7, 35-42). Table 2 lists selected features of the results obtained in these various studies and, although it was not possible to make uniform comparisons between them, it demonstrates the diversity of the findings that is most likely related to a similarly diverse array of antibody-tumor systems investigated. Monoclonal antibodies against the soluble CEA and cell-surface antigens on colon and mammary carcinomas, osteogenic sarcomas, and teratocarcinomas have been shown to localize tumors in various experimental animal models (1,3,4,6,7,35-38,40-42). Furthermore, both anti-CEA and anti-human osteogenic sarcoma MAs have been shown to image colonic adenocarcinomas in patients (2,5). Studies with MAs were first initiated by Ballou et al. (1), who demonstrated that murine teratocarcinomas could be imaged with an MA reactive with the stage-specific embryonal antigen-1 (SSEA-1). This antibody had an IgM isotype and, as depicted in Table 2, MAs belonging to IgG_1, IgG_{2a}, and IgG_{2b} subclasses also have tumor-localizing qualities. One study has used rat MA (35), and the magnitude of tumor localization appeared to be less than that obtained with murine MA in other investigations, but this may have been due to a special property of the tumor model investigated rather than the species origin of the antibody.

Table 2 Tumor Localization with Monoclonal Antibodies

Animal system	Antigen (antibody isotype)	Day[a]	Tumor/tissue ratio		Percentage of injected dose in tumor		Reference
			Blood	Lungs	Per gram	Total	
Mouse teratocarcinoma, mouse host	SSEA-1 (IgM)	5	15.0	35.0	15.0	NA[b]	37
Human osteogenic sarcoma, immunosuppressed mouse host	Surface (IgG_{2b})	3	2.2	3.3	41.0	3.6	7
Rat mammary carcinoma, rat host	Surface (IgG_{2b})	3	1.0	2.7	0.8	0.6	35
Human melanoma, athymic (nude) mouse host	Surface (IgG_{2a})	6	6.6	16.0	NA	NA	3
Human teratoma, immunosuppressed mouse host	Surface (IgG_{2a})	4	9.1	36.3	NA	NA	6
Human colon carcinoma, athymic (nude) mouse host	Surface (IgG_1)	6 hr	NA	NA	NA	6.0	40
Human colon carcinoma, athymic (nude) mouse host	CEA (IgG_1)	4	6.0	14	NA	4.2	4

Human colon carcinoma, athymic (nude) mouse host	CEA (NA)	3	7	NA	5	NA	41
Normal lymph node, mouse host	Thy-1.1 (IgG_{2a})	20 hr	6.7^c	NA	4^c	NA	39
Human colon carcinoma, human host	Surface (IgG_{2b})	2	NA	2.8^d	0.005	NA	2
Human colon carcinoma, human host	CEA (IgG_1)	NA	1.2^e	4.1^e	NA	NA	5

[a] Day postinjection of radiolabeled antibody.
[b] NA, not available.
[c] Lymph node/blood ratio or percentage of injected dose per gram of lymph node.
[d] Tumor/normal adjacent mucosa ratio.
[e] Tumor/serum ratio.

Of the studies listed in Table 2, MA localization in mouse teratocarcinomas (37) and human teratomas (6) in experimental animals yielded improved tumor/blood and tumor/normal tissue ratios over those obtained with polyclonal antibodies in other systems (18,20,22). Ghose et al. (3) directly compared the localization of a murine MA and a goat polyclonal antibody in a human melanoma xenograft. They showed that the MA gave more distinct tumor images and a 10-fold greater tumor/blood ratio than the polyclonal antibody. However, there are three aspects of this study that limit a generalization concerning the relative efficacy of tumor localization with MA compared to polyclonal antibodies. The two antibody types reacted with different antigens or determinants on melanoma cells, and their quantitative expression on these cells was not compared. The percentage of active antibody in the radiolabeled preparations was not established, suggesting that the poorer localization obtained with the polyclonal antibody might have been due to its higher content of irrelevant IgG. Finally, the MA was cleared from the circulation at a much faster rate than the polyclonal antibody, resulting in enhanced tumor images coincident with a lower blood background level. In other studies by Mach et al. (5), MA and polyclonal antibodies against CEA gave similar images and tumor uptake based on a comparison of a limited number of patients. The average tumor/normal adjacent tissue ratio for MA was 4.1 compared to 3.6 for the polyclonal antibody. Only 0.1% of the injected dose was found in the tumor after administration of either antibody type. Thus these studies indicate that an MA and suitably prepared polyclonal antibodies against the same antigen, having similar affinity constants, can have comparable localization characteristics.

In an effort to compare the localization qualities of MAs and polyclonal antibodies, we have initiated studies in the GW-39 hamster host model (18,20) using antibodies of both types prepared against CEA. Goat anti-CEA antibody was affinity purified and was shown to contain 70% specifically reactive antibody in the radiolabeled preparation (22). Monoclonal antibodies against CEA were prepared, as described in detail elsewhere (43), by fusion of spleen cells from immunized mice with the nonsecreting P3-x63-Ag8.653 myeloma cell line. Three clones were selected and shown to recognize separate epitopes on the CEA molecule (43). They were designated NP-1, which reacted with a site shared between CEA and the nonspecific cross-reacting antigen, and NP-2 and NP-3, both of which cross-reacted with a related antigen in meconium but not the nonspecific cross-reacting antigen. NP-1, NP-2, and NP-3 all had an IgG_1 isotype and average binding constants of 5.3×10^{11}, 1.9×10^{11}, and 4.5×10^9 M^{-1}, respectively. The K value for the goat antibody was 6.3×10^{11} M^{-1}. The MAs were purified from ascites fluid by ammonium sulfate precipitation and ion exchange chromatography. After radioiodination, between 60 and 80% of the radiolabeled MA preparations bound to a CEA immunoadsorbent. Groups of five hamsters each, all bearing GW-39 cheek pouch tumors, were injected intraperitoneally with 5 μg of antibody labeled with $5\mu Ci$ of ^{125}I. The animals also received a similar amount of MOPC 21 IgG_1 or normal goat IgG labeled with ^{131}I.

Table 3 Localization of Radiolabeled Monoclonal and Polyclonal Antibodies Against Carcinoembryonic Antigen in GM-39 Tumors 3 Days After Injection

Antibody	Tumor weight (g)	Tumor/tissue ratio			Percentage of injected dose in tumor	
		Blood	Lung	Muscle	Per gram	Total
Goat polyclonal	0.4 ± 0.1[a]	2.4 ± 0.6	4.4 ± 0.7	24.3 ± 4.5	4.4 ± 0.4	1.7
Murine monoclonal						
NP-1	0.6 ± 0.3	1.3 ± 0.5	3.4 ± 0.7	18.6 ± 3.0	3.3 ± 0.8	1.9
NP-2	0.4 ± 0.2	1.8 ± 0.6	4.0 ± 0.8	25.0 ± 7.1	4.0 ± 0.5	1.6
NP-3	0.7 ± 0.2	1.5 ± 0.2	3.6 ± 0.7	23.3 ± 3.8	2.6 ± 0.4	1.9
NP-1, NP-2, NP-3 mixture	0.3 ± 0.1	2.6 ± 0.6	4.4 ± 0.9	21.2 ± 7.8	4.3 ± 0.5	1.3

[a]Mean ± SE.

Table 3 compares selected tumor/tissue ratios and percentages of injected dose in the tumor for the different groups 3 days after injection. A fifth group is also shown that consists of animals injected with an equal mixture of the MAs equivalent to a total dose of 15 μg of antibody. It is apparent that the different MAs were very similar to one another as well as to the goat polyclonal antibody in their localization of GW-39 tumors. This relationship between the different groups at days 1 and 7 after injection did not appreciably deviate from the results depicted on day 3. Furthermore, there was no significant difference in the rate of clearance of the different antibody preparations from the circulation. A tissue localization ratio was computed for the different groups according to the formula

$$\frac{\text{Anti-CEA IgG/normal IgG in tissue}}{\text{Anti-CEA IgG/normal IgG injected}}$$

These values were also quite similar between groups, ranging from 2.0 to 3.0 on day 3 for tumors, compared to about 1.0 for the reference tissues (lung, liver, spleen, kidney, muscle, blood). The increase in the localization ratio above 1.0 for tumors demonstrates that the accretion of antibody in this tissue was due to its specific selective uptake. It was unexpected that the MA mixture did not improve localization. Reciprocal blocking experiments in vitro using soluble antigen (43) showed that NP-1 and NP-2 cross-inhibited one another, although only NP-1 reacted with nonspecific cross-reacting antigen, while both MAs failed to cross-block NP-3. However, it is possible that antigen in situ behaves differently, and its combination with any one of the MAs injected may inhibit binding by the others. Nonetheless, these preliminary studies demonstrate that MAs and polyclonal antibodies against the same soluble antigen give comparable localization based on tissue counting techniques, supporting the initial clinical findings of Mach et al. (5,44), who studied the same antigen system. Whether the same is true for imaging GW-39 tumors is currently being investigated.

The importance of evaluating the localizing qualities of a newly prepared MA in an animal model prior to clinical application is demonstrated by the recent studies of Hedin et al. (4). The localization of three MAs recognizing different epitopes on CEA was studied in nude mice grafted with LS174T colonic tumors. Although all three MAs showed similar potency when reacted with CEA in vitro (45), one failed to localize in tumors, while the second gave an intermediate localization in comparison to the third. It would be of interest in this latter study to determine by tumor extraction or immunohistochemistry, if the CEA expressed by LS174T contains the epitope recognized by the MA that failed to localize. Masking of certain antigenic epitopes in situ or heterogeneity in their expression among different tumors of the same type may necessitate the formulation of artificial "polyclonal" antibodies with MAs of differing specificities. Hedin et al. (4) also showed a correlation between tumor localization and antigen content by comparison of three CEA-producing tumors that varied in their antigen expression.

Variability in antigen synthesis probably accounted for the differences noted in the localization of germ cell tumor xenografts with an anti-teratoma MA (6). Tumor size as well as quantitative and qualitative differences in antigen production could all explain the failure by Mach et al. (5,44) to obtain positive tumor images in about 50% of their patients studied with MAs to CEA.

The possibility that MAs may show enhanced selective tumor uptake over that obtained with polyclonal antibodies would be a major asset in improving clinical imaging procedures with radioantibodies. With an increased accretion of radio-labeled antibody in the tumor, one might be able to eliminate sophisticated background subtraction procedures currently in clinical use that have the potential to generate positive scans, not on the basis of an immunochemical reaction between antigen and antibody in the tumor, but as a result of differences in the metabolic distribution patterns of the antibody and background subtracting agent (46). However, studies in experimental animal tumors suggest that the need for background subtraction depends more on the rate of antibody clearance and properties of the tumor rather than whether the antibody is polyclonal or monoclonal in nature, assuming that both have a similar percentage of immunoreactivity with antigen. Ballou et al. (1) showed that scintigraphic detection of tumors during the first 2 days after MA injection required subtraction of background monitored by the distribution of ^{123}I-labeled irrelevant mouse immunoglobulin. Imaging at 4–5 days did not require background subtraction and corresponded to a decrease in circulating radioactivity that was accompanied by 10-fold increase in tumor/blood ratios over this time period (37,38). It was also shown that $F(ab')_2$ MA fragments were cleared from the circulation much faster than intact antibody, and positive tumor images without background subtraction could be obtained at 2 days following injection of antibody fragments. In the study of Houston et al. (39), almost all of the $F(ab')_2$ fragments of an IgG_{2a} MA against Thy-1.1 were eliminated from circulation of mice within 24 hr compared to a 6-day half-life for intact antibody. When $F(ab')_2$ fragments were used instead of intact antibody, there was over a 20-fold increase in the antibody distribution ratio between lymph nodes and blood. It will be important to evaluate further whether the use of $F(ab')_2$ fragments, irrespective of their mono- or polyclonal source, results in enhanced preferential localization of antibody, as observed by Houston et al. (39) in their studies of anti-Thy-1.1 targeting to normal lymph nodes and spleen, but not by others using animal tumor models (38,47). The rate of dissipation of antibody from the circulation in conjunction with its rate of accretion, level of uptake, and retention characteristics in tumors will all contribute to the quality of scans obtained at any given time point. In this context, it appears that both MAs and polyclonal antibodies reach their maximum levels in tumors within 24–48 hr after injection and begin to decrease thereafter (6,18). Thus manipulations during this early time period that facilitate clearance of antibody without interfering with tumor uptake would create the ideal setting for improving the sensitivity and clarity of tumor imaging. The use of F (ab')$_2$ or smaller fragments as well as the recently described use of liposome-entrapped second antibody to enhance clearance of circulating radiolabeled antibody (48) are two strategies that may fulfill the latter goal. In five patients with gastrointestinal cancer, Begent et al. (48) showed that injection of liposome-entrapped second antibody accelerated the clearance of polyclonal antibody against CEA and enhanced tumor images in three patients.

Size is another factor that influences the ease by which tumors are detected by scanning. In studies of an anti-human osteogenic sarcoma MA in a xenograft model, Pimm et al. (7) found that smaller tumors, while having the same blood ratio but only one-half the total radioactivity as tumors twice their size, were not clearly localized by external scintigraphy. Thus the tumor mass and its radioactivity relative to the total burden of the whole animal influences to a great extent the outcome of attempts at tumor imaging. In fact, it is of no surprise that imaging studies in experimental animals with MAs were successful based on the size (> 0.5 g) of the tumors that were imaged, especially since they were transplanted to a superficial location (3–5,37,40). Our earlier work with polyclonal antibodies against CEA showed that even irrelevant IgG or antibody itself in a nonspecific manner can result in positive scans if tumors in the size range normally reported are used for imaging (20). Paired-label experiments by Moshakis et al. (6), who used an anti-human teratoma MA in a xenograft model, showed that even specific accretion of antibody decreases in tumors of increasing size. This effect was also noted in animals carrying both small and large tumors, indicating that it was related to a property of the larger tumors, perhaps vascularity (40) or decreased antigen expression, rather than neutralization of antibody in the circulation by released antigen or masking of tumor antigenic sites by antibody elicited in the host. We also had reported that larger xenografted colonic tumors showed reduced selective uptake of polyclonal anti-CEA antibody, although the mechanism of this effect was not explored (18). The ultimate value, then, of imaging studies with MAs is not that positive scans can be obtained but, rather, that a meaningful determination of the level of detectability is assessed with respect to tumor size and its body burden.

A potential problem area in radioimmunodetection applications using MAs or polyclonal antibodies against soluble antigens is their peripheral neutralization by secreted, circulating antigen. Although very high levels of CEA have been present in some of the patients imaged with goat polyclonal CEA antibodies, there has been a surprising lack of interference with the imaging results by circulating antigen (5, 25,27). Circulating complexes between CEA and polyclonal antibody have been found in both clinical (29,49) and experimental animal studies (50), the presence of which was not correlated with the success or failure of imaging or localization. Studies with MAs (4) and polyclonal antibodies (50) against CEA using human colonic and breast tumor xenograft models, respectively, suggest that the level of antigen production by the tumor is a more important factor in determining the degree of localization. Other studies in experimental animal models with MAs against cell-surface antigens have not found circulating complexes between antigen and the injected radioactive MA (6,7). However, interference by circulating antigen was felt to be responsible, based on in vitro blocking assays with tumor-bearing serums, for the failure of MA against human HLA to localize in xenografted human colonic HT29R tumors, although the existence of antigen–radioactive antibody complexes was not proven (34).

The actual site at which radioactive antibody is deposited is somewhat similar between different antigen–tumor systems. With a known soluble antigen such as CEA, autoradiographic studies have shown that both MAs (5) and polyclonal antibodies (51,52) are predominantly found in extracellular locations and very rarely within tumor cells or on their membranes. Sites of radioactive antibody deposition also generally corresponded to areas of antigen localization, as assessed by immunoenzyme staining procedures. Polyclonal antibody was located in a few cells suggestive of macrophage origin in the study by Lewis et al. (52), whereas Mach et al. (5) found no evidence of CEA MA uptake by macrophages residing in tumors. Thus the lack of extensive resident macrophage uptake of radioactive antibodies against CEA argues against engulfment of antibody-antigen complexes, particularly those in the circulation, by these cells as being the main mechanism by which CEA antibody localizes to or is retained in tumors (51). Monoclonal antibodies to cell-surface antigens were retained in connective tissue surrounding and invaginating tumor areas (7,40) and, in addition, Moshakis et al. (53) found anti-human teratoma MA in close association with tumor cell membranes. Although the apparent relative absence of direct interaction of radioactive MAs and polyclonal antibodies with tumor cells may not have important consequences for diagnostic imaging, it may be a major limiting factor concerning the efficacy of antibody-targeted therapeutic agents that depend upon close proximity to, or internalization by, tumor cells for their action.

Clinical localization studies with MAs have almost been exclusively carried out in patients with colorectal cancer. Farrands et al. (2) found that an MA prepared against osteogenic sarcomas and cross-reactive with other tumor types, but not certain normal cells (54), localized colon tumors in 9 of 11 patients by imaging procedures using background subtraction. The tumor from one patient that was negative by imaging in vivo gave a positive scan of the resected specimen. The average tumor/adjacent normal tissue ratio obtained by tissue counting of resected specimens from five patients was 2.8, and about 0.005% of the injected dose was in the tumor on a per gram basis. The smallest primary tumor detected by imaging had a volume of 18 cm^3, comparable to the lower size limits of detectability experienced so far with polyclonal antibodies to CEA (25-27). Disseminated cancer was localized in 5 patients, including three with liver and 1 with brain metastasis. Furthermore, a synchronous occult tumor was imaged in the transverse colon of a patient with a second rectal primary. In an earlier study by Mach et al. (5) of 28 patients, 26 with colon and 2 with pancreatic carcinomas, positive scans of primary tumors were obtained by using subtraction techniques in 14 cases with MA against CEA. Four patients were simultaneously injected with [125] I-labeled normal mouse IgG and the levels of radioactivity for both antibody, labeled with [131] I, and normal mouse IgG were measured in resected specimens. Tumor/ adjacent normal tissue ratios were 4.1 and 1.25 for the MA and normal mouse IgG, respectively, demonstrating the specificity of the localization. The percentage of patients with positive scans, the degree of tumor uptake of antibody, and the specificity of the reaction observed with MAs were comparable to those achieved with goat polyclonal CEA antibodies under similar imaging conditions (5,29,44). When transaxial tomoscintigraphy was used without background subtraction, 13 of 14 patients gave positive localization with radioactive MA in areas known to contain tumor, but many regions of nonspecific activity were noted, questioning the utility of the approach in terms of its specificity (5). Recent clinical radioimmunodetection studies by us with radiolabeled monoclonal antibodies against CEA or AFP have generally confirmed these observations of tumor imaging, but without any apparent increase in nonspecific background activity. Figure 1 (Plate 4) presents the imaging (subtraction) results in two patients receiving either AFP or CEA monoclonal antibodies labeled with [131] I. Both images show liver uptake in patients with hepatocellular carcinoma (AFP) or metastatic colorectal cancer (CEA).

Berche and co-workers (55) recently were able to improve the apparent specificity of tomoscintigraphy, without sacrificing its sensitivity, such that 16 of 17 tumor sites were identified with radioactive MA in patients with gastrointestinal or medullary thyroid carcinomas. Since only two patients with no evidence of disease and negative by tomoscintigraphy were studied, it may be premature to judge the specificity of this new approach to radioimmunodetection. The size of the lesions detected by tomoscintigraphy were also within the same range of those clinically detected by rectilinear scanning that incorporates computer processing for background subtraction (2,25-27). Thus, it is also too early to assess the sensitivity of tomoscintigraphy in terms of tumor size in comparison to rectilinear scanning with background subtraction, whereby the experience of others with the latter method (2,25-27) indicates a similar false-negative rate to that obtained with tomoscintigraphy by Berche et al. (55).

OUTLOOK

Although major improvements in radioimmunodetection will undoubtedly come from the development of new antibody preparations, particularly the use of antibody fragments of more-tumor-specific reagents, advances at the levels of the radionuclide and the scanning instrumentation can also be made (41,55-57). Short-lived radionuclides of low energy, such as [111] In, [99m] Tc, and [123] I, are more

Plate 4

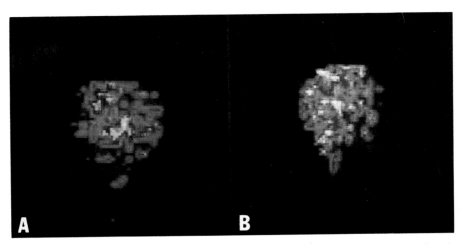

Figure 1 (A) Carcinoembryonic antigen radioimmunodetection (patient) scan showing abnormal radioactivity (white and red areas) in liver with colorectal cancer metastases after subtraction of ^{99m}Tc from ^{131}I-labeled anti-CEA monoclonal antibody. (B) Alphafetoprotein scan performed with monoclonal AFP antibody labeled with ^{131}I and processed by subtraction method. Image shows abnormal radioactivity consistent with confirmed hepatocellular carcinoma.

advantageous for imaging, and methods for improved labeling of antibodies with these isotopes need to be developed further. Single-photon emission computer-ized tomography may provide better image resolution while reducing or elimi-nating the need for computer-assisted image subtraction (5,55), but further work comparing this modality with rectilinear scanning needs to be done before the true contribution of this approach is evaluable.

Finally, it is our view that single antibody preparations, particularly highly speci-fic and restricted MAs, may not be as effective for localization (or therapy) as antibody mixtures. Such mixtures may be antibodies directed against different determinants of the same antigen (as we have pursued with mixtures of CEA MAs), or against different antigens of the same tumor cells (58; Nelson et al., manuscript submitted for publication). This should afford an increased accretion of radio-activity in tumors, especially tumors with heterogeneous cell populations having variable quantities of different epitopes of an antigen or different tumor-associated antigens expressed. This problem of variable and differential expression of tumor markers within a tumor is easily appreciated when a tumor section is stained for such a marker, and in the case of CEA, for example, abundant evidence has shown that only certain areas and populations of cells within a tumor section stain for this antigen when immunohistochemical methods are applied (59). The effect of in-creased accretion of radioactivity in the tumor may be improved resolution and better tumor/nontumor ratios, perhaps thereby reducing the requirements for back-ground subtraction techniques. Such antibody mixtures for tumor localization and, presumably, therapy may be considered to be "engineered" polyclonal anti-bodies, since different mixtures of epitope-specific MAs are consolidated (mixed) to produce a more effective cancer detection and/or cancer therapeutic agent. It is our view that this may be the principal contribution of MA technology—development of the proper ingredients of an "engineered" polyclonal antibody.

With the advent of tumor-localizing antibodies, it is an obvious expectation that such antibodies should be investigated as agents for directing therapeutic measures to cancer cells selectively, and considerable efforts are in progress with regard to arming tumor-localizing antibodies with toxins, radiation, and anti-cancer drugs (8,9,60–64). Suffice it to say that the problems of tumor localization with radiolabeled antibodies are only compounded when there is a desire to retain the integrity of a toxic molecule bound to an antibody until it reaches the tumor, and then to permit a selective uptake by the tumor cells while not comprising the cytotoxic effects of the anti-cancer agent. Nevertheless, the first step in this direct-ion is the development and demonstration of tumor-localizing antibodies, and it is to be expected that the further advancement of cancer radioimmunodetection will be commensurate with improvements in methods of specific cancer immuno-therapy.

CONCLUSION

As a cancer detection modality, radioimmunodetection is still in its infancy, even though almost three decades have elapsed since its inception. Throughout its history, improvements in antibody preparation, identification of new tumor markers, and advances in imaging instrumentation and techniques have all stimulated a renewed interest in the use of radiolabeled antibodies for specifically detecting tumor sites. The advent of MAs with their exquisite specificity and potential for identifying more tumor-distinct markers will likely represent a further contribution toward the goal of establishing radioimmunodetection as a standard detection method. Although MAs have been used successfully for radioimmunodetection, it is still unclear whether these reagents are superior to affinity-purified conventional antibodies, in terms of either tumor resolution or a reduced need for computer processing. However, we have cited several areas in which MAs provide new opportunities to improve the primary immunological detection agent that should complement and meet coincident progress in radionuclide labeling of antibodies and in imaging instrumentation. Finally, the ability to localize cancer with anti-tumor antibodies serves as an obvious basis for developing such antibodies for therapy, particularly those MAs that are more organ- and tumor- distinct in their localization.

ACKNOWLEDGMENTS

Our research has been supported by grants CA-17742, CA-25584, CA-31226, and CA-24376 from the National Institutes of Health, a grant from the Veterans Administration, and by American Cancer Society Grant RD-134. We thank our collaborators for their assistance and support, especially Dr. E. Ruoslahti of the La Jolla Cancer Research Foundation, California for his alpha-fetoprotein monoclonal antibody-producing clone, and Drs. S. J. Bennett and R. M. Sharkey.

REFERENCES

1. B. Ballou, G. Levine, T. R. Hakala, and D. Solter, *Science 206*:844 (1979).
2. P. A. Farrands, M. V. Pimm, M. J. Embleton, A. C. Perkins, J. D. Hardy, R. W. Baldwin, and J. D. Hardcastle, *Lancet 2*:397 (1982).
3. T. Ghose, S. Ferrone, K. Imai, S. T. Novell, Jr., S. J. Luner, R. H. Martin, and A. H. Blair, *J. Nat. Cancer Inst. 69*:823 (1981).
4. A. Hedin, B. Wahren, and S. Hammarström, *Int. J. Cancer 30*:547 (1982).
5. J. -P. Mach, F. Buchegger, M. Forni, J. Ritschard, C. Berche, J. -D. Lumbroso, M. Schreyer, C. Girardet, R. S. Accolla, and S. Carrel, *Immunol. Today 2*:239 (1981).
6. V. Moshakis, R. A. J. McIlhinney, D. Raghavan, and A. M. Neville, *Br. J. Cancer 44*:91 (1981).

7. M. V. Pimm, M. J. Embleton, A. C. Perkins, M. R. Perkins, M. R. Price, R. A. Robins, G. R. Robinson, and R. W. Baldwin, *Int. J. Cancer 30*:75 (1982).
8. P. Casellas, J. P. Brown, O. Gros, P. Gros, I. Hellström, F. K. Jansen, P. Poncelet, R. Roncucci, H. Vidaliand, K. E. Hellström, *Int. J. Cancer 30*:437 (1982).
9. D. G. Gilliland, Z. Steplewski, R. J. Collier, K. F. Mitchell, T. H. Chang, and H. Koprowski, *Proc Nat. Acad. Sci. U.S.A.* 77:4539 (1980).
10. D. Pressman and L. Korngold, *Cancer 6*:610 (1953).
11. W. F. Bale, I. L. Spar, R. L. Goodland, and D. E. Wolfe, *Proc. Soc. Exp. Biol. Med. 89*:564 (1955).
12. W. F. Bale and I. L. Spar, *Adv. Biol. Med. Phys. 5*:285 (1957).
13. I. L. Spar, W. F. Bale, D. Marrack, W. C. Dewey, R. J. McCardle, and P. V. Harper, *Cancer 20*:865 (1967).
14. W. F. Bale, M. A. Contreras, and E. D. Goody, *Cancer Res. 40*:2965 (1980).
15. M. S. Mahaley, Jr., and E. D. Day, *J. Neurosurg. 23*:363 (1965).
16. K. D. Bagshawe, F. Searle, J. Lewis, P. Brown, and P. Keep, *Cancer Res. 40*:3016 (1980).
17. J. Quinones, G. Mizejewski, and W. H. Beierwaltes, *J. Nucl. Med. 12*:69 (1971).
18. F. J. Primus, R. H. Wang, D. M. Goldenberg, and H. J. Hansen, *Cancer Res. 33*:2977 (1973).
19. D. Pressman, E. D. Day, and M. Blan, *Cancer Res. 17*:845 (1957).
20. D. M. Goldenberg, D. F. Preston, F. J. Primus, and H. J. Hansen, *Cancer Res. 34*:1 (1974).
21. J. -P. Mach, S. Carrel, C. Merenda, B. Sordat, and J. C. Cerottini, *Nature 248*:704 (1974).
22. F. J. Primus, R. MacDonald, D. M. Goldenberg, and H. J. Hansen, *Cancer Res. 37*:1544 (1977).
23. A. E. Reif, L. E. Curtis, R. Duffield, and I. A. Shauffer, *J. Surg. Oncol. 6*:133 (1974).
24. J. -P. Mach, S. Carrel, C. Merenda, D. Heumann, and U. Roenspies, *Eur. J. Cancer Suppl. 1*:113 (1978).
25. D. M. Goldenberg, F. DeLand, E. Kim, S. Bennett, F. J. Primus, J. R. van Nagell, Jr., N. Estes, P. DeSimone, and P. Rayburn, *N. Engl. J. Med. 298*:1384 (1978).
26. D. M. Goldenberg, E. E. Kim. S. J. Bennett, M. O. Nelson, and F. H. DeLand, *Gastroenterology 84*:524 (1983).
27. D. M. Goldenberg, E. E. Kim, F. H. DeLand, S. Bennett, and F. J. Primus, *Cancer Res. 40*:2984 (1980).
28. F. J. Primus and D. M. Goldenberg, *Cancer Res. 40*:2979 (1980).
29. J. -P. Mach, M. Formi, J. Ritschard, F. Buchegger, S. Carrel, S. Widgren, A. Donath, and P. Alberto, *Oncodev. Biol. Med. 1*:49 (1980).
30. D. M. Goldenberg, E. E. Kim, F. H. DeLand, E. Spremulli, M. O. Nelson, J. P. Gockerman, F. J. Primus, R. L. Corgan, and E. Alpert, *Cancer 45*:2500 (1980).
31. E. E. Kim, F. H. DeLand, M. O. Nelson, S. Bennett, G. Simmons, E. Alpert, and D. M. Goldenberg, *Cancer Res. 40*:3008 (1980).
32. D. M. Goldenberg, E. E. Kim, F. H. DeLand, J. R. van Nagell, Jr., and N. Javadpour, *Science 208*:1284 (1980).

33. D. M. Goldenberg, E. E. Kim, and F. H. DeLand, *Proc. Nat. Acad. Sci. U.S.A.* *78*:7754 (1981).
34. H. M. Warenius, G. Galfré, N. M. Bleehen, and C. Milstein, *Eur. J. Clin. Oncol.* *17*:1009 (1981).
35. M. V. Pimm, J. A. Jones, M. R. Price, J. G. Middle, M. J. Embleton, and R. W. Baldwin, *Cancer Immunol. Immunother.* *12*:125 (1982).
36. V. Moshakis, R. A. J. McIlhinney, D. Raghavan, and A. M. Neville, *J. Clin. Pathol.* *34*:314 (1981).
37. G. Levine, B. Ballou, J. Reiland, D. Solter, L. Gumerman, and T. Hakala, *J. Nucl. Med.* *21*:570 (1980).
38. D. Solter, B. Ballou, J. Reilan, G. Levine, T. R. Hakala, and B. B. Knowles, *Prog. Cancer Res. Ther.* *21*:241 (1982).
39. L. L. Houston, R. C. Nowinski, and I. D. Bernstein, *J. Immunol.* *125*:837 (1980).
40. A. A. Epenetos, C. C. Nimmon, J. Arklie, A. T. Elliott, L. A. Hawkins, R. W. Knowles, K. E. Britton, and W. F. Bodmer, *Br. J. Cancer 46*:1 (1982).
41. P. Stern, P. Hagan, S. Halpern, A. Chen, D. David, T. Adams, W. Desmond, K. Brautigan, and I. Royston, *Prog. Cancer Res. Ther.* *21*:245 (1982).
42. J. -P. Mach, F. Buchegger, C. Giradet, M. Formi, J. Ritschard, R. S. Accolla, and S. Carrel, in *Markers for Diagnosis and Monitoring of Human Cancer, Proceedings of the Serono Symposia*, Vol. 2 (M. I. Colnaghi, G. L. Buraggi, and M. Ghione, eds.), Academic, New York, 1982, p. 189.
43. F. J. Primus, K. D. Newell, A. Blue, and D. M. Goldenberg, *Cancer Res. 43*: 686 (1983).
44. J. -P. Mach, S. Carrel, M. Formi, J. Ritschard, A. Donath, and P. Alberto, *N. Engl. J. Med. 303*:5 (1980).
45. A. Hedin, S. Hammarström, and O. Larsson, *Mol. Immunol. 19*:1641 (1982).
46. D. C. Sullivan, J. S. Silva, C. E. Cox, D. E. Haagensen, Jr., C. C. Harris, W. H. Briner, and S. A. Wells, Jr., *Invest. Radiol. 17*:350 (1982).
47. S. A. Gaffar, S. J. Bennett, F. H. DeLand, F. J. Primus, and D. M. Goldenberg, *Proc. Am. Assoc. Cancer Res. 23*:249 (1982).
48. R. H. J. Begent, A. J. Green, K. D. Bagshawe, B. E. Jones, P. A. Keep, F. Searle, R. F. Jewkes, G. M. Barratt, and B. E. Ryman, *Lancet 2*:739 (1982).
49. F. J. Primus, S. J. Bennett, E. E. Kim, F. H. DeLand, M. C. Zahn, and D. M. Goldenberg, *Cancer Res. 40*:497 (1980).
50. V. Moshakis, M. J. Bailey, M. G. Ormerod, J. H. Westwood, and A. M. Neville, *Br. J. Cancer 43*:575 (1981).
51. V. Moshakis, M. G. Ormerod, J. H. Westwood, S. Imrie, and A. M. Neville, *Br. J. Cancer 46*:18 (1982).
52. J. C. M. Lewis, K. D. Bagshawe, and P. A. Keep, *Oncodevel. Biol. Med. 3*:161 (1982).
53. V. Moshakis, R. A. J. McIlhinney, and A. M. Neville, *Br. J. Cancer 44*:663 (1981).
54. M. J. Embleton, B. Gunn, V. S. Byers, and R. W. Baldwin, *Br. J. Cancer 43*: 582 (1981).
55. C. Berche, J. -P. Mach, J. -D. Lumbroso, C. Langlais, F. Aubry, F. Buchegger, S. Carrel, P. Rougier, C. Parmentier, and M. Tubiana, *Br. Med. J. 285*:1447 (1982).

56. D. M. Goldenberg, *Cancer Res. 40*:2957 (1980).
57. D. A. Scheinberg, M. Strand, and O. A. Gansow, *Science 215*:1511 (1982).
58. S. A. Gaffar, K. D. Pant, D. Shochat, S. J. Bennett, and D. M. Goldenberg, *Int. J. Cancer 27*:101 (1981).
59. F. J. Primus, C. A. Clark, and D. M. Goldenberg, in *Diagnostic Immunohisto-chemistry* (R. A. DeLellis, ed.), Masson, New York, 1981, p. 263.
60. D. M. Goldenberg, S. A. Gaffar, S. J. Bennett, and J. L. Beach, *Cancer Res. 41*:4354 (1981).
61. T. Ghose, A. Guda, J. Tai, A. S. MacDonald, and S. T. Norvell, *Cancer 36*: 1646 (1975).
62. T. Ghose and A. H. Blair, *J. Nat. Cancer Inst. 61*:657 (1978).
63. S. E. Order, J. L. Klein, D. Ettinger, P. Alderson, S. Siegelman, and P. Leichner, *Cancer Res. 40*:3001 (1980).
64. R. Arnon and M. Sela, *Immunol. Rev. 62*:5 (1982).

13 APPROACHES TO CANCER THERAPY USING MONOCLONAL ANTIBODIES

Mary E. Kirch/Sloan-Kettering Institute, New York, New York

INTRODUCTION

It has been a long-standing hope that the specificity of the immune system might one day provide a modality for the treatment of human neoplasia. Attempts at passive immunotherapy in experimental systems date back to the demonstration of Gorer and Amos (1) that antibody could suppress the growth of transplanted murine leukemia cells. Even in this early study, one of the major limitations of antibody therapy was already apparent: There was a requirement that antibody be administered concomitantly with the tumor inoculum, or very soon thereafter.

Among the other obstacles to overcome were difficulties in defining suitable target antigens for immunotherapy and numerous ways by which tumor cells can "escape" from antibody-mediated destruction (see below). In general terms, experimental trials of passive immunotherapy of neoplasia over the past 25 years have proved disappointing. Antibody has proved to be relatively ineffective in abrogating tumor growth, although enhanced survival times of experimental hosts bearing transplanted tumors could frequently be achieved (2,3). However, it is now apparent that the antisera employed in those studies may have been inappropriate for definitive evaluation of passive immunotherapy. Despite extensive efforts to raise specific antisera, and great care in absorption, therapy trials were limited by the then existing technology. Because the specificity of the antisera were often incompletely defined, it was difficult to analyze the underlying causes of tumor cells escape. Furthermore, the antisera consisted of complex immunoglobulin mixtures and did not permit an assessment of the relative contribution of each antibody subclass to effective therapy, or lack thereof. The monoclonal antibodies (MAs) produced by hybridoma technology (4,5) eliminate some of these problems. Even in those cases where heteroimmunization yields MAs that define previously unrecognized antigens, the monospecificity of the identifying antibody simplifies the task of characterizing the target antigen. The restriction of MAs to a single immunoglobulin isotype will also make it possible to select antibody of that class that is most effective in completely eliminating tumor cells. Thus, the development of hybridoma technology provides a rationale for a reassessment of the role of antibody in passive immunotherapy of neoplasia.

Historic Perspective

Experimental Models of Passive Immunotherapy: An excellent review by Rosenberg and Terry (2) summarizes experiences with passive immunotherapy. The reader is referred to this article for a résumé of experimental models of passive immunotherapy that predate 1977. Since that time, two features of murine leukemias have made it possible to study passive immunotherapy under conditions where the target antigen is well defined, even when heteroantisera are employed. First, murine leukemia virus (MuLV) is an etiological agent of many murine T-cell derived leukemias, and the well-characterized MuLV antigens constitute a suitable target for passive immunotherapy. Second, B-cell tumors are monoclonally derived (6,7). As a result, the idiotypic determinants (Id) associated with the cell-surface immunoglobulin are shared among the tumor cells, but only an extremely small fraction of normal B lymphocytes express the relevant Id that represents, in practice, a tumor-specific antigen. These two types of antigens have been used to study the effects of antibody on both primary and transplanted tumors. Of particular interest are those studies directed at elucidating the mechanism by which antibody effects target cell destruction in vivo.

Antigens expressed by virally induced tumors have provided one system in which the efficacy of passively administered antibody has been explored. Mice of the AKR strain usually die of spontaneously occurring T-cell-derived leukemia.

Development of this disease is related to the presence of endogenous C-type virus providing a rationale for preventive serotherapy with antibodies directed at MuLV. Huebner and co-workers (8) found that administration of type-specific anti-MuLV prior to evolution of disease would suppress virus expression and leukemogenesis later in life. Passive administration of antibodies to a mixture of MuLV resulted in a similar suppression in wild mice (9) with a high incidence of spontaneous leukemia. Schafer and co-workers (10) found that administration of antibody to Friend leukemia virus delayed leukemia onset. There was a striking diminution of leukemia incidence in the offspring up to 55 weeks of age (less than 15%, versus 60% of control mice). Passively administered anti-MuLV has also been shown to inhibit x-ray-induced leukemogenesis (11). Thus passive immunotherapy bears some promise as a prophylactic means to control viral oncogenesis, but at present, although antibody prolongs host survival, viremia and the ensuing leukemia ultimately occur.

Antibodies directed at virus-associated antigens have also been found to influence the growth of transplanted tumors. Early studies by Old and co-workers (12) showed that rat antiserum with specificity for the cell-surface antigen (G) associated with Gross virus-induced leukemia suppressed the growth of syngeneically transplanted murine leukemias bearing the target antigen. A number of important points were elucidated by these studies: (a) Antibody administration within 24 hr after tumor cell transfer was effective in eradicating a tumor inoculum. If antibody transfer was delayed until 3 days after tumor inoculation, the effect was to prolong host survival without curing, although free antibody was available in the serum. (b) The mechanisms by which antibody eradicated the tumor cells appeared to be a direct one. Activity immunity of protected hosts was not demonstrated by a second tumor challenge in the absence of antibody. (c) Antibody was effective over an extended dose range. Even antibody doses that were below the minimum effective dose required for cures produced some beneficial effect (i.e., extended survival time).

In other studies, syngeneic hyperimmune serum was produced by immunization with murine adenocarcinoma 755 (13). Extremely small quantities of serum were able to protect syngeneic hosts if transferred concomitantly with, but not necessarily at the same site as, the tumor cells. The effective antibody was apparently IgG rather than IgM and recognized virus-related cell-surface antigens (14). To determine whether increasing amounts of antibody could compensate for an increase in tumor burden, a careful titration of antibody versus tumor cell number was performed. In this system, increased amounts of antiserum abrogated the growth of tumor inocula (5×10^5 cells) that were up to 5000 times the number of tumor cells that were lethal to 100% of host mice in the absence of therapy, but larger inocula were not tested (13). Similar passive immunotherapy experiments in allogeneic hosts revealed a marked strain specificity in the ability of antiserum to curtail tumor growth, suggesting that a host effector component was involved in tumor cell destruction. Microscopic analysis of peritoneal aspirates suggested that cells of the monocyte/macrophage lineage were participating in target cell destruction.

Immunization of A2G mice with cell-free preparation of Ehrlich ascites tumor cells previously infected with influenza virus confers protection against subsequent challenge with the same tumor (15). Serum from immunized hosts contained an IgG antibody (16) that provided transient protection against tumor implantation when transferred to unimmunized recipients (17). The antiserum mediated target cell damage but not lysis in vitro in the presence of peritoneal exudate cells (18), whereas in vivo target cell lysis could be detected within 30 min of inoculation of tumor cells and specific antiserum (19). Treatment of experimental mice with silica prior to tumor cell transfer abrogated the accelerated clearance of labeled tumor cells (20). These experiments suggested that antibody-dependent cellular cytotoxicity (ADCC) was involved in target cell destruction, but the nature of the effector cell was not established.

The C3H lymphoma has been studied as a target for allo- or syngeneic antiserum-mediated suppression in a thorough series of experiments (21–26). Antibody of the IgG_1 class was effective in suppressing the growth of syngeneically transplanted lymphoma cells (21). Macrophages or platelets were effective in restoring tumor suppression in mice that had been irradiated to abrogate responsiveness to passive immunotherapy (22). Among the factors that limited the effectiveness of antibody therapy were the time of tumor residency prior to antibody administration and the size of tumor inoculum (24). In this system, an increase in cell number after tumor cell transfer appeared to be the limiting factor when antibody administration was delayed; there was no inherent difference in susceptibility of tumor cells to regulation at different times after cell transfer. On the other hand, antibody was not the limiting factor when suppression of large (10^6) tumor inocula was attempted, suggesting that a host effector component might be present in limiting amounts. In other experiments (25) therapy-sensitive numbers of tumor cells (10^5) were transferred to one leg muscle of syngeneic hosts, and therapy-insensitive numbers (10^6) to the other leg of the same host; systemic administration of antibody was achieved by intraperitoneal injection. The lower dose of tumor cells was completely suppressed in 62% of the mice, whereas the larger inocula, in the same mice, were not suppressed. Transfer of exogenous macrophages with the tumor cells partially restored antibody-mediated suppression of large tumor inocula (10^6 cells). The authors concluded that a local deficiency in macrophages was responsible for the ineffectiveness of antibody in suppressing the growth of large numbers of tumor cells injected at a single site. It was suggested that the macrophage inadequacy was due either to a deficiency in activation of macrophages within the tumor, or to inadequate mobilization of macrophages to the tumor site. In vitro studies gave further support to the involvement of macrophages in inhibiting tumor cell proliferation in the presence of specific antiserum (24,25). Both cytostatic and cytolytic effects of antibody plus effector cells were detected by in vitro assays. Together, macrophages and antibody rapidly reduced the proliferative capacity of the target cell (26). These cells remained metabolically active in the cytostatic state, but did not resume proliferation, and eventually died in culture (27).

The idiotypic determinants (Id) associated with cell-surface immunoglobulin of neoplastic B cells would seem to provide an ideal opportunity to study immunotherapy in a situation where the target antigen is well characterized. However, idiotype-directed immunotherapy may employ unique regulatory avenues that may not apply to antibody-mediated control of tumors of non-B-cell origin. The growth and differentiation of normal B lymphocytes is subject to T-cell regulation (28) and may be under antibody-mediated, or "network," control (29). Similarly, the growth and differentiation of a transplantable murine myeloma has been shown to be subject to normal immunoregulatory controls (30). Thus in the case of B-cell tumors, anti-tumor antibody (anti-Id) might intervene to bring the tumor back under the control of the normal regulatory system. In this sense, immunotherapy trials involving B-cell neoplasms may represent a case of unique complexity, but some features of host responsiveness to passive immunotherapy may be shared with tumors of other origins.

The first attempts to exploit immunoglobulin as a target antigen for passive immunotherapy were performed with murine plasmacytomas. In one report, an alloantiserum was produced that recognized idiotypic determinants of the TEPC-15 plasmacytoma (31). The antiserum was administered intraperitoneally 1 day prior to tumor cell inoculation at the same site. Although antibody significantly prolonged survival time, in no case were the experimental mice cured. As only a single experiment was reported, it is possible that if the number of tumor cells had been reduced, or if the amount of antiserum had been varied, increased therapeutic effectiveness could have been achieved (see below). The first report of cures effected by passively administered anti-Id reagents used tumor inocula that were minimally above the number of tumor cells required for engraftment, and below the tumor dose that was lethal to 100% of recipient mice in the absence of therapy (32). Plasmacytomas, LPC-1 or MOPC-300, were transplanted subcutaneously into syngeneic mice and antibody was administered intraperitoneally within 30 min, and 24 and 48 hr after tumor cell transfer. In each case, some of the mice failed to show any sign of tumor growth (45% of LPC-1- and 57% of MOPC-300-bearing mice), whereas in others, initial growth was followed by regression. Thus administration of heterologous anti-Id antibody may have allowed the host's immune system to bring the tumor under control.

In the experiments outlined above, antibody was available for combination with surface immunoglobulin immediately after tumor cell transfer. As myelomas secrete large amounts of Id-bearing immunoglobulin, circulating antigen might impose serious limitations to passive immunotherapy of established, immunoglobulin-secreting myelomas. Furthermore, tumors that represent different stages of B-cell differentiation might respond differently to anti-Id attachment at the cell surface, or require the participation of different host mechanisms to effect tumor ablation. Although relatively uncommon in mice, tumors that reflect earlier stages of B-cell differentiation (e.g., chronic lymphocytic leukemia and Burkitt's lymphoma) are important in human clinical oncology. Recognition of these facts has lead several investigators to develop models with which to explore passive, anti-Id-mediated therapy of B-cell lymphomas.

The development of antigen-induced murine B-cell lymphomas (33) provided the first opportunity to study passive Id-directed immunotherapy of a tumor that represented an "early" stage of B-cell differentiation (34). In contrast to results with plasmacytomas, initial therapy trials with heteroantiserum containing antibodies directed at the Id of a B lymphoma, Ch1, were extremely promising (35). In experiments designed to elucidate the requirements for effective immunotherapy, a number of important parameters were identified (36): (a) Early transplant generations were more susceptible to anti-Id-mediated cures than were higher passage generations of the same tumor. If this finding can be verified in other experimental models, the clinical implications are obvious, as it suggests that primary tumors, early in the course of the disease, may be most susceptible to antibody-mediated regulation. (b) The amount of antiserum transferred was critical to the outcome of the experiment. Transfer of 2.0 ml of antiserum resulted in 78% cures, whereas none of the mice receiving 0.5 ml of antiserum survived beyond the time period of untreated controls. Although immunoglobin may represent unique target antigen in terms of the response to excessive amounts of antibody, this parameter should be probed with other models. (c) As has been observed in other experimental systems, excessive delay of antibody administration resulted in failure to cure. However, it could not be determined whether this difference was attributable to tumor burden, to other changes in the tumor population following transplantation, or simply to antibody insufficiency. (d) By combining cyclophosphamide chemotherapy (50 mg/kg body weight on day 11) with anti-Id (0.2 ml on day 16) the number of cures (100%) exceeded that which could be achieved by either treatment alone. Thus combination chemoimmunotherapy was effective in eradicating a well-established tumor. In other experiments (37) there was an upper limit to the number of tumor cells that could be eradicated by a single injection of 0.1 ml of antiserum. The minimum lethal dose of the CH1 lymphoma is a single cell, and significantly increased numbers of cures could be effected in mice bearing initial tumor inocula of up to 10^4 cells if antibody was inoculated within 24 hr of tumor. The therapeutic effects were attributable to IgG antibodies. Complement was not required for tumor cell destruction, as therapy was effective in genetically C5-deficient mice, or in mice in which C3 has been pharmacologically depleted.

The authors reported an interesting correlation between host age and response to immunotherapy, as the response of young adult mice was superior to that of very young (7 weeks) or older (1 year) hosts. The correlation with maturation and decline in natural killer (NK) activity (38,39) and the fact that NK cells are able to mediate ADCC in vitro (40,41) suggested that this mechanism might contribute to target cell destruction in vivo.

The spontaneous murine B-cell leukemia BCL_1, resembles the prolymphocytic form of human chronic lymphocytic leukemia. Krolick and co-workers (42) have used this tumor as a model in which to study anti-Id therapy. Administration of rabbit anti-Id at the time of tumor transfer completely suppressed the growth of 1×10^4 tumor cells in blood and spleen. In accord with the results of Lanier and co-workers (37), this was highly significant, as a single BCL_1 tumor cell is sufficient to kill the host. To evaluate the effectiveness of anti-Id in treating mice with established tumors, 10^6 BLC_1 cells were inoculated intravenously into syngeneic BALB/c mice. Splenectomy 2 weeks after tumor transfer retarded the appearance of circulating tumor cells. Administration of anti-Id after splenectomy further postponed the appearance of tumor cells, but this combination of immunotherapy with surgery was ineffective in eliminating the tumor.

Tumor Cell "Escape" from Antibody-Mediated Destruction: The survival and subsequent proliferation of even a single clonogenic tumor cell following treatment will have the result that such therapy will prolong survival, but not cure. However, an understanding of the mechanism(s) by which therapy is evaded may provide an opportunity to devise protocols of improved therapeutic effectiveness. Experiences with transplanted tumors have defined several means by which tumor cells avoid antibody-mediated destruction (43,44). In general terms, tumor cell "escape" may be due to inherent features of the tumor cell population and/or to deficiencies in a required host effector system.

At the level of the tumor cell itself, examples of tumor resistance to immune destruction include those that are attributable to (a) spontaneous shedding or rapid turnover of cell-surface antigen (45), (b) reversible antibody-induced modulation of cell-surface antigen (46-48), and (c) selection of stable, antigen-negative (or low) variants (49,50). Furthermore, other cyclic changes that occur during the transplantation cycle may render the population sensitive to antibody-mediated destruction at one time, while conferring resistance at another (51). In this context, variations in cell-surface antigens (52) and/or membrane lipid constituents (53,54) may confer cyclic resistance to cytolysis and may be secondary to changes in the cell cycle distribution of the population (55-60).

Antibody may act in concert with complement, macrophages, and/or natural killer cells to abrogate tumor cell growth in vivo. In the face of established neoplastic disease, each of these effector systems may become depleted (61-68). Thus, by virtue of its immunosuppressive properties, the tumor may escape antibody-mediated destruction. Furthermore, the effect of passively administered antibody may be to enhance or facilitate the growth of transplanted tumors (69-73), resulting in *decreased* host survival time. In this case, antibody may interfere with the host's ability to develop an effective cytotoxic T-cell response. In addition, antibody attachment at the cell surface may increase the ability of the tumor cells to lodge and grow in secondary sites (i.e., increase metastasis). Attempts to elucidate the causes of enhancement have indicated that antibody class or concentration are important, but the data often present apparent contradictions (74-

78). Regardless of the mechanism(s) involved, a better understanding of the events of tumor "escape" will be required as a foundation for defining those conditions under which antibody therapy will be effective.

Selection of Target Antigens for Passive Immunotherapy

Conventional and monoclonal antibodies have defined many antigens that are preferentially associated with neoplastic tissues, some of which may constitute targets for passive immunotherapy. Diagnostic assays for circulating tumor antigens have been limited by the restrictions imposed by the expression and release of antigens in association with nonmalignant disease. On the other hand, once a diagnosis of malignancy has been made, these restrictions do not apply to antibody therapy. A new set of criteria for the ideal target antigen for passive immunotherapy by antibody transfer can be defined:

1. Absence of antigen from the surface of normal cells of the individual
2. Presence on the surface of all tumor cells, to minimize the possibility of tumor cell escape
3. Absence of large quantities of free, circulating antigen
4. Common representation among tumors of similar derivation (i.e., not unique to the individual)
5. Cytolysis or cytostasis to follow as an inevitable consequence of antibody attachment at the cell surface

It may ultimately prove to be the case that only the truly "tumor-specific" antigens are those that are attributable to a chemical or viral oncogenic event. All other tumor markers may represent inappropriately expressed, but otherwise normal, gene products or differentiation antigens. Tumor cells frequently express high levels of oncodevelopmental gene products (79,80). The expression of these antigens in normal adult cells is usually limited to a small number of cells; alternatively, there may be a relative paucity of antigen on the surface of normal cells. In either case, the pattern of expression of the target antigen would provide a basis for the selective destruction of tumor cells. In this regard, hematological neoplasms present several advantages that may not be shared with solid tumors, as there may be greater latitude in choosing suitable target antigens for passive immunotherapy. The fact that hemopoietic stem cells persist in the adult makes it possible to consider target antigens that are shared among tumor cells and normal cells. Although normal cells bearing the "target" differentiation antigen will be "sacrificed," this can be tolerated if the normal compartment can be replenished with time.

One of the challenges of MA therapy is the presence of large quantities of circulating antigen of patients bearing leukemias and solid tumors. The problems associated with circulating antigen stem from the fact that (a) this antigen represents an accessible reservoir that may prohibit free antibody from reaching the target cell and (b) large quantities of circulating antigen–antibody complexes may contribute to pathophysiological effects of MA therapy. The development of MAs that recognize cell-surface-associated antigens that are not readily shed into the bloodstream offers one approach to this problem; however, other avenues exist. It may be possible to cause a diminution in circulating tumor-associated antigen by surgically removing the primary tumor in the case of solid tumors or by reducing the tumor burden by cytoreductive chemotherapy in the case of hematological neoplasms. Moreover, it may be possible to treat tumors that are not susceptible to this approach by simply increasing the dose of MA, as shown by the example of anti-Id therapy of human B lymphoma that was successful in the face of low levels of idiotype-positive immunoglobulin (81). Furthermore, studies with murine and rat alpha-fetoprotein-producing hepatomas have shown that anti-alpha-fetoprotein antibodies can effectively diminish circulating alpha-fetoprotein without significant pathological consequences (82–84). The consequences of circulating antigen–antibody complexes may also be reduced with monoclonal reagents as opposed to conventional antibodies, since MAs recognize only a single antigenic determinant on most protein antigens, and would therefore be expected to form smaller antigen-antibody complexes, which may be cleared without imposing kidney damage.

If therapy by passive administration of antibody is to become an effective modality in the treatment of human neoplastic disease, there is a requirement that antibody eradicate all clonogenic tumor cells. In view of the well-documented heterogeneity of human and murine primary neoplasms (85,86), this would appear to be a formidable obstacle. Thus the heterogeneity of primary tumors could lead to the outgrowth of stable, antigen-negative, therapy-resistant cells or variants (49). Although it may be true that spontaneously occurring human tumors may not be analogous to many of our experimental models in terms of the degree of heterogeneity within the tumor cell population, this consideration does not obviate the possibility of antibody therapy. There undoubtedly are cases where individual tumors are heterogeneous with respect to expression of an individual target antigen, but it may be possible to select target antigens that *are* consistently expressed at least on the surface of the clonogenic tumor cells. On the other hand, it may be possible to circumvent this problem by directing antibodies to more than one target antigen, hoping to achieve complete eradication of the tumor burden by fractional cell killing, akin to the approach that has proved fruitful in combination protocols with conventional chemotherapeutic agents.

The suggestion that target antigens should be widely distributed among similar patient populations is a purely practical limitation. For example, although the Id determinants present on the surface of B-cell-derived neoplasms constitute an ideal target antigen in terms of exquisite specificity for the tumor cell, it would clearly be preferable, in terms of time and commitment of resources, if a more widely distributed antigen were suitable as a therapeutic target (e.g., heavy-chain isotypic determinants). Thus, if a decision were made to include antibody in a treatment protocol, the requisite reagents would be available immediately. Al-

though heavy-chain markers are shared with circulating and cell-associated immunoglobulin of normal lymphocytes, as discussed previously, neither of these facts
obviate their potential usefulness as therapeutic targets. Furthermore, each of
these sources of normal antigen is diminished by chemotherapy and by neoplastic
disease, making this approach quite feasible in terms of relative specificity.

The criterion that antibody attachment at the cell surface must necessarily
abrogate the potential of that cell to propagate itself is the most difficult to satisfy.
As mentioned above, tumor cells may escape from antibody-mediated destruction
either by direct means or by subverting host effector systems that may be required
for their destruction. As MAs recognize a single antigenic determinant on most
protein antigens, the degree of cross-linking, and hence antibody-induced clearance of cell-surface antigen, may be reduced relative to conventional antisera.
Furthermore, as it is clear that the target antigen itself has some "control" over
whether modulation ensues (48), in vitro studies with MAs should prove informative as to whether newly defined antigens are likely to constitute effective targets
in vivo. Other approaches to circumventing the problem of tumor cell "escape"
are discussed later.

TREATMENT OF TRANSPLANTED MURINE LEUKEMIAS WITH MONO-
CLONAL ANTIBODIES DIRECTED AT LYMPHOCYTE DIFFERENTIATION
ANTIGENS: A MODEL FOR PASSIVE IMMUNOTHERAPY

Recognizing that differentiation antigens constitute potential targets for therapy
of human hematological neoplasms, we have developed a parallel murine model
system for MA therapy. Murine leukemias derived from cells of T-cell lineage
display many of the differentiation antigens present on their normal cell counterparts (87–89). Antibody directed at the T-lymphocyte differentiation antigen
Thy-1 had previously been shown by others to suppress the growth of murine T
lymphoma cells in vivo (90,91) and in vitro (92,93). The studies of Bernstein
and co-workers (90,91) were important in showing that syngeneically transplanted
tumors were susceptible to regulation by MAs directed at differentiation antigens
that were present on normal host lymphoid cells, which might have been expected
to remove large quantities of circulating antibody, thereby contributing to pathophysiological effects, as well as reducing the amount of MA available for combination with tumor cells. The fact that Thy-1 shared by the tumor, T-cells, and
a subset of NK cells (94) makes the effector mechanism of antibody-mediated
regulation difficult to analyze. In order to establish a model that might facilitate
in vivo analysis of requisite effector function, we have transported murine T-cell
leukemias into hosts that were congenic for the target lymphocyte differentiation
antigen [i.e., displayed the antithetical form of the antigen (95)]. The normal
differentiation antigen mimics the situation where the tumor cell displays antigen(s)
not represented on normal host tissues. This model avoids perturbations of

naturally occurring (and perhaps biologically significant) tumor–host interactions that might otherwise occur as a consequence of administration of lymphocyte-reactive antibody. The objective was to define those parameters that contribute to curtailment of tumor growth and the limitations of passive immunotherapy. By using this information to define the effector mechanisms of MA therapy, it was hoped that it could be possible to define more effective therapeutic protocols.

Experimental Protocol

Suitable target antigens for this study included the lymphocyte differentiation antigens Thy-1.2, and Lyt-2.2, to which MA had previously been developed in this laboratory (U. Hammerling, Sloan-Kettering Institute). Established tumor cell lines expressing the relevant antigen and appropriate congenic hosts were made available by Dr. E. A. Boyse of the Sloan-Kettering Institute in New York. Although lymphocyte differentiation antigens are only weakly immunogenic (if at all) on congenic immunization, it was first necessary to establish the transplantation characteristics of each tumor in the prospective congenic host. Pertinent characteristics of the tumor used in these studies are shown in Table 1. In each case, it was possible to define a tumor challenge dose that would quickly and consistently kill the congenic recipient in the absence of therapy. In initial therapy experiments, tumor cells were inoculated subcutaneously at the nape of the neck. This site of injection was chosen, as it also permitted an evaluation of the ability of the antibody to interfere with the normal dissemination of these tumors, which is to lodge and grow in lymphoid organs (e.g., spleen and lymph node.) In order to provide the requirement that antibody "home" to the site of tumor inoculation to eradicate the tumor, antibody was administered intraperitoneally. To determine the cause of death and extent of disease, mice were routinely autopsied within 24 hr of death. The general protocol for these experiments is illustrated by example with ASL.1 in Figure 1.

Parameters That Contribute to Effective Therapy

Immunoglobulin Class: Early experiments using conventional antibodies indicated that antibody class was a major determinant in the outcome of therapy trials of tumor-bearing animals, but this issue remains to be conclusively resolved. The homogeneity of MAs provides antibodies of a single immunoglobulin subclass and with defined and restricted specificity. Since different classes of immunoglobulin mediate different biological effector functions, differences in therapeutic effectiveness are also potentially informative as to the means by which antibody is prolonging host survival or effecting cures. Monoclonal antibodies of the IgG_3 and IgM classes, with specificity for the alloantigenic determinants of Thy-1.2, were available in this laboratory to study differential effects on host survival. Clone 9/37 was derived from cell fusion of spleen cells of an AKR mouse immunized with B6 thymocytes; the antibody is IgG_3 (κ). Ascites containing 9/37 anti-

Table 1 Characteristics of Murine T-Cell Leukemias

Tumor	Strain of origin	Phenotype (target antigen)	Congenic host	LD_{50}[a]
ASL.1	A	Thy-1.2	A/Thy-1.1 ♂	10^2
			(A/Thy-1.1 $\times$ B6/Thy-1.1)F$_1$ ♂	10^2
			(A/Thy-1.1 $\times$ AKR/H-2^b)F$_1$ ♂	10^2
ERLD	C57BL/6 (B6)	Lyt-2.2	B6/Lyt-2.1 ♂ or ♀	10^2
EL4	B6	Lyt-2.2	B6/Lyt-2.1 ♂ or ♀	10^1

[a]LD_{50} = number of tumor cells (derived from syngeneic passage) required to kill 50% of host mice upon subcutaneous inoculation.

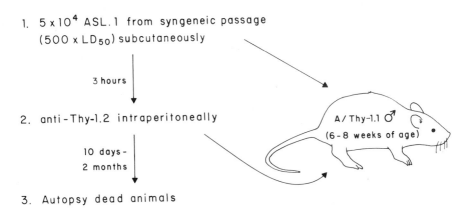

1. 5×10^4 ASL.1 from syngeneic passage
   $(500 \times LD_{50})$ subcutaneously

   3 hours

2. anti-Thy-1.2 intraperitoneally

   A/Thy-1.1 ♂
   (6-8 weeks of age)

   10 days-
   2 months

3. Autopsy dead animals

4. Reinject survivors* at 2 months with ASL.1

5. Statistical analysis

Figure 1 Protocol for anti-Thy 1.2 MA treatment of ASL.1 (Thy-1.2$^+$, A strain-derived leukemia) grown in congenic hosts. * Representative animals have been observed for a period of 6 months. Those animals that are still alive at 2 months following tumor challenge do not subsequently develop leukemia. We operationally refer to those animals that pass the 2-month survival point as "cured."

body was generated by growing the hybridoma in (BALB × AKR)F$_1$ hosts (pristane-treated 1 week prior to hybridoma cell transfer). Clone 6/68 was derived from (A/Thy-1.1 × AKR/H-2^b)F$_1$ spleen cells after immunizations with the Thy-1.2$^+$ tumor ASL.1; the antibody is IgM (κ). As the fusion resulted in a hybridoma of triple genetic heritage, clone 6/68 was grown in Swiss nude mice, from which serum was obtained.

In order to evaluate the relative therapeutic effectiveness of clone 9/37 versus 6/68 antibody, 5×10^4 ASL.1 tumor cells (derived from syngeneic passage) were transferred subcutaneously to A/Thy-1.1 male mice; this tumor challenge dose is 500 times the LD$_{50}$ in this strain. Antibody was administered intraperitoneally 3 hr later. In initial trials, antibody doses were chosen that resulted in circulating antibody titers of 1:400 (measured by cytotoxicity assays) after antibody transfer. As shown in Figure 2, antibody of the IgG$_3$ subclass was extremely effective in generating long-term survivors ($P < 0.001$ relative to controls). On the other hand, the IgM antibody significantly increased the survival time of treated mice ($P < 0.05$) relative to controls, without significantly increasing the percentage of cured mice [25% cures, $P < 0.1$ relative to controls (95)].

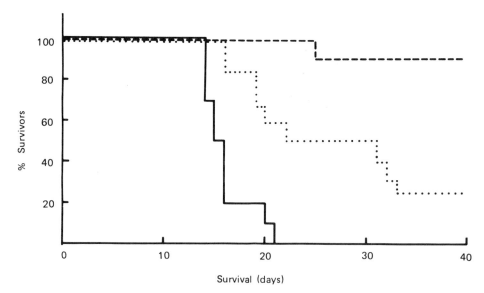

Figure 2 Therapy of ASL-1 with monoclonal antibody directed at Thy-1. A/Thy-1.1 male mice (8–10 weeks of age) were injected subcutaneously (at the nape of the neck) with 5×10^4 viable ASL.1 tumor cells derived from syngeneic passage. Antibody injections were given intraperitoneally 3 hr after tumor inoculation and on alternate days for 1 week. Control animals (10) received MOPC-70A (0.2 ml ascites, diluted 1:4) as nonspecific, myeloma-derived immunoglobin (—); experimental groups (10 mice per group) received anti-Thy-1.2 from clone 9/37, IgG_3 anti-Thy-1.2 (0.2 ml ascites, diluted 1:4) (- - -), or clone 6/68, IgM anti-Thy-1.2 (0.2 ml nude mouse serum, diluted 1:10) (•••) (From Ref. 95.)

As A/Thy-1.1 mice are deficient in the fifth component of complement (96), it was possible that IgM antibodies would be more effective than IgG_3 if the experiments were repeated in mice with an intact hemolytic complement system. This does not prove to be the case: When the experiment was performed in (A/Thy-1 $\times$ B6/Thy-1.1)F_1 mice, the result of IgM antibody administration was again to prolong host survival time, without effecting cures (97). Similar results were obtained if antibody was administered chronically in order to compensate for the shorter in vivo half-life of IgM antibody (98) or if antibody was administered at the site of tumor, in order to compensate for differences in the abilities of IgG and IgM antibodies to penetrate into extravascular spaces (99) and "home" to the tumor.

IgM anti-Thy-1 antibodies extended the survival time of congenic host mice bearing the transplanted ASL.1 leukemia; in contrast, Bernstein and co-workers (90,91) found that anti-Thy-1 antibodies of the IgM class were completely ineffective in suppressing the growth of syngeneically transplanted AKR leukemias. Furthermore, IgG_3 antibodies produced no cures in the AKR leukemia system (90,91), whereas they generated long-term survivors in the ASL.1 system (95). More work must be done to determine the reasons for these disparate results, but the observation of Palladino and co-workers (100) that IgM MAs retard the growth of syngeneically transplanted Meth-A sarcoma cells supports our observation that IgM antibodies prolong survival time in hosts bearing transplanted tumors.

An important difference between antibodies of the IgM and IgG classes lies in their ability to mediate cytolysis by alternate mechanisms. IgM antibodies are generally considered to be more efficient, on a molar basis, than are IgG antibodies in mediating complement-dependent target cell lysis. On the other hand, IgG antibodies are effective in mediating target cell lysis by antibody-dependent cellular cytotoxicity (ADCC) when either spleen cells or activated macrophages are used as the effector cells against antibody-coated nucleated targets (91,101). IgM antibodies do not mediate ADCC under these conditions (91, 101). Although it is tempting to speculate that the reason for the greater therapeutic effectiveness of IgG antibodies is related to the fact that antibodies of that class mediate ADCC, whereas IgM antibodies do not, one is reluctant to draw this conclusion without more direct evidence. The very homogeneity of MA favors an idiosyncratic result that may be due to other factors. For example, slight differences in the antigenic determinant recognized by the antibody or differences in affinity may also play a critical role in the outcome of the therapeutic trials.

Tumor Burden: Results of other investigators have suggested that one of the limitations to passive immunotherapy is the extent of tumor mass; that is, there is an upper limit to the number of tumor cells that can be eradicated by antibody therapy. Although anti-Thy-1.2 treatment was capable of eradicating tumor inocula of 500 times the LD_{50}, it was of interest to determine whether similar restrictions would apply in this system. It had previously been demonstrated that 100 μg of 9/37 (IgG_3) anti-Thy-1.2 antibody was the minimum effective dose when 5×10^4 tumor cells were transferred (95). To examine the effectiveness of therapy on animals bearing larger tumor burdens, a 1-mg dose of antibody was chosen. Although antibody extended host survival time by 52% for tumor cell inocula of 5×10^5 and by 23% for mice inoculated with 5×10^6 cells, the maximum number of cells that could be treated (i.e., resulting in cures) was 5×10^4 (Table 2).

In considering the causes for tumor cell escape, antibody does not appear to be the limiting factor, as the antibody dose was 10 times the amount required to destroy lower cell numbers, and circulating antibody could be detected in all mice up to 10 days following tumor inoculation. If the ASL.1 tumor were heterogenous with respect to susceptibility to antibody-mediated suppression, then the rela-

Table 2 Maximum Therapy-Sensitive Tumor Burden

Number of ASL.1 cells (subcutaneous)	Immunoglobulin (intraperitoneal)	Survivors (%)	Survival time (days)[a]
5×10^4	9/37 anti-Thy-1.2	89	not applicable
5×10^4	MOPC 70A	0	11.3 (10–12)
5×10^5	9/37 anti-Thy-1.2	11	14.3 (12–16)[b]
5×10^5	MOPC 70A	0	9.3 (9–12)
5×10^6	9/37 anti-Thy-1.2	0	10.7 (9–14)[b]
5×10^6	MOPC 70A	0	8.7 (8-9)

[a]Average survival time of animals that die of tumor, with the range in parentheses.

[b]Survival time significantly increased with respect to controls ($P < 0.05$).

Source: Ref. 102.

tive insensitivity of large tumor inocula might be attributable to the selection of stable, therapy-insensitive variants (49). To test this possibility, tumor cells were removed from moribund mice and transferred to previously unchallenged recipients in therapy-sensitive numbers. If variant selection had occurred, the tumor would have been expected to be refractory to therapy. In experiments of this kind, the tumor was found to be sensitive to therapy (Table 3), indicating that variant selection had not occurred.

Timing of Antibody Administration: It has frequently been reported that there is a critical time period after tumor cell transfer during which the tumor will respond to antibody therapy (1,12,24,36), but the causes often remain to be elucidated. It had previously been found that a similar critical time point existed for treatment of ASL.1; that is, antibody administration at 2 or 24 hr was equally effective in curing the host, but if antibody was administered at 48 hr, the result was to prolong survival, without curing (95). In view of the fact that there is an upper limit to the number of tumor cells that can be eradicated by antibody therapy, it was possible that at 48 hr the tumor burden exceeded this limit. In order to test this possibility, similar experiments were performed using fewer tumor cells (102). However, when antibody treatment of mice bearing a reduced tumor burden was delayed for 48 hr, a similar time dependency was observed; a delay of 48 hr resulted in prolonged host survival, but failed to cure (Table 4). Thus tumor cell "escape" as the result of inappropriately timed antibody administration did not appear to be secondary to a tumor burden that exceeded a critical threshold. An extremely short in vivo doubling time of less than 6 hr would be required to bring the tumor burden above the therapy sensitive level of 5×10^4 cells. A possible explanation is that only the

Table 3 Test for Variant Selection In Vivo

Experiment	Antibody	Survival[a] time (days)	Percentage of survivors
1.1[b]	Anti-Thy-1.2	12.0	0
	Control	10.0	0
1.2A[c]	Anti-Thy-1.2	NA[d]	80
	Control	13.0	0
1.2B[c]	Anti-Thy-1.2	NA	90
	Control	14.5	0
2.1[b]	Anti-Thy-1.2	18.7	0
2.2A[c]	Anti-Thy-1.2	NA	70
	Control	13.7	0
2.2B[c]	Anti-Thy-1.2	NA	100
	Control	15.7	0

[a]Days after tumor cell transfer.

[b]ASL.1 tumor cells from syngeneic passage (5×10^5) were inoculated subcutaneously. Immunoglobulin (9/37 anti-Thy-1.2 or MOPC 70A control) was inoculated intraperitoneally 2 hr after tumor.

[c]Tumor cells from an individual moribund mouse were adjusted to $5 \leqslant 10^4 /0.2$ ml injection and transferred to new hosts for standard therapy trials.

[d]NA, not applicable.

Source: Ref. 102.

tumor cells at the subcutaneous inoculation site were susceptible to regulation, and that between 24 and 48 hr the tumor was able to reach sites that were inaccessible. Although one cannot rule out the possibility that some tumor cells are able to sequester themselves, the fact that there was a tumor mass at the site of inoculation (on autopsy) suggests that there was another underlying cause. In general terms, it is likely that the tumor cell population undergoes a critical change with respect to susceptibility to antibody regulation, or that the tumor imposes restrictions on a required host effector function.

Choice of Target Antigen/Tumor: To expand the number of target antigens under study, Lyt-2 was chosen as a second target for therapy trials. Tumors derived from C57BL/6 (B6) mice were transplanted into B6/Lyt-2.1 congenic hosts. Serum containing monoclonal anti-Lyt-2.2 (IgG_{2b}) was injected intraperitoneally into mice bearing subcutaneously transplanted tumors. Mice bearing ERLD were cured, or showed increased survival time as the result of specific antibody therapy (Table 5). In contrast, antibody caused a small but significant *decrease* in the survival time

Table 4 Delayed Antibody Administration: Effect on Host Survival

Number of ASL.1 cells (subcutaneous)	Survivors (%)	Survival time (days)[a]
5×10^4 (E)[b]	20	16.1 (15–17)
5×10^4 (C)[c]	0	12.7 (11–19)
1.25×10^4 (E)	10	23.9 (20–29)
1.25×10^4 (C)	0	14.2 (12–27)
3.125×10^3 (E)	10	21.2 (19-29)
3.125×10^3 (C)	0	14.6 (13–18)

[a]Average survival time of animals that die, with the range in parentheses.

[b]E, experimental group, treated intraperitoneally with 9/37 antibody 48 hr after subcutaneous tumor inoculation → A/Thy-1.1♂.

[c]C, control group, treated with MOPC 70A-containing ascites intraperitoneally 48 hr after tumor inoculation.

Source: Ref. 102.

of mice bearing EL4. Although Snell (69) proposed that the target cell itself was one of the arbiters of enhancement, this is the first definitive experimental evidence that inherent features of the *target* cell may ultimately determine whether the host is helped or hindered by antibody administration.

Considerations of Effector Mechanisms of Passive Immunopatherapy

Complement-Mediated Cytolysis: It is unlikely that complement cytolysis is required for passive immunotherapy of the ASL.1 tumor. Maximum cure rates were achieved in mice that do not possess an intact hemolytic complement system (i.e., the C5-deficient strain A/Thy-1.1). Furthermore, IgM antibodies, which are considered to be more effective on a molar basis than IgG antibodies in complement-mediated cytolysis, were ineffective in generating long-term survivors, even in experiments in mice that are not C5 deficient, or under experimental conditions where the antibody was injected at the tumor inoculation site, to accommodate for differences in the ability of IgG and IgM antibodies to reach the site of the tumor. Although complement-mediated cytolysis does not appear to cause target cell destruction, it is possible that complement is indirectly involved in tumor cell destruction, possibly via C3-mediated chemotactic activity to recruit macrophages to the tumor site.

Endogenous Host Response: One way in which antibody might curtail tumor growth is to allow the host to establish an effective, endogenous response to the tumor, either by temporarily curtailing tumor growth, thereby providing sufficient time for the host to respond to the tumor, or by reducing the immunosuppressive

Table 5 Treatment of B6-Derived Leukemias with MA Directed at Lyt-2.2

Tumor:Host	Number of tumor cells[a]	Immunoglobulin	Survival time (days)[b]	Percentage of survivors
ERLD:B6/Lyt-2.1	1×10^4	Anti-Lyt-2.2	$31.1 (29-36)^c$	60^c
		Control	25.9 (21–29)	10
EL4:B6/Lyt-2.1	5×10^4	Anti-Lyt-2.2	$23.9 (22-27)^d$	0
		Control	26.1 (22–30)	0
EL4:(C3H/An $\times$ B6/Lyt-2.1)F$_1$	1×10^5	Anti-Lyt-2.2	$25.0 (22-31)^d$	10
		Control	30.7 (26–39)	10

[a]Number of tumor cells (from syngeneic passage) injected subcutaneously.

[b]Average survival time of those animals that die of tumor, with the range in parentheses.

[c]Significantly increased with respect to control ($P < 0.05$).

[d]Significantly decreased with respect to control ($P < 0.05$).

effects of the tumor. The inherent limitations of passive immunotherapy have led to speculation that cytotoxic T lymphocytes may be the only effective means of eradicating tumor cells (2). However, delayed hypersensitivity reactions have been shown to be effective in curtailing the growth of chemically induced fibrosarcomas (103,104), and there is some evidence that lymphoid tumors may represent a special case of tumor immunity as administration of anti-Id antibodies may act to bring transplanted B lymphoma cells under normal regulatory control (30). In any case, if the regulation of the ASL.1 tumor by anti-Thy-1.2 depended upon an immune response by the host, this should manifest itself with increased survival times or cures if the host were rechallenged with the same tumor. To test this possibility, A/Thy-1.1 mice that had previously been challenged with 5 × 10⁴ ASL.1 tumor cells, and "cured" by anti-Thy-1 antibody treatment, were rechallenged with tumor 2 months after the original inoculation. Age-matched controls were injected at the same time with tumor cells derived from syngeneic passage. Animals that had previously been exposed to tumor died within the same time course as animals that had not previously been exposed to tumor, even if the secondary tumor challenge was reduced to 1/100 of the original challenge dose (Table 6). Thus, an immune response by the host does not appear to contribute to passive immunotherapy in this system.

Antibody-Dependent Cellular Cytotoxicity: In studies with murine effector cells ADCC activity has been attributed to thymocytes (105,106), cells of the NK lineage (40,41,107), and effector cells of the monocyte/macrophage lineage (108-113). Several observations on the requirements for effective immunotherapy of ASL.1 were consistent with the possibility that one or both of the latter cell types might be involved: (a) IgM antibody, which is active in thymocyte-mediated ADCC (105,106) does not function in ADCC mediated by spleen cells or macrophages (91,101) and was relatively ineffective therapeutically. (b) The IgG₃ antibody used for treatment mediates ADCC against EL4 lymphoma target cells when macrophage cell lines (101) or spleen cells (unpublished data, Kirch) are used as effector cells. (c) The limitations with respect to tumor burden and timing of antibody administration suggest that a host effector function might be the limiting factor.

Other investigators have noted a correlation between the efficiency of antibodies of different immunoglobulin classes in in vitro ADCC assays and the ability to suppress tumor growth in vivo (91, 114–116). A more definitive way to demonstrate an in vivo role of ADCC would be to establish that depletion of a putative effector cell ablated the effectiveness of passive immunotherapy. Recognizing that NK cells and macrophages were the most likely candidates of ADCC, established pharmacological treatments were used to deplete these cell types prior to the initation of therapy trails. Iota-carrageenan was used to deplete macrophages (MPs) and NK cells according to the method of Cudkowitz and Hochman (117). Chronic admin-

Table 6 Secondary Tumor Challenge of Previously "Cured" Mice[a]

Number of ASL.1 cells	Group[b]	Survival time (days)	Number of mice
5×10^2	Control	17.0 ± 3.3[c]	10
	Experimental	15.6 ± 3.3[d]	24
5×10^3	Control	18.2×5.8	10
	Experimental	12.6 ± 2.8[d]	25
5×10^4	Control	12.0 ± 2.0	13
	Experimental	10.9 ± 0.8[d]	16

[a]"Cured" mice had previously been challenged with 5×10^4 ASL.1 tumor cells and treated with 9/37 anti-Thy-1.2.

[b]Experimental mice received the indicated number of tumor cells at 2 months following the initial challenge; age-matched control mice had not previously been exposed to tumor, and neither group received antibody.

[c]Survival time following tumor cell inoculation, ± 1 standard deviation.

[d]Not significantly different from control by Student's t test.

Source: Ref. 95.

istration of estrogen was used to selectively deplete NK cells (118,119). As shown in Table 7, administration of agents known to depress NK and/or macrophage activity did not reduce the ability of anti-Thy-1.2 to suppress the growth of the ASL.1 tumor. Although these experiments *suggest* that ADCC may not be involved as an effector mechanism in this system, conclusive proof is lacking. It would be necessary to confirm that ADCC activity is severely depressed at the site of tumor inoculation. These experiments have not yet been performed, and it remains a possibility that antibody attachment at the tumor cell surface leads to local activation or recruitment of a sufficient number of ADCC effector cells to bring about target cell destruction. The only experimental results that clearly indicate that the status of the host may play a role in the efficacy of therapy are those in which host age was the variable (Table 7). Although other investigators have noted a correlation between host age and NK/ADCC activities (38,39) other environmental factors may play a role in limiting therapeutic effectiveness in the older animals.

Effector Cell-Independent Effects of MAs. Although antibody may effect target cell lysis via an immunologically mediated process, it is possible that the consequence of antibody attachment at the surface of the target cell would be a reduced proliferative capacity. One method of approaching this question is to examine the effects of antibody on cultured tumor cell lines, in the absence of host effector systems. In early studies of this kind, heteroantisera directed at antigens on the surface of murine leukemia cells (120) and at AFP on the surface

Table 7 Depletion of Host Effector Function: Effect on MA Therapy of ASL.1[a]

Effector	Function	Method of depletion	Treatment	9/37 (anti-Thy-1.2)	Survivors (%)	Survival time[b] (days)
NK	Natural cell-mediated cytotoxicty (ADCC?)	Iota-carrageenan i.v. Dose: 0.8 mg Timing: days −2,0	Iota-carrageenan −	−	0	12.8
			−	+	100	>2 mo.
MP	MP-mediated cytotoxicity (ADCC?)		+	−	0	12.7
			+	+	100	>2 mo.
NK	Natural cell-mediated cytotoxicity (ADCC?)	Estrogen Dose: 15-mg implant at 3–4 weeks of age Timing: chronic experiment begun at host age of 8–9 weeks	Estrogen −	−	0	13.4
			−	+	70	17.3
			+	+	0	10.3
			+	3	100	>2 mo.
NK	Natural cell-mediated cytotoxicity (ADCC?)	Natural: host age	Host age 1 year	−	0	11.4
			1 year	+	0	16.2
			6 months	−	0	11.9
			6 months	+	54	18.4
			6–8 weeks	−	0	11.4
			6–8 weeks	+	80	17.0

[a]All mice received 5×10^4 ASL.1 tumor cells subcutaneously on day 1 of the experiment. Where indicated, MA was inoculated 2 hr later, intraperitoneally. All host mice, A/Thy-1.1 or (A/Thy-1.1 X B6/Thy-1.1)F_1, were 6–8 weeks of age at the initiation of the experiments, except where noted.

[b]Average survival time of animals that die of tumor.

[c]>2 months survival = cured.

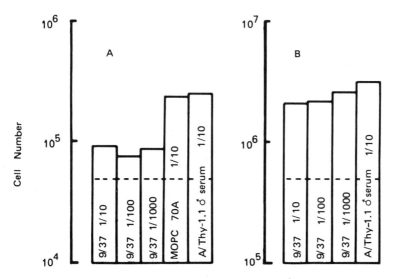

Figure 3 Cultured ASL.1 cells were plated in 25-cm^2 tissue culture flasks in a total volume of 5 ml of media (RPMI 1640 with 10% heat-inactivated fetal bovine serum). Antibody, control immunoglobulin, or mouse serum was added at the indicated final dilutions. Cultures containing (A) 5 × 10^4 or (B) 5 × 10^5 cells initially (- - -) were incubated at 37°C for 48 hr. *Source: Ref. 102.*

of rat hepatoma cells (121) significantly inhibited proliferation in vitro. Proliferation of neoplastic murine B cells can be inhibited in the presence of the appropriate anti-immunoglobulin reagents (122, 123). The observation of McGrath and co-workers (92,93) that murine T lymphoma proliferation was inhibited when cells were cultured in the presence of anti-Thy-1 or anti-MuLV MA suggested that ASL.1 might also be susceptible to some degree of regulation in the absence of host effector systems. In order to evaluate direct effects of antibody, cultured ASL.1 tumor cells were exposed to various concentrations of anti-Thy-1.2 (Fig. 3). The antibody that was effective in abrogating tumor growth in vivo also inhibited proliferation in vitro if the cells were plated at low density. Sensitivity to antibody was lost when cells were plated at higher density. This loss of sensitivity at the higher cell density was apparently not due to antibody insufficiency. A 1:1000 dilution of antibody inhibited proliferation when the cell density was 1 × 10^4 per milliliter, but when the cell number was increased only 10-fold (to 1 × 10^5/ml), even 100-fold greater amounts of antibody (i.e., 1:10 dilution) did not inhibit proliferation.

Clearly the inhibition of proliferation that occurred in vitro is not equal in magnitude to that achieved by anti-Thy-1.2 in vivo. The survival data from in vivo experiments indicate that greater than 99.2% of the tumor cells must have been eradicated to bring the tumor burden below the LD$_{50}$ level, whereas only a partial diminution of proliferation was observed in vitro. It may be that antibody does exert a portion of its therapeutic effects by direct interaction with vital cell membrane components, but that other in vivo effects contribute to the final eradication of the tumor. Alternatively, it may be that the in vitro experiments that have been performed to date do not adequately reflect in vivo conditions. In any case, the correlation between the in vivo experiments with respect to the limitations imposed by cell numbers suggests that it may be of value to probe between the two culture conditions, and to explore the possibility that further correlates exist between susceptibility to inhibition in vivo and in vitro.

APPROACHES TO INCREASING THE EFFECTIVENESS OF MONOCLONAL ANTIBODY THERAPY

Minimize Tumor Cell "Escape" via Modulation of Cell-Surface Antigen

Regardless of the mechanism(s) by which antibody-mediated cell destruction is effected in vivo, it is clear that premature clearance of cell-associated antibody precludes effective therapy. The problem of antibody-induced modulation of cell surface antigen may be reduced by using monoclonals, as opposed to conventional antibodies. However, experiences with treatment of human neoplasia indicate that otherwise promising target antigens do undergo modulation (124,125). Modulation represents a situation where antibody attachment leads to reversible clearance of antigens; thus the antigen will reappear when circulating antibody is removed (48). It has therefore been suggested that multiple injections of MA should be timed to coincide with maximal reexpression of the target antigen (126). Alternatively, it may be possible to circumvent this problem by biochemical modification of the antibody molecule, as suggested by Glennie and Stevenson (127). Although antigenic modulation may occur in the presence of univalant, Fab antibody fragments, the murine thymus leukemia antigen may be unique in this regard (128). Redistribution by bivalent antibody was required to modulate the surface immunoglobulin of the guinea pig $L_2 C$ leukemia (129). This suggested that a modified antibody molecule, which retained an intact Fc portion but was univalent, might alleviate the difficulties of modulation while providing the requisite effector function. Limited papain digestion of rabbit antibody to produce Fab/c molecules was found to fulfill this requirement (127). Fab/c derivatives of anti-Id antibody retained the ability to effect complement-mediated target cell lysis in vitro. The antibody fragments were much more effective than the parent molecule in prolonging survival of $L_2 C$-bearing hosts (127). Taken together, these results suggest that the problems of antibody-induced clearance of cell-surface antigen can be significantly reduced or eliminated by appropriately timed administration of intact or modified MAs that are directed at suitable antigens.

Maximize Host Effector Systems

In experimental situations, antibody may require complement (130,131) or macrophages (20,22,108,113,131,132) to curtail the growth of transplanted tumors. The ADCC effector function attributed to NK cells (40,41) suggests that these cells may also play a role in antibody-mediated tumor cell destruction. With the exception of tumors of viral etiology (8-11), there is virtually no information on the role that antibody may play in regulating the growth of primary tumors. Thus, in terms of defining optimal clinical conditions for application of monoclonal antibody therapy, the possible effector mechanism(s) of the antibody therapy remain an unresolved but crucial question. The issue is further complicated by the fact that each of the putative mechanisms of tumor cell destruction can be depressed as the result of tumor residence and/or prior chemotherapy (63,66-68,133). Thus, a better understanding of the events of tumor ablation by MA is fundamental to effective therapeutic applications. It may be that one mechanism of cytolysis is generally more efficient in killing tumor cells in situ. Alternatively, tumors of similar derivation may be preferentially susceptible to a particular form of lysis, but resistant to another. For example, CEA-bearing colon tumor cell lines have been reported to be relatively resistant to C'-mediated cytolysis (134) while retaining susceptibility to ADCC. Similar studies have examined the cytolytic capacity of MAs which recognize (a) a colorectal carcinoma antigen that is distinct from CEA or (b) a melanoma-associated antigen. Although significant target cell lysis was achieved by spleen cell-mediated ADCC, complement-dependent lysis did not occur (125). If in vitro studies reflect differential effectiveness of alternative mechanisms of target cell destruction in vivo, this may provide a basis for improved applications of MA in therapy protocols. The simplest approach would be to monitor the experimental host/patient to determine whether requisite host effector functions are adequate as a prerequisite to initiating therapy. Alternatively, it may be possible to manipulate the host into a more responsive state by immunopharmacological agents (113,135-137).

Pharmacological Agents

Antibody-Toxin Conjugates: In view of the well-documented ability of tumor cells to evade destruction by the biological action of passively administered antibody, in some clinical applications it may be advantageous to ignore the biological effector role(s) of antibody, and to utilize the specificity of anti-tumor antibodies to "target" foreign toxins in tumor cells. The status of this field prior to the introduction of hybridoma antibodies has been exhaustively reviewed (138,139) and a summary of these results is beyond the scope of this chapter. It is sufficient to note that the possibility of achieving selective toxicity was inherent in earlier studies. This provides impetus for further study with MA, where the specificity of the antibody is better defined and more restricted. Early efforts concentrated on improving the specificity of conventional chemotherapeutic agents for tumor cell targets, hoping to spare normal cells from cytotoxic effects and reduce systematic toxicity. This approach is highly promising in cases where it is feasible to effect a cure with chemotherapeutic agents, as shown by recent attempts to "target" conventional chemotherapeutic agents to tumors with a high proliferative fraction (140,141). As most conventional chemotherapeutic agents preferentially kill dividing cells, an improved localization in tumor tissues would not necessarily be expected to improve the fractional kill of tumor cells in cases where a low proliferative fraction exists, as is the case for most solid tumors and many hematological neoplasms. For this reason, current efforts have been directed at defining agents that are capable of killing noncycling as well as actively dividing cells. Highly promising candidates as the toxin partner are potent plant polypeptide toxins such as ricin and abrin and bacterial diphtheria toxin, which are cytotoxic by virtue of their ability to catalytically inhibit protein synthesis, and thus capable of eradicating both proliferating and "resting" tumor cell populations. The term *immunotoxin* has been adopted to describe toxins covalently linked to intact antibody molecules or fragments thereof.

In early experiments, diphtheria toxin conjugated to rabbit antibodies directed at antigens present on the surface of SV-40-transformed hamster cells was partially effective in inhibiting (25-65% complete regression) the growth of transplanted lymphoma cells (142). Since deliberate immunization of human subjects against diphtheria toxin is a regular practice, circulating antibodies might reduce the efficacy of tumor therapy by immunotoxins or increase pathophysiological effects. Therefore ricin is now considered to be of greater potential in human applications, and research in animal models is currently focused on the ricin toxin.

The biological properties of the intact ricin molecule reside in two distinct polypeptide chains, of which the A chain is responsible for inhibition of protein synthesis, whereas the B chain determines binding to galactose-containing receptors and, presumably, internalization of the toxin (143). The A chain inhibits protein synthesis at the level of the 60-S ribosmal subunit (144). The alternative approaches to "designing" immunotoxins are (1) to attempt to increase the specificity of the intact toxin by "targeting" with highly specific antibody or (b) to use antibody or antibody fragments to "substitute" for the functions of the B chain. When assayed under conditions where binding via B chains is competitively inhibited (i.e., in the presence of galactose or lactose), immunotoxins involving the intact toxin molecule are preferentially toxic for tumor cells bearing the target antigen (145,146). In the absence of inhibitors of B-chain binding, however, immunotoxins comprised of covalently linked antibody-ricin conjugates are effective in inhibiting protein synthesis in cells that do not bear the target antigen (145,148). Thus in vitro studies with ricin molecules that retain B chains show the restriction of this approach in vivo.

The principal concerns over the application of immunotoxins composed of antibody and toxin fragments lacking binding (B) chains (e.g., antibody–ricin A chain), are the uncertainty over whether such complexes can be effectively internalized, and whether the A chain will retain toxic activity. In practice, in vitro studies show that antibodies directed at the murine Thy-1 antigen can facilitate entry of antibody-ricin conjugates into murine lymphoma/leukemia cell lines when B-chain function is competitively blocked (145,146). Anti-Thy-1.2-ricin A chain conjugates have been shown to selectively inhibit protein synthesis in vitro (147). Immunotoxins (ricin A chain) directed at immunoglobulin determinants (mu, delta, and idiotypic) have been shown to be highly effective in killing normal and neoplastic murine B cells expressing the relevant immunoglobulin (148). Immunotoxins prepared using Fab fragments of rabbit anti-human immunoglobulin were also effective in selectively inhibiting growth of surface immunoglobulin-positive cells (149). Other antigens that have proved to be suitable targets for immunotoxins in vitro include a human colorectal carcinoma-associated antigen (150), a human breast carcinoma-associated antigen (151), a human transferrin receptor (152), and the common acute lymphoblastic leukemia antigen (153). Until the mechanism(s) by which antibody facilitates toxin A chain entry into tumor cells are better understood, no definitive conclusions can be drawn, but it seems unlikely that immunotoxins of this type will prove to be universally applicable to all potential tumor-associated target antigens.

Despite the encouraging results in vitro, there have been few reports on the efficacy of antibody–toxin conjugates in eliminating tumor cells in vivo. Anti-Thy-1.2 immunotoxins produced a modest increase in survival time of BALB/c mice bearing the syngeneic (Thy-1.2 positive) WEHI-7 tumor if immunotoxin was injected within 1 hr at the same site as the tumor cells. Survival time was not affected in mice bearing a larger tumor burden. In this case, failure to achieve a significant cure rate may be due to the extremely short in vivo half-life of the conjugate (30 min) and to the large numbers of normal lymphocytes that bear the target antigen. Using a synthetic antigen (TNP), Blythman and co-workers (154) showed that the growth of TNP-HeLa cells in nude mice was significantly reduced if conjugate was administered within 1 hr after tumor cell transfer.

As mentioned previously, anti-transferrin receptor-A conjugates effectively inhibit protein synthesis in vitro. 200- to 100-fold higher concentrations of antibody alone or antibody plus free A chain were required to inhibit protein synthesis in vitro (152). When a similar comparison was made in vivo, antibody was equally as effective as immunotoxin (each administered intravenously) in inhibiting the growth of a human melanoma cell line subcutaneously transplanted into nude mice (152). It remains to be determined whether immunotoxins may have advantages under other experimental conditions. Immunotoxins may prove to be more effective than unconjugated antibody in eradicating large tumor inocula or well-established tumors. On the other hand, in this particular case, the transferrin receptor may represent a unique target on the target cell, and antibody may be effectively inhibiting iron uptake and killing the target cell metabolically, as suggested in the following section.

The potential application of immunotoxins to clinical management of neoplastic disease include (a) elimination of resident tumor cells prior to autologous bone marrow reconstitution (155) and (b) eradication of tumor cells in situ. Vitetta and co-workers (156) have addressed both possibilities in elegant experiments involving the transplantable murine tumor BCL_1. The tumor represents an animal model of the prolymphocytic variant of human chronic lymphocyte leukemia. The absence of circulating immunoglobulin bearing BCL_1 idiotypic determinants circumvented the potentially formidable obstacle of circulating target antigen.

Although the idiotypic determinants present on clonally derived B-cell tumors constitute an "ideal" target antigen in terms of specificity, the practical limitation of preparing anti-idiotypic reagents in clinical situations provides a rationale for exploring more broadly reactive antibodies as carriers for cytotoxic agents. As a model for autologous bone marrow rescue (155), bone marrow derived from mice bearing the BCL_1 tumor was treated with rabbit anti-mouse immunoglobulin prior to transfer to syngeneic recipients. Antibody-complement mediated cytolysis was ineffective in preventing the appearance of BCL_1 idiotype-bearing cells in recipient mice. In contrast, the same antibody, when employed as a carrier for ricin A chain, was extremely efficient in preventing the appearance of tumor cells. The antibody moiety of the immunotoxin used in these studies was not tumor specific, but reacted with a differentiation antigen immunoglobulin shared with normal B cells. By using lethally irradiated recipients, these investigations showed that reconstitution of both the B- and T-cell lineages could be achieved by transferring immunotoxin-treated bone marrow cells derived from tumor-bearing mice. Clearly, the practical limitations of this approach with respect to human neoplasia are diminished if one can employ antibody carriers of broad specificity, with the assurance that the "sacrifice" of normal B cells will result in only a transient diminution of the normal lymphoid compartment. It is equally clear that in this case, as in any application of antibody therapy, the complete eradication of tumor cells requires the absence of a more primitive clonogenic tumor stem cell that lacks the target antigen, a criterion that may *not* be fulfilled by some human hematological neoplasms (157-159).

In experiments designed to evaluate the efficacy of the immunotoxin in vivo, Vitetta and co-workers again chose a target antigen that would be shared with normal B cells. Mice bearing well-established BC_1 tumors were treated with total lymphoid irradiation to reduce the tumor burden prior to immunotoxin therapy. Although the survival time of treated mice was significantly increased, it was apparent that the residual tumor burden precluded "cures." By further reducing the number of tumor cells (total lymphoid irradiation plus splenectomy), it was possible to generate long-term survivors only in experimental mice that were also treated with immunotoxin. The authors concluded that (a) therapy was most effective when the tumor burden was not massive, (b) the reappearance of tumor cells following unsuccessful therapy was not due to selection of immunoglobulin-negative variants, and (c) reversible damage occurred in liver, spleen, and lymph nodes, as reported by others (160).

Combination Chemoimmunotherapy: The classic approach to passive immuno-therapy by antibody transfer is ιο consider antibody as the specific component in an immunological reaction. Thus the consequence of antibody attachment at the target cell would be to call into play otherwise nonspecific components of the immune system, and target cell lysis would be effected by complement activation or ADCC, or macrophages would clear antibody-coated target cells. It is also pos-sible to consider antibody as a highly specific pharmaceutical reagent. Thus it may be possible to define target structures on the surface of the tumor cell membrane such that antibody attachment would result in metabolic disorders that would be directly cytotoxic or would render the cell incapable of further proliferation even in the absence of host effector systems. As suggested by Trowbridge and Domingo (152), the transferrin receptor offers an attractive candidate for this type of target. The transferrin receptor is selectively expressed on proliferating cells and is thought to be essential for iron transport (161–163). Therefore either direct blocking of the receptor by antibody or antibody-induced clearance of the receptor would have the effect of inhibiting proliferation by interfering with the requirement for iron uptake.

The clinical value of drug protocols involving combinations of chemotherapeutic drugs often dramatically exceeds that of a single drug. Unfortunately, further de-velopments of this approach have been limited by difficulties in selecting combin-ations of drugs that are not prohibitively toxic toward normal cells in concert with increased anti-tumor activity (164). However, if antibody can inhibit proliferation by interacting with vital cell membrane components, then we may regard antibody as a drug. By employing MA as a highly selective partner in combination drug therapy, it may be possible to effect synergistic tumor cell kill without concomi-tant increases in systemic toxicity.

An alternative approach to combination chemoimmunotherapy is offered by the observation that the cell cycle may influence accessibility of cell-surface anti-gens or susceptibility to lysis (55–60). If the cell cycle status of a tumor popu-lation reflects a differential susceptibility to regulation by MA, identification of the sensitive phase (or alternatively, of relatively resistant phases) would provide a basis for improved therapeutic applications of MA. If a discrete antibody-sensitive phase of the cell cycle can be identified, it may be possible to use cell blocking agents (e.g., thymidine, hydroxyurea, cytosine arabinoside) in nontoxic dosages to accumulate cells within that phase (164). This approach has the advantage that it may apply to target antigens that depend upon host effector systems for eradi-cation of the tumor population.

SUMMARY AND CONCLUSIONS

The past several decades of research on the feasibility of passive tumor immuno-therapy have led to the definition of conditions where such therapy ιs of benefit to the host. Unfortunately, interspersed among the beneficial effects of antibody therapy are those situations where antibody is ineffective or in which antibody apparently acts to enhance the growth or metastasis of the tumor. Hybridoma-derived MAs provide the basis for improved diagnostic/prognostic assays for neoplasia, as well as constitute probes for the analysis of normal and tumor cell biology. An exciting extension of these applications is to reconsider the question of whether MA directed at cell-surface constituents can be effectively integrated into therapeutic protocols for the control of neoplastic disease.

Experiences with transplanted murine and human tumors indicate that antibody can eradicate tumor inocula in vivo, but that strict limitations exist with respect to "cures." The boundaries of effective therapy are generally defined by (a) the class of antibody transferred, (b) the timing of antibody administration relative to tumor cell transfer, (c) the extent of tumor burden, and (d) the adequacy of host effector systems. In general terms, the factors that are responsible for tumor cell "escape" from antibody-mediated destruction may be attributable to inherent features of the tumor cell population or to deficiencies in host-derived cellular or humoral effector systems. Preliminary experiences with monoclonal antibody treatment of human hematological neoplasms (166, see Ch. 8) suggest that an understanding of the events of tumor ablation or escape will be crucial in the construction of optimally effective therapeutic protocols. Among the possible modification of antibody treatment regimens are attempts to preferentially stimulate host effector functions or to use antibody in conjunction with conventional chemotherapeutic agents or as a carrier for drugs or nonspecific cell toxins.

ACKNOWLEDGMENTS

The collaboration of Drs. U. Hammerling and J. Abbott is gratefully acknowledged, as is the expert technical assistance of Ms. T. Lee. The author's work was supported by grant IM-239 from the American Cancer Society.

REFERENCES

1. P. A. Gorer and D. B. Amos, *Cancer Res. 16*:338 (1956).
2. S. A. Rosenberg and W. D. Terry, *Adv. Cancer Res. 25*:323 (1977).
3. R. Motta, *Adv. Cancer Res. 14*:161 (1971).
4. G. Köhler and C. Milstein, *Nature 256*:495 (1975).
5. G. Köhler and C. Milstein, *Eur. J. Immunol. 6*:511 (1976).
6. K. R. Schroer, D. E. Briles, J. A. Van Boxel, and J. M. Davie, *J. Exp. Med. 140*:1416 (1974).
7. P. J. Fialkow, *Biochim. Biophys. Acta 458*:283 (1976).
8. J. J. Huebner, R. V. Gilden, R. Toni, R. W. Hill, R. W. Trimmer, D. D. Fish, and B. Sass, *Proc. Nat. Acad. Sci. U.S.A. 73*:4633 (1976).
9. M. B. Gardner, V. Klement, J. D. Estes, R. V. Gilden, R. Toni, and T. J. Heubner, *J. Nat. Cancer Inst. 58*:1855 (1977).
10. W. Schafer, H. Schwartz, H. J. Thiel, P. J. Fischinger, and D. P. Bolognesi, *Virology 83*:207 (1977).

11. R. L. Peters, B. Sass, J. R. Stephenson, I. K. Al -Ghazzouli, S. Hino, R. M. Donahoe, M. Kende, J. A. Aaronson, and G. J. Kelloff, *Proc. Nat. Acad. Sci.* 74:1697 (1977).

12. L. J. Old, E. Stockert, E. A. Boyse, and G. Geering, *Proc. Soc. Exp. Biol. Med.* 124:63 (1967).

13. D. E. Haagensen, Jr., G. Roloson, J. J. Collins, S. A. Wells, Jr., D. P. Bolognesi, and H. J. Hansen, *J. Nat. Cancer Inst.* 60:131 (1978).

14. J. J. Collins, G. Roloson, D. E. Haagensen, Jr., P. J. Fischinger, S. A. Wells, Jr. W. Holder, and D. P. Bolognesi, *J. Nat. Cancer Inst.* 60:141 (1978).

15. J. Lindenmann and P. A. Klein, *J. Exp. Med.* 126:93 (1967).

16. P. A. Klein, *Pathol. Microbiol.* 30:222 (1967).

17. J. Lindenmann and P. A. Klein, *Recent Res. Cancer Res.* 9:1 (1967).

18. J. C. Scornik and P. A. Klein, *Transplantation* 26:356 (1978).

19. J. C. Scornik and P. A. Klein, *J. Nat. Cancer Inst.* 61:1143 (1978).

20. J. C. Scornik and P. A. Klein, *J. Nat. Cancer Inst.* 61:1149 (1978).

21. R. J. Johnson, G. R. Pasternack, and H. S. Shin, *J. Immunol.* 118:489 (1977).

22. R. J. Johnson, G. R. Pasternack, and H. S. Shin, *J. Immunol.* 118:494 (1977).

23. R. J. Johnson, G. R. Pasternack, B. -E. Drysdale, and H. S. Shin, *J. Immunol.* 118:498 (1977).

24. H. S. Shin, J. S. Economou, G. R. Pasternack, R. J. Johnson, and M. L. Hayden, *J. Exp. Med.* 144:1274 (1976).

25. R. J. Johnson, R. F. Siliciano, and H. S. Shin, *J. Immunol.* 122:379 (1979).

26. G. R. Pasternack, R. J. Johnson, and H. S. Shin, *J. Immunol.* 120:1560 (1978).

27. G. R. Pasternack, R. J. Johnson, and H. S. Shin, *J. Immunol.* 120:1567 (1978).

28. R. K. Gershon, *Contemp. Top. Immunobiol.* 3:1 (1974).

29. Jerne, N. K., *Ann. Immunol.* 125c;373 (1974).

30. R. G. Lynch, J. W. Rohrer, B. Odermatt, H. M. Gebel, J. R. Autry, and R. G. Hoover, *Immunol. Rev.* 48:45 (1979).

31. P. G. Beatty, B. S. Kim, D. A. Rowley, and L. W. Coppelson, *J. Immunol.* 116:1391 (1976).

32. Y. Chen, V. Takulis, and P. Heller, *Proc. Soc. Exp. Biol. Med.* 151:121 (1976).

33. L. Lanier, M. A. Lynes, P. J. Wettstein, and G. Haughton, *Nature* 271:554 (1978).

34. M. A. Lynes, L. L. Lanier, G. F. Babcock, P. J. Wettstein, and G. Haughton, *J. Immunol.* 121:2352 (1978).

35. G. Haughton, L. L. Lanier, G. F. Babcock, and M. A. Lynes, *J. Immunol.* 121:2358 (1978).

36. L. L. Lanier, G. F. Babcock, M. A. Lynes, and G. Haughton, *J. Nat. Cancer Inst.* 63:1417 (1979).

37. L. L. Lanier, G. F. Babcock, R. B. Raybourne, L. W. Arnold, N. L. Warner, and G. Haughton, *J. Immunol.* 125:1730 (1980).

38. R. B. Herberman, M. E. Nunn, and D. H. Lavrin, *Int. J. Cancer* 16:216 (1975).

39. R. Kiessling, E. Klein, H. Pross, and H. Wigzell, *Eur. J. Immunol.* 5:117 (1975).

40. E. Ojo and H. Wigzell, *Scand. J. Immunol.* 7:297 (1978).

41. A. Santoni, R. B. Herberman, and H. T. Holden, *J. Nat. Cancer Inst.* 62:109 (1979)

42. K. A. Krolick, P. C. Isakson, J. W. Uhr, and E. S. Vitetta, *Immunol. Rev.* 48:81 (1979)

43. E. Hawrylko, in *The Handbook of Cancer Immunology*, Vol. 2 (H. Waters, ed.), Garland STPM Press, New York, 1978, p. 2.
44. R. B. Faanes, in *The Handbook of Cancer Immunology*, Vol. 5 (H. Waters, ed.), Garland STPM Press, New York, 1978, p. 2.
45. P. Alexander, *Cancer Res. 34*:2077 (1974).
46. E. A. Boyse, E. Stockert, and L. J. Old, *Proc. Nat. Acad. Sci. 58*:954 (1967).
47. J. Gordon, D. F. Robinson, and G. T. Stevenson, *Immunology 42*:7 (1981).
48. C. Stackpole and J. Jacobson, in *The Handbook of Cancer Immunology*, Vol. 2 (H. Waters, ed.), Garland STPM Press, New York, 1978, p. 55.
49. E. M. Fenyö, E. Klein, G. Klein, and K. Swiech, *J. Nat. Cancer Inst. 40*:69 (1968).
50. W. W. Young, and S. -I. Hakomori, *Science 211*:487 (1981).
51. E. Celis, A. H. Hale, J. H. Russell, and H. N. Eisen, *J. Immunol. 122*:954 (1979).
52. A. H. Hale, E. Celis, J. H. Russell, and H. N. Eisen, *J. Immunol. 122*:959 (1979).
53. S. I. Schlager and S. H. Ohanian, *Science 197*:773 (1977).
54. S. I. Schlager, S. H. Ohanian, and T. Borsos, *J. Immunol. 120*:463 (1978).
55. M. Cikes, *Transplant. Proc. 3*:1161 (1971).
56. R. A. Lerner, M. B. A. Oldstone, and N. R. Cooper, *Proc. Nat. Acad. Sci. 6 68*:2584 (1971).
57. P. Dombernowsky, P. Bichel, and N. R. Hartman, *Cell Tissue Kinet. 6*:347 (1973).
58. N. V. Leneva and G. J. Svet-Moldavsky, *J. Nat. Cancer Inst. 52*:699 (1974).
59. M. A. Pellegrino, S. Ferrone, N. R. Cooper, M. P. Dierich, and R. A. Reisfeld, *J. Exp. Med. 140*:578 (1974).
60. P. J. Leibson, M. R. Loken, S. J. Shapiro, and H. Schreiber, *Cancer Res. 40*:56 (1980).
61. W. P. Drake, P. C. Ungaro, and M. R. Mardiney, Jr., *Biomedicine 18*:284 (1973).
62. S. Becker and E. Klein, *Eur. J. Immunol. 6*:892 (1976)
63. R. B. Herberman, M. E. Nunn, H. T. Holden, S. Staal, and J. Y. Djeu, *Int. J. Cancer 19*:555 (1977).
64. R. J. North, D. P. Kirstein, and R. L. Tuttle, *J. Exp. Med. 143*:559 (1976).
65. S. J. Normann and E. Sorkin, *J. Nat. Cancer Inst. 57*:135 (1976).
66. G. R. Pasternack, R. Snyderman, M. C. Pike, R. J. Johnson, and H. S. Shin, *J. Exp. Med. 148*:93 (1978).
67. S. J. Normann, M. Schardt, and E. Sorkin, *J. Nat. Cancer Inst. 66*:157 (1981).
68. I. Kamo and H. Friedman, *Adv. Cancer Res. 25*:271 (1977).
69. G. D. Snell, *Cancer Res. 17*:2 (1957).
70. N. Kaliss, *Cancer Res. 18*:992 (1958).
71. G. Moller, *J. Nat. Cancer Inst. 30*:1153 (1963).
72. K. E. Hellström, I. Hellström, and J. T. Nepom, *Biochem. Biophys. Acta 473*:121 (1977).
73. V. V. Likhite, in *The Handbook of Cancer Immunology*, Vol. 4 (H. Waters, ed.), Garland STPM Press, New York, 1978, p. 236.
74. S. Tokuda and P. F. McEntee, *Transplantation 5*:606 (1967).
75. R. G. Kinsky, G. A. Voisin, and H. T. Duc, *Transplantation 13*:452 (1972).
76. T. N. Harris and S. Harris, *Immunology 25*:409 (1973).

77. P. Rubinstein, F. DeCary, and E. W. Streun, *J. Exp. Med. 140*:591 (1974).
78. H. I. Duc, R. G. Kinsky, J. Kanellopoulos, and G. A. Voisin, *J. Immunol. 115*: 1143 (1975).
79. K. H. Ibsen and W. H. Fishman, *Biochim. Biophys. Acta 56*:243 (1979).
80. P. Gold and J. Shuster, *Cancer Res. 40*:2973 (1980).
81. R. A. Miller, D. G. Maloney, R. Warnke, and R. Levy, *N. Engl. J. Med. 306*:517 (1982).
82. G. J. Mizejewski and R. P. Allen, *Nature 250*:50 (1974).
83. S. Sell, H. W. Sheppard, Jr., R. Nickel, D. Stillman, and M. Michaelson, *Cancer Res. 36*:476 (1976).
84. E. Engvall, H. Pihko, H. Jalanko, and E. Ruoslahti, *J. Nat. Cancer Inst. 59*:277 (1977).
85. R. T. Prehn, *Adv. Cancer Res. 23*:2 (1976).
86. I. R. Hart and I. J. Fidler, *Biochim. Biophys. Acta 651*:37 (1981).
87. E. A. Boyse, M. Miyawawa, T. Aoki, and L. J. Old, *Proc. R. Soc. London B 170*:175 (1968).
88. L. J. Old and E. Stockert, *Annu. Rev. Genet. 11*:127 (1977).
89. B. J. Mathieson, P. S. Campbell, M. Potter, and R. Asofsky, *J. Exp. Med. 147*:1267 (1978).
90. I. D. Bernstein, M. R. Tam, and R. C. Nowinski, *Science 207*:68 (1980).
91. I. D. Bernstein, R. C. Nowinski, M. R. Tam, B. McMaster, L. L. Houston, and E. A. Clark, in *Monoclonal Antibodies. Hybridomas: A New Dimension in Biological Analyses* (R. H. Kennett, T. J. McKearn, and K. B. Bechtol, eds.), Plenum, New York, 1980, p. 275.
92. M. S. McGrath, E. Pillemer, and I. L. Weissman, *Nature 285*:259 (1980).
93. M. S. McGrath, E. Pillemer, D. A. Kooistra, S. Jacobs, L. Jerabek, and I. L. Weissman, *Cold Spring Harbor Symp. Quant. Biol. 44*:1297 (1980).
94. G. Koo and A. Hatzfeld, in *Natural Cell-mediated Immunity Against Tumors*, (R. Herberman, ed.) Academic, New York, 1980, p. 105.
95. M. E. Kirch and U. Hammerling, *J. Immunol. 127*:805 (1981).
96. B. Cinader, S. Dubiski, and A. C. Wardlaw, *J. Exp. Med. 120*:897 (1964).
97. M. E. Kirch, T. Lee, and U. Hammerling, in *Monoclonal Antibodies and T-cell Hybridomas: Perspectives and Technical Advances* (G. Hammerling, U. Hammerling, and J. Kearney, eds.), Elsevier/North-Holland, Amsterdam, 1981, p. 221.
98. H. L. Spiegelberg, *Adv. Immunol. 19*:259 (1974).
99. J. G. Hall, M. E. Smith, P. A. Edwards, and K. V. Shooter, *Immunology 16*:773 (1969).
100. M. Palladino, Sloan-Kettering Institute, New York, personal communication.
101. P. Ralph, in *Macrophage-mediated Antibody-dependent Cellular Cytotoxicity* (H. S. Koren, ed.), Marcel Dekker, New York, 1983, p. 71.
102. M. E. Kirch, T. Lee, and J. Abbott, in *B and T Cell Tumors: Biological and Clinical Aspects* (E. Vitetta and C. F. Fox, eds.), Academic, New York, 1982, p. 267
103. M. A. Palladino and G. J. Thorbecke, *Cell. Immunol. 38*:350 (1978).
104. M. A. Palladino and G. J. Thorbecke, *Eur. J. Immunol. 8*:257 (1978).

105. E. W. Lamon, M. W. Shaw, S. Goodson, B. Lidin, A. S. Walia, and E..W. Fuson, *J. Exp. Med. 145*:302 (1977).
106. E. W. Lamon, B. R. Williams, E. W. Fuson, H. D. Whitten, and A. S. Walia, *J. Immunol. 120*:244 (1978).
107. A Santoni, R. B. Herberman, and H. T. Holden, *J. Nat. Cancer Inst. 63*:995 (1979).
108. J. Zighelboim, B. Bonavida, and J. L. Fahey, *J. Immunol. 111*:1737 (1973).
109. M. Yamazaki, H. Shinoda, Y. Suzuki, and D. Mizuno, *Gann 67*:741 (1976).
110. P. Ralph and I. Nakoinz, *J. Immunol. 119*:950 (1977).
111. M. -L. Lohmann-Mathes, W. Domzig, and H. Taskov, *Eur. J. Immunol. 9*:261 (1979).
112. W. Domzig and M. -L. Lohmann-Mathes, *Eur. J. Immunol. 9*:267 (1979).
113. C. Nathan, L. Brukner, G. Kaplan, J. Unkeless, and Z. Cohn, *J. Exp. Med. 152*:183 (1980).
114. H. Kaprowski, Z. Steplewski, D. Herlyn, and M. Herlyn, *Proc. Nat. Acad. Sci. 75*:3405 (1978).
115. D. Herlyn, M. Herlyn, Z. Steplewski, and H. Kaprowski, *Eur. J. Immunol. 9*:657 (1979).
116. D. M. Herlyn, Z. Steplewski, M. F. Herlyn, and H. Kaprowski, *Cancer Res. 40*:717 (1980).
117. G. Cudkowitz and P. S. Hochman, *Immunol. Rev. 44*:13 (1979).
118. W. E. Seaman, M. A. Blackman, T. D. Gindhart, J. R. Roubinian, J. Loeb, and N. Talal, *J. Immunol. 121*:2193 (1978).
119. W. E. Seaman and N. Talal, in *Natural Cell-mediated Immunity Against Tumors* (R. Herberman, ed.) Academic, New York, 1980, p. 765.
120. T. -J. Yang and S. I. Vas, *Cancer Res. 30*:1231 (1970).
121. Y. Tsukada, M. Mikuni, H. Watabe, S. Nishi, and H. Hirai, *Int. J. Cancer 13*:187 (1974).
122. P. C. Isakson, K. A. Krolick, J. W. Uhr, and E. S. Vitetta, *J. Immunol. 125*:886 (1980).
123. A. W. Boyd and J. W. Schrader, *J. Immunol. 126*:2466 (1981).
124. R. A. Miller, D. G. Maloney, J. McKillop, and R. Levy, *Blood 58*:78 (1981).
125. J. Ritz, J. M. Pesando, S. E. Sallan, L. A. Clavell, J. Notis-McConarty, P. Rosenthal, and S. F. Schlossman, *Blood 58*:141 (1981).
126. R. A. Miller and R. Levy, *Lancet 2*:226 (1981).
127. M. J. Glennie and G. T. Stevenson, *Nature 295*:712 (1982).
128. M. E. Lamm, E. A. Boyse, L. J. Old, B. Lisowska-Bernstein, and E. Stockert, *J. Immunol. 101*:99 (1968).
129. J. Gordon and G. T. Stevenson, *Immunology 42*:13 (1981).
130. L. Bellelli and M. L. Sezzi, *Oncology 33*:215 (1976).
131. K. Nishioka, *Adv. Cancer Res. 14*:231 (1971).
132. B. Bennett, L. J. Old, and E. A. Boyse, *Transplantation 2*:183 (1964).
133. C. Riccardi, T. Barlozzari, A. Santoni, R. B. Herberman, and C. Cesari, *J. Immunol. 126*:1284 (1981).
134. S. Carrel, M. C. DeLisle, and J. P. Mach, *Cancer Res. 37*:2644 (1977).
135. E. Ojo, O. Haller, A. Kimura, and H. Wigzell, *Int. J. Cancer 21*:444 (1978).

136. J. Y. Djeu, J. A. Heinbaugh, H. T. Holden, and R. B. Herberman, *J. Immunol.* *122*:175 (1979).

137. H. S. Koren, M. S. Meltzer, and D. O. Adams, *J. Immunol. 126*:1013 (1981).

138. T. Ghose and A. H. Blair, *J. Nat. Cancer Inst. 61*:657 (1978).

139. F. L. Moolten, B. M. Schreiber, and S. H. Zajdel, *Immunol. Rev. 61*:47 (1982).

140. R. Arnon and M. Sela, *Immunol. Rev. 62*:5 (1982).

141. R. A. DeWeger, H. F. J. Dullens, and W. Den Otter, *Immunol. Rev. 62*:29 (1982).

142. F. L. Moolten, N. J. Caparell, S. H. Zajdel, and S. R. Cooperhand, *J. Nat. Cancer Inst. 55*:473 (1975).

143. S. Olsner and A. Pihl, *Biochem. 12*:3121 (1973).

144. S. Benson, S. Olsnes, and A. Pihl, *Eur. J. Biochem. 59*:573 (1975).

145. R. J. Youle and D. M. Neville, Jr., *Proc. Nat. Acad. Sci. U.S.A. 77*:5483 (1980).

146. L. L. Houston and R. C. Nowinski, *Cancer Res. 41*:3913 (1981).

147. F. K. Jansen, H. E. Blythman, D. Carriere, P. Casellas, O. Gros, P. Gros, F. Paolucci, B. Pau, P. Poncelet, G. Richer, H. Vidal, and G. A. Voisin, in *Monoclonal Antibodies and T-cell Hybridomas: Perspectives and Technical Advances* (G. Hammerling, U. Hammerling, and J. F. Kearney, eds.), Elsevier/ North-Holland, Amsterdam, 1981, p. 229.

148. K. A. Krolick, C. Villemez, P. Isakson, J. W. Uhr, and E. S. Vitetta, *Proc. Nat. Acad. Sci. 77*:5419 (1980).

149. V. Raso and T. Griffin, *J. Immunol. 125*:2610 (1980).

150. D. G. Gilliland, Z. Steplewski, R. J. Collier, K. F. Mitchell, T. H. Chang, and H. Koprowski, *Proc. Nat. Acad. Sci. 77*:4559 (1980).

151. K. A. Krolick, D. Yuan, and E. S. Vitetta, *Cancer Immunol. Immunother. 12*:39 (1981).

152. I. S. Trowbridge and D. L. Domingo, *Nature 294*:171 (1981).

153. V. Raso, *Immunol. Rev. 62*:93 (1982).

154. H. E. Blythman, P. Casellas, O. Gros, P. Gros, F. K. Jansen, F. Paolucci, B. Pau, and H. Vidal, *Nature 290*:145 (1981).

155. R. P. Gale, *J. Am. Med. Assoc. 243*:540 (1980).

156. E. S. Vitetta, K. A. Krolick, and J. W. Uhr, *Immunol. Rev. 62*:159 (1982).

157. P. J. Fialkow, A. L. Reddy, and J. I. Bryant, *Int. J. Cancer 26*:603 (1980).

158. P. J. Martin, V. Najfeld, J. A. Hansen, G. K. Penfold, R. J. Jacobson, and P. J. Fialkow, *Nature 287*:49 (1980).

159. P. J. Fialkow, J. W. Singer, J. W. Adamson, K. Viadya, L. W. Dow, J. Ochs, and J. W. Moohr, *Blood 57*:1068 (1981).

160. F. K. Jansen, H. E. Blytham, D. Carriere, P. Casellas, O. Gros, P. Gros, J. C. Laurent, F. Paolucci, B. Pau, P. Poncelet, G. Richer, H. Vidal, and G. A. Voisin, *Immunol. Rev. 62*:185 (1982).

161. T. A. Hamilton, H. G. Wada, and H. H. Sussman, *Proc. Nat. Acad. Sci. 76*: 6406 (1979).

162. J. W. Larrick and P. Cresswell, *J. Supramol. Struct. 11579* (1979).

163. R. Sutherland, D. Delia, C. Schneider, R. Newman, J. Kemshead, and M. Greaves, *Proc. Nat. Acad. Sci. 78*:4515 (1981).

164. W. B. Pratt and R. W. Ruddon, *The Anticancer Drugs*, Oxford University Press, New York, 1979.
165. L. M. Nadler, P. Stashenko, R. Hardy, W. D. Kaplan, L. N. Button, D. W. Kufe, K. H. Antman, and S. F. Schlossman, *Cancer Res. 40*:3147 (1980).
166. R. O. Dillman, R. E. Sobol, M. R. Green, H. A. Collins, J. C. Griffiths, and I. Royston, *Proceedings of the AACR and ASCO,* p. 376 (1981).

14 RECENT DEVELOPMENTS

INTRODUCTION

This chapter was included to provide an opportunity for those authors who wished to update their contributions so that this book would be as current as possible at the time of publication. Updates for eight of the contributions are presented below. No attempt was made to make this chapter a comprehensive review of the literature published between mid-1982 and the end of 1983. Only the pertinent recent citations relevant to the author's own research or to the advancement of a specific type of human cancer are presented. Not all contributors elected to update their chapters; however, the material that is presented in this chapter provides a good cross section of the types of advances being made in the use of monoclonal antibodies for diagnosis and therapy of human cancer.

CHAPTER 1: APPLICATIONS OF MONOCLONAL ANTIBODIES TO THE STUDY OF HUMAN CANCER

A large number of articles describing the production and specificity of monoclonals to human tumor cells has accumulated since submission of the manuscript for Chapter 1. Most of these have to be regarded as preliminary in nature, and as such, do not provide substantial new information not already adequately described in this book. However, there have been recent developments in the areas of antigen characterization, phenotyping of tumors, generation of human monoclonal antibodies, and therapeutic application of monoclonals that will be described in this addendum to Chapter 1.

Characterization of Tumor-Associated Antigens

Several recent papers have described tumor-associated glycolipid antigens defined by monoclonal antibodies (1–8), especially those associated with colorectal or gastrointestinal tumors (2–8). Of particular interest is the further characterization and distribution of the monosialoganglioside gastrointestinal cancer-associated antigen (GICA). This antigen was originally claimed to be detectable in colorectal tissue and meconium (7). On this basis, GICA was considered to be of an oncofetal nature and potentially useful for the detection and study of colorectal carcinomas (8). A kit (Centocor CA 19-9 RIA) for assessment of antigen levels in serum and urine was marketed for use in gastrointestinal cancer. However, immunoperoxidase studies have shown the GICA to be more widely distributed than originally proposed (9) and the oncofetal nature of the antigen has been challenged (5). A most recent study was undertaken to further delineate the characteristics of the GICA and to evaluate its usefulness as a marker in colorectal carcinoma (6). These investigators tested the immunoreactivity of monoclonal antibody (1116NS 19-9) that specifically binds this monosialoganglioside antigen in histologic sections of a large series of carcinomas of the large bowel and compared the results with gross and histological characteristics and with flow-cytometrical data. Their results indicated the presence of GICA is correlated neither with the localization nor with the stage of tumor. In addition, there was no statistically significant correlation with the histological degree of differentiation of colorectal cancers, nor with DNA histograms. Since 7.2% of the negative carcinomas showed a positive adjacent normal mucosa, genetically determined polymorphism, as suggested by the finding of a blood group Lewis A sugar sequence in the antigen (4), cannot be the sole factor for absence of immunoreactivity in certain tumors. The results of this study indicate that the practical significance of its immunocytochemical detection for histopathological use for diagnosis or prognosis is limited because the expression of GICA is not strongly related to factors known to be correlated with prognosis, such as extension and degree of differentiation, DNA content, and percentage of S-phase cells.

Antigenic Phenotyping and Heterogeneity

Two recent papers illustrated the effective use of monoclonal antibody panels for classification of benign and malignant tumors and for dissecting the antigenic specificities of tumor-associated antigens.

Stramignoni et al. (10) analyzed the reactivity of three monoclonal antibodies generated against metastatic mammary carcinoma tissues with formalin-fixed tissue sections of human colon adenocarcinoma and adenomas by an immunoperoxidase assay. The panel of antibodies used were B72.3, B6.2, and B1.1 (see Chap. 5). Antibody B1.1, reactive with the 180 kilodalton glycoprotein carcinoembryonic antigen (CEA) was most selective in its reactivivity to colon carcinoma as compared with adenoma. The B72.3 antibody demonstrated the most selective reactivity for carcinomas and also reacted with cells in areas of "atypia" within adenomas. Since the B72.3 antibody reacted to both malignant and atypical lesions, these investigators examined patients with ulcerative colitis, whose risk of developing colorectal cancers is 5-11 times greater than that of the normal population. In three out of seven cases, positive staining was observed only when morphological glandular atypia and active inflammation were present. These results indicated that the ulcerative colitis patients could be divided into positive and negative groups. If confirmed in a larger study, the B72.3 marker may be useful as an indicator of malignant propensity. Considerable antigenic heterogeneity was observed in most all colon carcinomas examined. Antigenic heterogeneity was also observed in another recent study of colon carcinomas using a monoclonal (19-9) that reacts to a monosialoganglioside antigen (12). Colon carcinoma, adenomas, and ulcerative colitis, respectively, could be antigenically phenotyped into several distinct groups based on the reactivity to the three monoclonal antibody panel. This immunohistological classification is significant, for it should not be possible to determine if a given antigenic phenotype correlates with a specific biological property such as response to a specific therapeutic modality or prognosis.

In another study, 14 monoclonal antibodies generated against CEA from six different laboratories were evaluated for the detection of CEA and related antigens in the sera of 311 patients with gastrointestinal diseases and normal donors using double-determinant immunoassays (11). Competitive binding studies indicated that 12 different antigenic determinants representing six different groups were detected on the CEA molecule(s). Group I monoclonal antibodies bound only to the classical 180 kd CEA group II monoclonal antibodies seemed to detect antigens closely associated with the classical CEA; groups III, V, and VI monoclonal antibodies also detected a glycoprotein that cross reacts with the CEA-related antigen NCA; and group IV monoclonal antibody, which is the B6.2 monoclonal antibody that detects a 90 kd protein antigen or breast carcinoma cells (13; Chap. 5), detected only NCA. Groups I and II showed the lowest number of false-positive reactions with sera of normal donors and with sera of patients with inflammatory and benign gastrointestinal diseases, in contrast to conventional CEA assays. One group III antibody, B1.1 (see page 3) seemed to be useful in detecting benign gastrointestinal disease. Antigen levels were elevated in 56-75% (depending on antibody used) of sera from patients with advanced gastrointestinal tumors. These results are similar to those obtained by standard assays. However, the use of various combinations of antibodies appeared to eliminate the false-positive results observed with normal sera and with sera from patients with gastrointestinal and noncancerous diseases. These results suggest that double-determinant immunoassays using a panel of monoclonal antibodies might improve conventional CEA assays by reducing the number of false-positive sera detected in patients with benign inflammatory bowel disease.

Human Monoclonal Antibodies

A few reports have appeared on the production of human monoclonal antibodies to tumor antigens (14-18). The study of Glassy et al. (14), describes the general properties of UC729-6, a 6-thioguanine-resistant human lymphoblastoid B-cell line suitable for generating human/human hybridomas which secrete immunoreactive human immunoglobulins and also for rescuing Ig from B-cell malignancies. The fusion frequency with lymphocytes from cancer patients was equal to or higher than the established murine hybridoma protocols.

Another group of investigators (15,16) fused lymphocytes from regional lymph nodes, peripheral blood, spleen and tumor infiltrates with either the SKO-007 (human myeloma line), LICR-LON-HMy2 (LICR-2), GM 4672 (human lymphoblastoid lines), or NS-1 (mouse myeloma line). In one of the studies reported by this group (15), fusion of lymph node lymphocytes with NS-1 resulted in a 3-4 times higher frequency of clones than fusion with LICR-2, and a ten times higher frequency than fusion with SKO-007 or GM 4672. In the case of peripheral blood lymphocytes, fusion with NS-1 gave greater than 25 times the frequency of clones than fusion with LICR-2 or SKO-007. Human immunoglobin heavy chains μ, γ, or α were detected in 50-80% of wells containing growing clones. The level of Ig production ranged from 0.2 to 40 μg/ml and the relative proportion of μ-, γ-, and α-positive wells varied from specimen to specimen. No apparent relation was found between level and/or class of Ig production and the different fusion partners or sources of lymphocytes. Ig secretion appeared to be a more stable property of LICR-2-derived clones than NS-1-derived clones; but in another study, stable Ig-secreting clones were isolated with approximately equal frequency from LICR-2 and NS-1 fusions (16). Less than 1% of the antibody secreting clones reacted with cell surface antigens, whereas 3-9% reacted with intracellular antigens. A new cell surface antigen with properties of a glycolipid was defined with an IgM monoclonal antibody secreted by a tetraploid cell derived from a fusion of LICR-2 with lymphocytes from the axillary lymph node of a patient with melanoma (15). Stable cell lines secreting human antibody that detected nuclei, nucleoli, cytoskeletal elements, Golgi complexes, or other cytoplasmic components were also isolated in these studies (15,16). One of these antibodies detected an intracellular antigen that is restricted to cells of neuroectodermal derivation, and a second antibody reacted primarily with cells of epithelial origin. A range of intracellular structures was identified by antibodies derived from lymphocytes of both normal individuals and patients with cancer, indicating that these autoantibodies need not be related to overt disease. The results reported by these investigators indicate that methods for construction of Ig-secreting human/human hybrids or human/mouse hybrids have been considerably improved. Although there are some technical problems still to be resolved, this approach may still be a shotgun exhibition in light of the propensity to produce monoclonal antibodies to autoantigens. However, the methods for generating human monoclonals against surface and intracellular antigens should give insight into the repertoire of humoral immune responses to autologous cellular antigens in cancer patients.

As illustrated in the studies described above, the human myeloma or lymphoblastoid lines appear to be clearly less than satisfactory as fusion partners. In contrast the mouse myeloma cell lines are remarkably efficient and reliable as fusion partners in mouse/mouse hybridoma production. Unfortunately, when these mouse myeloma cell lines are fused with antigen-primed human B lymphocytes, the capacity to retain stable human Ig-secreting clones is often transient due to selective elimination of human chromosomes. A recent report by Teng et al. (17), describes a strategy aimed at retaining the high fusion frequency of a mouse myeloma cell line under selected conditions in which it is forced to retain one or more human chromosomes. They took the FU-266 mutant human myeloma cell line sensitive to hypoxanthine/aminopterin/thymidine (HAT) and transfected it by protoplast fusion with DNA of the recombinant plasmid vector pSV2-neo^R, thus acquiring a dominant marker conferring resistance to the antibiotic G-418. One of the neo^R clones (E-1), was fused to irradiated or unirradiated cells of the HAT-sensitive, G-418-sensitive, non-producer myeloma line x63-Ag8-653. Hybrid clones were selected in G-418 plus ouabain to preserve their HAT sensitivity. Small numbers of human chromosomes were retained in cell hybrids and most ceased secreting IgE and lambda light chain of the human myeloma parent. Selected hybrid clones were then tested as fusion partners with either polyclonally activated B lymphocytes or antigen-primed human B lymphocytes. Some of the heteromyelomas have consistently generated high yields of variable human Ig-secreting hybridomas which grow well and can be readily subcloned. Ig secretion of the clones has been stable for over six months and several antigen-specific human monoclonal antibodies were generated. The high yield of viable hybridomas, their capacity for sustained secretion of relatively high levels of human immunoglobulin, and the absence of secreted Igs from the human myeloma or mouse myeloma cells indicate that these heteromyeloma clones appear to provide a significant advantage as malignant fusion partners for the generation of human/human monoclonal antibodies.

Monoclonal Antibodies in Cancer Therapy

As has been stated in several preceding chapters, monoclonal antibodies may be useful alone as serotherapeutic agents if they can induce sufficient cytotoxicity for the cancer cells through activation of the complement system or by cell-mediated phenomena. However, the use of antibody conjugated to drugs, toxins, or radioisotopes seems to offer the greatest hope for the development of cancer-specific cytotoxic reagents. The current status of the use of monoclonal antibodies for the immunotherapy of cancer and of the phase I clinical trials presently being conducted in the United States has been presented in recent reviews by Oldham (19,20). Although many monoclonal antibody trials are being initiated, few have been underway for a sufficient period of time to have reported any results. The larger number of patients treated with antibody alone thus far have had leukemia or lymphoma (see Chaps. 1, 8, and 13). While most of these trials involved individual patients or very small series of patients, early indications are that monoclonal antibody alone can have therapeutic effects in certain human malignancies. Based on the preliminary trials using mouse-derived monoclonal antibodies, it is clear that these mouse immunoglobulin reagents can be administered to human patients without severe acute toxicity. Clinical phase I trials investigating different doses and schedules of intravenous administration are underway. A major difficulty with antibody alone appears to be that of antigenic modulation, where apparent loss of the antigen involved in the reaction can occur within a few minutes to an hour or two after exposure to some of the monoclonal antibodies. This modulation, however, appears to be a temporary problem, often with return of the antigen within 24-36 hr, but modulation does not occur with all antibodies. A possible solution to antigenic modulation is to use two monoclonal antibodies directed against different epitopes on the same antigen or against different antigens on the same tumor cell. There are several other approaches to enhance the efficacy of monoclonal antibodies, such as infusing more than one monoclonal antibody using different antibody subclasses, developing polyclonal heteroantisera raised to monoclonal purified antigens, or using monoclonal antibodies conjugated to drugs, toxins, or isotopes. Many of these approaches are being tried in animal tumor models (21) and in preliminary trials in man. In addition to the clinical trials underway at Sidney Farber, Stanford, and the University of California at San Diego to evaluate monoclonals for the serotherapy of T-cell leukemias, lymphomas, and T-antigen-bearing chronic lymphocytic leukemia (CLL), the Biological Response Modifiers Program (BRMP) of the National Cancer Institute has several clinical trials with anti-T-cell antigen monoclonal antibodies for these disorders. It is already clear from these trials that there are certain problems in addition to antigenic modulation implicit in the use of antibody alone. One of these problems is the release of free antigen which forms immune complexes with the infused monoclonal, eliminating its effect on the tumor cell. Plasmapheresis over an immunoabsorbent column or scheduling monoclonal antibody treatment at 3-day intervals may offer solutions to this problem. The generation of anti-mouse antibodies causing immune elimination of the mouse monoclonal antibodies may be overcome by using low dosage immunosuppressive drug treatments or plasmapheresis with immunospecific absorption. Another problem has been the nonsustained reduction of leukemic cells. A solution to this problem may be obtained with repeated intermittent monoclonal antibody infusions. The inability of bone marrow neoplastic cells to be killed may be resolved using immunotoxins or antibody-drug conjugates (see Chaps. 3 and 8). These clinical trials are identifying these kinds of problems and the solutions are being investigated.

Preliminary results have been reported on the use of monoclonal antibody for serotherapy of only a few solid tumors, such as melanoma and gastrointestinal cancer. Sears et al. (22), reported the preliminary results of a phase I trial using an IgG_{2a} anti-colorectal monoclonal antibody 17-1A. This antibody previously was shown to specifically inhibit the growth of human colon carcinomas xenografted in athymic mice. Four patients received 15-200 mg of purified antibody. The monoclonal antibody persisted in the circulation for more than one week when more than 15 mg of the antibody was administered. Antibodies against mouse Ig developed in three of the four patients. In one of the patients this caused a large fall in circulating mouse Ig; this change accompanied the patient's adverse clinical reaction to the last injection of antibody 17-1A. Because it was previously shown (see Chap. 1) that this antibody activates effector cells which are responsible for the destruction of the colorectal tumors in athymic nude mice, the peripheral blood lymphocytes were isolated from one patient,

mixed with antibody 17-1A, and the antibody-exposed lymphocytes returned to
the patient. The hepatic metastasis in this patient became smaller, the echogenic
characteristics changed, and a heightened monocyte infiltration was observed
in histological sections of a resected metastasis. Although the bone metastasis
apparently became smaller during treatment, there was no histologic evidence of
tumor destruction. The lack of tumor destruction might be attributed to antigenic modulation of the metastatic cells, as indicated by the absence of the
tumor-associated antigen in this lesion. Although these investigators concluded
that this mouse monoclonal antibody can be safely administered directly to the
diseased organ, the problems of antigenic modulation and the production of
anti-mouse antibodies were very much evident in this study.

At present there are two phase I trials using monoclonal antibodies to treat
melanoma. One of these is being conducted at the Fred Hutchinson Cancer
Center (23) using the anti-p97 monoclonal antibody (see Chap. 2). The second
trial is being conducted at the National Cancer Institute with the IgG_2 anti-
melanoma monoclonal antibody 9.2.27 (see Chap. 2). These are both phase I
trials where increasing doses will be evaluated to determine the biological effects
of these monoclonal antibodies.

While many problems remain to be defined, such as the class of immunoglobulin (24), the use of highly purified antibody, use of whole antibody or antibody fragments, the route, dosage, and schedule of administration, the immune
reactions to the mouse immunoglobulin, and the development and use of immunoconjugates, as this review points out, the production and use of monoclonal antibodies for serotherapy is the most fertile field for laboratory and clinical
investigation of cancer-specific reagents. However, extensive phase I trials are
needed to document the biological and toxic effects of antibody alone prior to
proceeding with immunoconjugate studies in human cancer patients. Extensive
animal model studies (21, 24-29; see also Chap. 13) with immunoconjugates
will also be necessary before in vivo trials with these reagents are initiated in
cancer patients.

CHAPTER 2: MONOCLONAL ANTIBODIES TO
MELANOMA-ASSOCIATED ANTIGENS

There has been much progress in this field since the literature review for Chapter
2 was completed. For example, work in our laboratory has resulted in the following additional findings: (1) the gene which codes for antigen p97 is located
on chromosome 3 (30), the same chromosome that carries the gene for the transferrin receptor and probably also for transferrin, a finding that is of interest in
view of the structural homology between p97 and transferrin and its ability to
bind iron; (2) cDNA sequences coding for p97 have been cloned (Brown et al.,
manuscript in preparation) which should provide a starting point for getting
definitive structural information about p97 and for performing transfection ex-

periments toward better understanding the function of p97 and developing a
very useful animal tumor model by introducing the p97 marker into mouse
tumor cells; (3) essentially all melanomas can be identified by using a combination of antibodies to p97, the GD3, and the proteoglycan antigens to stain frozen sections with the peroxidase-antiperoxidase technique (31); (4) ^{131}I-label-
led Fab fragments specific for p97 can be used to image metastatic melanoma
in patients and for concentrating a potentially therapeutic radiation dose into
tumor tissue (23); and (5) unlabelled anti-p97 or anti-proteoglycan antibodies,
given in large doses to patients with metastatic melanoma, localize throughout
the tissues of sections of metastatic melanoma (I. Hellström et al., manuscript
in preparation).

We continue to believe that antigens such as p97, and GD3, and the proteoglycan antigens, in view of their relative specificity for melanoma, offer great
promises both as diagnostic markers and therapeutic targets and that the need
for antibodies that define antigens of absolute tumor specificity (if such antigens
exist at all) is not as great as many had anticipated when work in this area was
first started. In view of the great promise of work on oncogenes, it is of interest
that the expression of many oncogenes in neoplastic, as compared to normal,
cells shows a quantitative rather than a qualitative difference, a situation similar
to the relative rather than absolute differences in the expression of tumor antigens in normal and neoplastic cells.

CHAPTER 4: MONOCLONAL ANTIBODIES TO GLIOMA TUMOR ANTIGENS

Recent developments show that in vivo localizations of monoclonal antibodies
in gliomas is possible and that their access to brain and tumor can be enhanced
by hyperosmotic blood-brain barrier disruption (32-37).

CHAPTER 7: MONOCLONAL ANTIBODIES TO OSTEOGENIC SARCOMA ANTIGENS

The antigen defined by monoclonal antibody α791T/36 has now been partially
characterized (38). Quantitative absorption studies have shown that it is associated with the plasma membrane, little or no antigenic activity being detected
in cytosol, nuclei, or cellular lipids. Treatment with various enzymes showed
that the antigen could be destroyed by papain, although milder proteolytic enzymes had minimal effect and glycosidases were inactive. Also, single-phase
aqueous butanol solutions failed to solubilize the α791T/36-defined antigen.
Following lactoperoxidase-catalyzed radioiodination of tumor cells, the antigen
could be extracted by nonionic detergent (Nonidet-P40) and precipitated using
α791T/36 antibody followed by Sepharose-protein A. The precipitated material
was characterized by electrophoresis on sodium dodecyl sulfate-polyacrylamide

gels (SDS-PAGE) and subsequent autoradiography, migrating as a monomeric protein of apparent molecular weight 72,000. This protein was shared by all cell lines which bind the α791T/36 antibody but was not detected in lysates of cells which do not bind α791T/36. Neuraminidase treatment reduced the molecular weight to 55,000, implying that the antigenic material is a glycoprotein with a high sialic acid content.

Localization of radiolabeled α791T/36 in tumor xenografts prompted clinical trials to evaluate the antibody for radioimmunodetection of tumors in patients, by imaging with a gamma camera. The first series evaluated were patients with primary or metastatic colorectal carcinoma (39), α791T/36 having previously shown reactivity in vitro with colorectal carcinoma cells (Chap. 7, Table 2). In 10 of 11 patients, labelled α791T/36 was localized to the tumor. In five cases with primary tumors the localization of the antibody was further confirmed by imaging of the resected specimens, and by in vitro counting of radioactivity in the tumor compared with adjacent normal colon. Since this study, the tumors of many more colorectal carcinoma patients have been imaged with similar success. Other tumors which effectively localize α791T/36 are osteogenic sarcoma (40) and ovarian carcinoma (41). The antibody has thus proved to have clinical potential exceeding initial expectations.

Studies on drug-targeting have advanced further since the demonstration of selective in vitro cytotoxicity by Vindesine- (VDS) 791T/36 conjugates (42). Vindesine-791T/36 conjugates were tested for therapeutic effects on xenografts of 791T in thymectomized CBA mice in comparison with free VDS or free α791T/36 antibody administrered in multiple doses (43). Free antibody had no effect compared with untreated controls, but both VDS and VDS-791T/36 significantly retarded tumor growth. Retardation by VDS was greater than with conjugates, but VDS was more toxic at the doses used. A cumulative dose of 20 mg VDS per kg body weight was highly toxic, but mice tolerated VDS-791T/ 36 conjugate containing up to 45 mg VDS per kg without evidence of toxicity. The acute LD_{50} for VDS in mice is established to be 6.3 mg/kg body weight (44). It is thus possible to administer greater amounts of conjugate than free drug, and if more efficient conjugates can be devised, they may have considerable potential for antitumor therapy.

One approach to greater efficiency is to use bridging agents to link drug and antibody, thereby achieving much greater numbers of drug molecules per antibody molecule without inactivating the antibody. We have recently described the preparation and properties of a conjugate of methotrexate (MTX) linked to α791T/36 by a human serum albumin (HSA) bridge, termed MTX-HSA-791T/36 (45). This was selectively cytotoxic to cells bearing the α791T/36-defined antigen and was as active against these cells as free MTX in a chronic exposure assay, unlike VDS-791T/36 which was less active than VDS in a similar assay (Chap. 7,

Fig. 8). The selectivity of the MTX-HSA-791T/36 conjugate was clearly anti-body-dependent, since competition by added excess free antibody abolished cytotoxic activity against otherwise susceptible cells. Current studies are aimed at evaluating further conjugates prepared with a wide range of drugs, several of which are proving in preliminary in vitro tests to be cytotoxic specifically toward cells expressing the relevant antigen. Despite the localization of α791T/36 to human tumors (39–41), there is as yet no reason to suggest that these conjugates could have therapeutic value in man, but their study in xenograft models will undoubtedly result in valuable information leading to the design of drug-antibody conjugates for eventual clinical use.

CHAPTER 8: MONOCLONAL ANTIBODIES TO HUMAN LEUKEMIA ANTIGENS

Identification of Appropriate Monoclonal Antibodies for Diagnosis and Treatment of T-ALL

Several groups have independently identified monoclonal antibodies which re-act with a cell surface glycoprotein of 40,000 molecular weight on T cells (46-49). This antigen is expressed on immature cells within the thymic cortex and is the most consistently expressed antigen in T-ALL (46,48,49) including cases in relapse and the "pre-T" subset that may lack other T-cell markers (48). The gp40K structure may also provide an appropriate "target" antigen for therapy with monoclonal antibodies either singularly or in combination with antibodies of different specificity. A ricin A chain conjugate of the monoclonal antibody WT1 (48), which recognizes the T cell 40K molecule, has been shown to be ex-tremely effective at inhibiting growth and protein synthesis of clonogenic T leu-kemic cells in vitro while leaving multipotential stem cells unharmed (50).

A Possible Leukemia Specific Monoclonal

Naito et al. (51) reported the production and characterization of a monoclonal antibody raised against T-leukemia (ALL) cell lines which appears to react with T-ALL but not cells in normal thymus.

Immunoglobulin Gene Rearrangements

Further studies have substantiated that non-T ALL (i.e., the common and null subgroups) have rearranged Ig genes (μ, and often κ and λ light chain also) (52), thus confirming that ALL can be divided into the major subtypes of "pre-T" and "pre-B." In addition, similar studies have shown that lymphoid blast crises of CML but not myeloid blast crises have rearranged μ genes (53,54).

Monoclonal Antibodies and the Antigenic Heterogeneity of Leukemias and Lymphomas

During the past year a plethora of reports on monoclonal antibody analysis of leukemias and lymphomas has appeared. Most of these document heterogeneity of expression of antigens which are poorly defined and of uncertain clinical significance. The distinction between lymphoid and nonlymphoid neoplasms in histopathological diagnoses can be conveniently made with appropriate monoclonal antibodies (55). Also preliminary studies indicate the evaluation of reactivity with monoclonal antibodies against the transferrin receptor (e.g., OKT9) may have prognostic value (56).

Monoclonal Antibodies Selective for Myeloid Cells

Many reports have appeared on monoclonal antibodies selectively reactive with myeloid cells (57-62). A substantial proportion of these reagents are directed towards fucosyl carbohydrate antigens, granulocytes, and neural tissue (63,64) and appear to be controlled by gene(s) on chromosome 11 (65). A substantial proportion of anti-carcinoma monoclonals appear to identify similar antigenic structures (66). Griffin et al., reported a series of monoclonal antibodies which appear to be very useful discriminators of myeloid leukemias (58,67); of these antibodies MY906 appears to be the best in terms of comprehensive reactivity with myeloblastic leukemias and lack of reactivity with non-myeloid cases (Ref. 68; and L. Chan and M. Greaves, unpublished observations).

Burkitt's Lymphoma Membrane Antigen

The monoclonal antibody 38-13 which appears to have specificity for Burkitt lymphoma cells (see Ref. 140 in Chap. 8) has been shown to identify a globotriaosylceramide (glycolipid) (69,70).

Relationship of Leukemic Phenotypes to Normal Differentiation Pathways

Studies with monoclonal antibodies continue to provide insight into the relationship between leukemias and their normal counterparts (e.g., CLL and ALL in Ref. 71). McCulloch and colleagues argue, however, that the lineage fidelity indicated by monoclonal antibody studies (72) is not always maintained in acute leukemias when certain markers are used (73).

CHAPTER 9: MONOCLONAL ANTIBODIES REACTIVE WITH HUMAN OVARIAN CARCINOMA

An immunoradiometric assay has been developed to measure CA125 antigen in human serum using the murine monoclonal antibody OC125 (74). By this assay only 1% of 888 apparently healthy individuals and 6% of 143 patients with non-malignant disease had serum CA125 levels above 35 U ml. In contrast, 83 of the 101 patients (82%) with surgically demonstrated ovarian carcinoma had elevated levels of the antigen. This is consistent with earlier studies of tissue sections in which more than 80% of nonmucinous epithelial tumors contained the CA125 antigen (75). In 38 patients with epithelial ovarian carcinoma monitored over 2-60 months, rising or falling levels of CA125 correlated with progression or regression of disease in 42 of 45 instances (93%).

Elevated CA125 levels were found in serum from 29% of patients with non-gynecological cancers, including carcinomas of the pancreas, stomach, colon, and breast. Consequently, the assay is not likely to differentiate ovarian cancers from other tumors that spread throughout the peritoneal cavity and produce ascites. The CA125 assay might, however, supplement more conventional markers in monitoring these other neoplasms.

The CA125 assay may provide the first generally useful marker for monitoring patients with epithelial ovarian carcinoma. Many patients with advanced ovarian carcinoma will receive intensive cytotoxic chemotherapy, and the majority will respond for various lengths of time. Such responses may often be documented objectively only through the use of invasive surgical restaging procedures. When conventional methods of noninvasive monitoring are used, many months may elapse before the success or failure of treatment becomes evident. Rapid and correct determination of the response to chemotherapy would prevent unnecessary toxicity associated with ineffective drugs and permit early evaluation of alternative agents. A rising level of CA125 could also lead to restaging after an apparently complete response to treatment.

CHAPTER 10: MONOCLONAL ANTIBODIES TO PROSTATE ADENOCARCINOMA ANTIGENS

We have confirmed in our laboratory the coexpression of a γFc receptor and the prostate tumor-associated antigen DU83.21 in membranes from prostate, bladder, and a few other urogenital tumor cell lines and on human cells transformed by cytomegalovirus (Wright, Campbell, Beckett, Starling, Schellhammer, Sieg, and Ladaga, manuscript in preparation). Neither the Fc receptor nor the DU83.21 antigen was detected on any of over 50 other human tumor and normal cell lines. An extensive study will be required to determine the significance of this coexpression on urogenital tumors.

Both antiprostate/bladder monoclonal antibodies DU83.21 and P6.2 have been successfully used to detect tumor cells in cytology specimens of prostate tumor biopsies and bladder washings from patients with transitional cell carcinoma of the urinary bladder (Wright, Beckett, Schellhammer, Starling, and Konchuba, manuscript in preparation). A study is now underway to develop a multiparameter analysis of cytology specimens based on RNA/DNA content, cell ploidy, nuclear size, and tumor marker (83.21 and 6.2) expression. If successful, this approach could provide both diagnostic and prognostic information about the patient's malignancy.

As discussed in Chap. 10, most of the antiprostate monoclonal antibodies described have been generated using prostate adenocarcinoma cell lines. Cell lines have largely been employed because of the difficulties in obtaining sufficient amounts of good quality prostate tumor tissue. We recently completed a fusion in which membrane extracts prepared from a pool of resected prostate tissues (both BPH and tumor tissue) were used to immunize mice (Starling, Sieg, Beckett, Schellhammer, Wirth, Ladaga, Poleksic, and Wright, manuscript in preparation). This fusion resulted in two hybrids secreting monoclonal antibodies, TP27 and TP73. Extensive evaluation of the specificity of these antibodies, using normal and malignant cell lines and tissues, demonstrated that TP27 does not react to any cell line tested (prostate or other) and binds only to prostate tissues (normal, BPH, and prostate carcinomas). TP73 binds to the DU145 and PC3, but not to the LNCaP, prostate tumor cell lines. Like TP27, it appears to bind only to prostate tissues. Neither of these antibodies bind to prostatic acid phosphatase (PAP or prostate antigen (PA). Both antibodies appear to identify two new prostate organ-specific antigens present in the membranes of prostate epithelial cells. A preliminary study in which these antibodies were compared with the reactivity of a monoclonal antibody against PA on formalin-fixed tissues showed considerable staining heterogeneity for all three monoclonal antibodies. In some cases cells not stained by one antibody were stained by one of the other antibodies. Using this panel of antibodies, 100% of the prostate tumor specimens were appropriately identified. The TP27 antibody appeared to be more efficient in staining metastatic lesions than either TP73 or anti-PA. The inclusion of the TP27 and TP73 antibodies with antibodies DU83.21 and P6.2 and antibodies to PAP and PA may provide an effective panel of antiprostate carcinoma reagents for identifying the various subpopulations of prostate tumors and for classifying prostate carcinomas. Both TP73 and TP27 are being evaluated for radioimmunological imaging and therapeutic applications.

A recent publication by Webb et al. (76), described the binding of two antiprostate monoclonals, αPro3 and αPro5, that bind to different epitopes on a 54,000 dalton (p54) antigen present in prostate tissues. They showed that antigenic modulation occurs upon interaction of p54 with either antibody, and that endocytosis of the immune complex appears to be the primary route of modulation. Endocytosis is more intense when both antibodies were used in combination than when either was used alone. This study points out the importance of a careful in vitro analysis of monoclonal antibodies in order to expedite the effectiveness of in vivo immunotherapeutic trials. This will be especially essential for immunotoxic conjugates which must be internalized by the tumor cell to achieve cytotoxicity. They suggest that if panels of different

epitope-same molecule and different tumor-associated molecule-directed monoclonal antibodies are carefully evaluated, it should be possible to generate a
defined synthetic antiserum that would be operationally specific in an immunotherapeutic context.

CHAPTER 11: DISSECTION AND CHARACTERIZATION OF HUMAN TUMOR-ASSOCIATED MACROMOLECULES USING MONOCLONAL ANTIBODIES

Recently, Wagener et al. (77,78), published companion papers which described
methods that they used to first determine the epitope specificity of monoclonal
antibodies to CEA and then to characterize the affinities and specificities of the
different monoclonal anti-CEA antibodies. By examining the competitive effects of ligand binding among the various monoclonal antibodies (see page 298),
they were able to identify five monoclonal antibodies which recognized five
different epitopes on the protein moiety of deglycosylated CEA. Using an
avidin-biotin-peroxidase technique, they were able to differentially detect three
different CEA-related antigens in normal and malignant tissues and peripheral
blood smears. Using biotin-labeled antibody, radiolabeled antigen, and avidin
as a precipitating agent in a solution phase, competitive radioimmunoassay, they
were able to quantitate the immunologic relationship between CEA, NCA, and
tumor-extracted CEA-related antigen (79). These studies suggested that at least
one of the monoclonal antibodies could be used in testing serum samples for
CEA and that heterogeneity of the radiolabeled CEA was due to an artefact
resulting from radioiodination damage.

Hedin et al. (80), produced eight different monoclonal antibodies to CEA.
Two of these cross-reacted strongly with NCA. Using gel filtration of radiolabeled CEA and monoclonal antibodies, they were able to identify at least five
different epitopes on the CEA molecule and showed that at least two of these
occurred twice in the molecule. The reactivity of the eight antibodies appeared
to be directed against conformation-dependent protein determinants. These
investigators have subsequently developed an enzyme immunoassay for serum
CEA which utilizes two of the monoclonal antibodies (81). The antibodies
recognize two different epitopes on the peptide moiety of CEA, and their combined use appeared to result in an increased specificity for CEA associated with
cancer when sera from healthy individuals and patients with malignant and nonmalignant diseases were tested. These findings are in contrast with those of
Buchegger et al. (82), who developed a sandwich enzyme immunoassay which
utilized a combination of three monoclonal antibodies against different epitopes of CEA. Their results, when assaying sera of patients with carcinoma,
benign disease and healthy volunteers, were comparable to those obtained using
a conventional goat anti-CEA antiserum. These investigators suggested that the
CEA associated with nonmalignant diseases is immunologically identical to the
CEA associated with colonic cancer.

Numerous other investigators have developed their own panels of monoclonal antibodies to CEA which define distinct epitopes (83-87). Whether or not any of the antibodies described to date or those to be described in the future truly recognize CEA determinants which would, in part, enhance specificity of clinical assays remains unresolved.

REFERENCES

1. S. Hakomori, *Bull. Cancer (Paris)* 70:118 (1983).
2. L. Lindholm, J. Holmgren, L. Svennerholm, P. Fredman, O. Nilsson, B. Persson, H. Myrovold, and T. Lagergard, *Int. Arch. Aller. Appl. Immunol.* 71:178 (1983).
3. H. Koprowski, *Ciba Found. Symp.* 96:204 (1983).
4. K. E. Falk, K. A. Karlsson, G. Larson, J. Thurin, M. Blaszczyk, Z. Steplewski, and H. Koprowski, *Biochem. Biophys. Res. Commun.* 110:383 (1983).
5. J. W. Arends, K. Verstunen, F. T. Bosman, J. Hilgers, and Z. Steplewski, *Hybridoma* 2:81 (1983).
6. J. W. Arends, T. Wiggers, B. Schutte, C. T. Thijs, C. Verstigen, J. Hilgers, G. H. Blijham, and F. T. Bosman, *Int. J. Cancer* 32:289 (1983).
7. J. L. Manani, M. Brockhaus, D. F. Smith, V. Ginsburg, M. Blaszczyk, K. F. Mitchell, Z. Steplewski, and H. Koprowski, *Science* 212:55 (1981).
8. Z. Steplewski, and H. Koprowski, In *Methods in Cancer Research*, Vol. XX, Academic Press, Inc., New York, 1982, p. 313.
9. B. F. Atkinson, C. S. Ernst, M. Herlyn, Z. Steplewski, H. Sears, and H. Koprowski, *Cancer Res.* 42:4820 (1982).
10. D. Stramignoni, R. Bowen, B. F. Atkinson, and J. Schlom, *Int. J. Cancer* 31:543 (1983).
11. M. Herlyn, M. Blaszczyk, H. F. Sears, H. Verrill, J. Lindgren, D. Colcher, Z. Steplewski, J. Schlom and H. Koprowski, *Hybridoma* 2:329 (1983).
12. B. F. Atkinson, C. S. Ernst, M. Herlyn, Z. Steplewski, H. F. Sears, and H. Koprowski, *Cancer Res.* 42:4820 (1982).
13. D. Colcher, P. Horan Hand, M. Nuti, and J. Schlom, *Cancer Invest.* 1:127 (1983).
14. M. C. Glassy, H. H. Handley, H. Hagiwara, and I. Royston, *Proc. Natl. Acad. Sci., USA* 80:6327 (1983).
15. R. J. Cote, D. M. Morrissey, A. N. Houghton, E. J. Beattie, Jr., H. F. Oettgen, and L. J. Old, *Proc. Natl. Acad. Sci., USA* 80:2026 (1983).
16. A. N. Houghton, H. Brooks, R. J. Cote, M. C. Taormina, H. F. Oettgen, and L. J. Old, *J. Exp. Med.* 158:53 (1983).
17. N. N. H. Teng, K. S. Lam, F. C. Riera, and H. S. Kaplan, *Proc. Natl. Acad. USA* 80:7308 (1983).
18. L. Olsson, H. Kronstrøm, A. Cambon-De Mouzon, C. Honsik, T. Brodin, and B. Jakobsen, *J. Immunol. Methods* 61:17 (1983).
19. R. K. Oldham, *Clin. Immunol. Newsletter* 4:131 (1983).
20. R. K. Oldham and R. V. Smalley, *J. Biol. Resp. Modif.*, in press.
21. K. A. Foon, M. I. Bernhard, and R. K. Oldham, *J. Biol. Resp. Modif.*, in press.

22. H. F. Sears, J. Mattis, D. Herlyn, P. Hayry, B. Atkinson, C. Ernst, Z. Steplewski, and H. Koprowski, *Lancet 1*:762 (1982).
23. S. M. Larson, J. A. Carrasquillo, K. A. Krohn, J. P. Brown, R. W. McGuffin, J. M. Ferens, M. M. Graham, L. D. Hill, P. L. Beaumier, K. E. Hellström, and I. Hellström, *J. Clin. Invest. 72*:2101 (1983).
24. M. Seto, T. Takahashi, S. Nakamura, Y. Matsudaira, and Y. Nishizuka, *Cancer Res. 43*:4768 (1983).
25. M. I. Bernhard, K. A. Foon, T. N. Oeltmann, M. E. Key, K. M. Hwang, G. C. Clarke, W. L. Christensen, L. C. Hoyer, M. G. Hanna, Jr., and R. K. Oldham, *Cancer Res. 43*:4420 (1983).
26. M. I. Bernhard, K. M. Hwang, K. A. Foon, A. M. Keenan, R. M. Kessler, J. M. Frincke, D. J. Tallam, M. G. Hanna, Jr., L. Peters, and R. K. Oldham, *Cancer Res. 43*:4429 (1983).
27. K. Imai, T. Nakanishi, M. Matsui, T. Noguchi, A. Yachi, S. Ferrone, *Protides Biol. Fluid Proc. Colloq. 30*:365 (1983).
28. R. W. Baldwin, M. J. Embleton, G. R. Fannery, J. M. Pelham, M. V. Primm, M. R. Price, and R. A. Robins, *Protides Biol. Fluid Proc. Colloq. 30*:381 (1983).
29. S. E. Halpern, P. L. Hagan, P. R. Garver, J. A. Koziol, A. W. N. Chen, J. M. Frincke, R. M. Bartholomew, G. S. David, and T. H. Adams, *Cancer Res. 43*:5347 (1983).
30. G. D. Plowman, J. P. Brown, C. A. Enns, J. Schröder, B. Nikinmaa, H. H. Sussman, K. E. Hellström, and I. Hellström, *Nature 303*:70 (1983).
31. I. Hellström, K. E. Hellström, and J. P. Brown, in *Progress in Cancer Research and Therapy*, Vol. 29, Raven Press, Inc., New York (1984).
32. J. G. Carncross, M. J. Mattis, H. R. Beresford, A. P. Albino, A. N. Houghton, K. O. Lloyd, and L. J. Old, *Proc. Natl. Acad. Sci. 79*:5641, (1982).
33. M. A. Bourdon, C. J. Wikstrand, H. Furthmayr, T. J. Matthews, and D. D. Bigner, *Cancer Res. 43*:2796 (1983).
34. C. J. Wikstrand, S. H. Bigner, and D. D. Bigner, *Cancer Res. 43*:3327 (1983).
35. B. de Muralt, N. de Tribolet, A. C. Diserens, S. Carrel, and J. P. Mach, *Anti-Cancer Res. 3*:106 (1983).
36. D. Stavrou, C. Süss, Th. Bilzer, U. Kummer, and N. de Tribolet, *Eur. J. Clin. Oncol. 19*:1439 (1983).
37. J. Phillips, T. Alderson, K. Sikora, and J. Watson, *J. Neurol. Neurosurg. Psychiatr. 46*:388 (1983).
38. M. R. Price, D. G. Campbell, R. A. Robins and R. W. Baldwin, *Eur. J. Cancer Clin. Oncol. 19*:81 (1983).
39. P. A. Farrands, A. C. Perkins, M. V. Pimm, J. G. Hardy, M. J. Embleton, R. W. Baldwin and J. D. Hardcastle, *Lancet 8295*:397 (1982).
40. N. C. Armitage, A. C. Perkins, M. V. Pimm, P. A. Farrands, R. W. Baldwin, and J. D. Hardcastle, *Br. J. Surg.*, submitted for publication.
41. E. M. Symonds, A. C. Perkins, M. V. Pimm, R. W. Baldwin, J. G. Hardy and D. A. Williams, *Am. J. Obstet. Gynecol.*, submitted for publication.
42. M. J. Embleton, G. F. Rowland, R. G. Simmonds, E. Jacobs, C. H. Marsden and R. W. Baldwin, *Br. J. Cancer, 47*:43 (1983).
43. R. G. Simmonds, M. V. Pimm, K. F. Hellström, G. F. Rowland, M. J. Emble-

ton, I. Hellström, C. Marsden, E. Jacobs, J. P. Brown and R. W. Baldwin, *Proc. Natl. Acad. Sci. (USA)*, submitted for publication.

44. G. C. Todd, W. R. Gibson, and D. M. Morton, *J. Toxicol. Environ. Health*, *1*:843 (1976).
45. M. C. Garnett, M. J. Embleton, E. Jacobs and R. W. Baldwin, *Int. J. Cancer 31*:661 (1983).
46. B. F. Haynes, *Immunol. Rev. 47*:127 (1981).
47. Y. Morishima, M. Kobayashi, S. Y. Yang, N. H. Collins, M. K. Hoffman, and B. Dupont, *J. Immunol. 129*:1091 (1982).
48. L. Vodinelich, W. Tax, Y. Bai, S. Pegram, P. Capel and M. Greaves, *Blood 62*:1108 (1983).
49. M. Link, R. Warnke, J. Finlay, M. Amylon, R. Miller, J. Dilley, and R. Levy, *Blood 62*:722 (1983).
50. C. D. Meyers, P. E. Thorpe, W. C. J. Ross, A. J. Cumber, F. E. Katz, and M. F. Greaves, *Blood* (in press).
51. K. Naito, R. W. Knowles, F. X. Real, Y. Morishima, K. Kawashima, and B. Dupont, *Blood 62*:852 (1983).
52. S. J. Korsmeyer, A. Arnold, A. Bakhshi, J. V. Ravetch, U. Siebenlist, P. A. Hieter, S. O. Sharron, T. W. LeBien, J. H. Kersey, D. G. Poplack, P. Leder, and T. A. Waldmann, *J. Clin. Invest. 71*:301 (1983).
53. A. M. Ford, H. V. Molgaard, M. F. Greaves, and H. J. Gould, *EMBO Journal 2*:997 (1983).
54. A. Bakhshi, J. Minowada, A. Arnold, J. Cossman, J. P. Jensen, J. Whang-Peng, T. A. Waldmann, and S. J. Korsmeyer, *N. Engl. J. Med. 309*:826 (1983).
55. R. A. Warnke, K. C. Gatter, B. Falini, P. Hildreth, R. E. Woolston, K. Pulford, J. L. Cordell, B. Cohen, C. de Wolf-Peters, and D. Y. Mason, *N. Engl. J. Med. 309*:1275 (1983).
56. J. A. Habeshaw, T. A. Lister, A. G. Stansfeld and M. F. Greaves, *Lancet i*: 498 (1983).
57. J. T. Kemshead, J. Fritschy, U. Asser, D. R. Sutherland, and M. F. Greaves, *Hybridoma 1*:109 (1982).
58. J. D. Griffin, J. Ritz, L. M. Nadler, and S. F. Schlossman, *J. Clin. Invest. 68*: 932 (1981).
59. B. Perussia, G. Trinchieri, D. Lebman, J. Jankiewicz, B. Lange, and G. Rovera, *Blood 59*:382 (1982).
60. E. D. Ball and M. W. Fanger, *Clin. Exp. Immunol 48*:655 (1982).
61. O. Majdic, K. Liszka, D. Lutz, and W. Knapp, *Blood 58*:1127 (1981).
62. E. D. Ball, R. F. Graziano, L. Shen, and M. W. Fanger, *Proc. Natl. Acad. Sci. (USA) 79*:5374 (1982).
63. C. Girardet, S. Ladisch, D. Heumann, J. P. Mach, and S. Carrel, *Int. J. Cancer 32*:177 (1983).
64. H. C. Gooi, S. J. Thorpe, E. F. Hounsell, H. Rumpold, D. Kraft, O. Förster and T. Feizi, *Eur. J. Immunol. 13*:306 (1983).
65. A. H. M. Geurts van Kessel, P. A. T. Tetteroo, A. E. G. Kr. Von dem Borne, A. Hagemeijer, and D. Boorsma, *Proc. Natl. Acad. Sci. (USA) 80*:3748 (1983).

66. J. L. Magnani, B. Nilsson, M. Brockhaus, D. Zopf, Z. Steplewski, H. Koprowski, and V. Ginsburg, *J. Biol. Chem. 257*:14365 (1982).
67. J. D. Griffin and S. F. Schlossman, In *Proceedings of the First International Conference on Leucocyte Differentiation Antigens*, Springer-Verlag, Berlin (in press).
68. J. D. Griffin, D. Linch, and S. F. Schlossman, *Blood* (in press).
69. E. Nudelman, R. Kannagi, S. Hakomori, M. Parsons, M. Lipinski, J. Wiels, M. Fellous, and T. Tursz, *Science 220*:509 (1983).
70. M. Lipinski, E. D. Nudelman, J. Wiels, and M. Parsons, *J. Immunol. 129*: 2301 (1982).
71. M. Gobbi, F. Caligaris-Cappio, and G. Janossy, *Br. J. Haematol. 54*:393 (1983).
72. M. F. Greaves, *J. Cell. Physiol. Suppl. 1*:113 (1982).
73. L. J. Smith, J. E. Curtis, H. A. Messner, J. S. Senn, H. Furthmayr, and E. A. McCulloch, *Blood 61*:1138 (1983).
74. R. C. Bast, Jr., T. L. Klug, E. St. John, E. Jenison, J. M. Niloff, H. Lazarus, R. S. Berkowitz, T. Leavitt, T. Griffiths, L. Parker, V. R. Zurawski, and R. C. Knapp, *N. Engl. J. Med. 309*:883 (1983).
75. S. E. Kabawat, R. C. Bast, Jr., W. R. Welch, R. C. Knapp, R. B. Colvin, *Am. J. Clin. Pathol. 79*:98 (1983).
76. K. S. Webb, J. L. Ware, S. F. Parks, W. H. Briner, and D. F. Paulson, *Cancer Immunol. Immunother. 14*:155-166 (1983).
77. C. Wagener, Y. H. Joy Yang, F. G. Crawford, and J. E. Shively, *J. Immunol. 130*:2308 (1983).
78. C. Wagener, B. R. Clark, K. J. Rickard, and J. E. Shively, *J. Immunol. 130*: 2302 (1983).
79. M. J. Kessler, J. E. Shively, D. G. Pritchard, and C. W. Todd, *Cancer Res. 38*:1041 (1978).
80. A. Hedin, S. Hammerström, and A. Larsson, *Molec. Immunol. 19*:1641 (1982).
81. A. Hedin, L. Carlsson, A. Berglund and S. Hammerström, *Proc. Natl. Acad. Sci. (USA) 80*:3470 (1983).
82. F. Buchegger, C. Mettraux, R. S. Accolla, S. Carrel, and J. P. Mach, *Immunol. Lett. 5*:85 (1982).
83. K. F. Mitchell, *Cancer Immunol. Immunother. 10*:1 (1980).
84. P. Oehr, H. D. Adolpho, A. Wurstrow and G. Derigs, *Tumor Diagn. 2*:189 (1981).
85. C. Stahli, V. Miggiano, M. LeDain, M. Ianelli, R. Fessler, P. Haring, J. Schmidt and T. Staehelin, *Res. Monogr. Immunol. 3*:201 (1981).
86. F. J. Primus, K. D. Newell, A. Blue and D. M. Goldenberg, *Cancer Res. 43*: 686 (1983).
87. F. Grunert, K. Wank, G. A. Luckenbach and S. von Kleist, *Oncodev. Biol. Med. 3*:191 (1982).

AUTHOR INDEX

C

SUBJECT INDEX